# REVISE EDEXCEL GCSE
# Combined Science
## Higher

# GUIDED
# REVISION
# WORKBOOK

Series Consultant: Harry Smith

Authors: Ann Fullick, Catherine Jones and Faye Thorndycroft

## Also available to support your revision:

**Revise GCSE Study Skills Guide**          9781447967071

The **Revise GCSE Study Skills Guide** is full of tried-and-trusted hints and tips for how to learn more effectively. It gives you techniques to help you achieve your best – throughout your GCSE studies and beyond!

**Revise GCSE Revision Planner**          9781447967828

The **Revise GCSE Revision Planner** helps you to plan and organise your time, step-by-step, throughout your GCSE revision. Use this book and wall chart to mastermind your revision.

**For the full range of Pearson revision titles across KS2, KS3, GCSE, Functional Skills, AS/A Level and BTEC visit:**
www.pearsonschools.co.uk/revise

**Question difficulty**
Look at this scale next to each exam-style question. It tells you how difficult the question is.

 Pearson

# Contents

## CHEMISTRY PAPER 4

## PHYSICS PAPERS 5 & 6

## PHYSICS PAPER 5

## PHYSICS PAPER 6

------------------

**A small bit of small print**

Edexcel publishes Sample
Assessment Material and the
Specification on its website. This is
the official content and this book
should be used in conjunction with it.
The questions have been written to
help you practise every topic in
the book. Remember: the real exam
questions may not look like this.

# Plant and animal cells

**1** In cell X, which structure is labelled A? Tick **one** box.

  ☐   **A**   nucleus

  ☐   **B**   mitochondria

  ☐   **C**   cell wall

  ☐   **D**   cell membrane       **(1 mark)**

> Cell X is a plant cell. Three of these structures are found in both animal **and** plant cells, so read through the whole list before putting your tick in one box.

cell X

**2** Which of the following is found in some plant cells but never in an animal cell? Tick **one** box.

  ☐   **A**   ribosomes

  ☐   **B**   nucleus

  ☐   **C**   cell membrane

  ☐   **D**   chloroplasts

> You may know the answer to multiple choice questions immediately. If not, read all the answers in case they remind you – and have a go anyway!

**(1 mark)**

**3 (a)** List **four** structures you will find in both animal and plant cells.

1 Cell membrane ...................................................................

2 Ribosome ...................................................................

3 ...................................................................

4 ...................................................................    **(4 marks)**

**(b)** Describe the function of each structure.

1 The cell membrane controls the movements of substances into and out of the cell.

2 The ribosomes are where proteins are made (protein synthesis takes place).

3 ...................................................................................................

4 ................................................................................................... **(4 marks)**

**4 (a)** What is a chloroplast?

................................................................................................... **(1 mark)**

Guided

**(b)** Name **one** type of plant cell that does not contain chloroplasts and explain why.

...................................................................................................

...................................................................................................

................................................................................................... **(3 marks)**

# Different kinds of cell

1  Which of these pairs of structures would you **only** find in a bacterial cell? Tick **one** box.

☐  **A**  plasmid DNA and a nucleus

☐  **B**  plasmid DNA and chromosomal DNA in the cytoplasm

☐  **C**  mitochondria and chloroplasts

☐  **D**  ribosomes and a nucleus

> Read each statement carefully. Some of the pairs have one structure found in animal cells and one found only in plant or bacterial cells. Some have structures found in animal cells. You are looking for two structures found only in bacterial cells.

**(1 mark)**

2  The diagram shows an egg cell and a sperm cell. They are not drawn to scale.

   (a)  Name the structures labelled A and B in the diagrams.

   A  ...................................................................................

   B  ...................................................................................

   **(2 marks)**

   > Structures A and B are very important to the function/purpose of these cells.

   (b)  Describe the function of the structures labelled A and B.

   A  The nutrients in the cytoplasm provide the egg with ...................................

   B  The mitochondria provide the energy needed ...................................   **(2 marks)**

   (c)  If the cells were drawn to scale, which cell would be bigger?

   ...............................................................................................   **(1 mark)**

   (d)  Give **two** reasons for the difference in size.

   The egg needs to be big to contain the nutrients and ...................................

   ...............................................................................................

   The sperm are small because they need to be able ...................................

   ...............................................................................................   **(2 marks)**

3  In smokers, the ciliated epithelial cells which line the tubes leading to the lungs do not work. Explain why this is a health risk.

Guided

   ...............................................................................................

   ...............................................................................................

   ...............................................................................................

   ...............................................................................................

   ...............................................................................................

   ...............................................................................................

   ...............................................................................................

   ...............................................................................................

   ...............................................................................................   **(3 marks)**

# Microscopes and magnification

**1** A student is given an image of a cell taken using a light microscope and asked to estimate the magnification used. Which of these answers cannot be correct? Tick **one** box.

☐ **A** ×40

☐ **B** ×100

☐ **C** ×1000

☐ **D** ×100 000  **(1 mark)**

> Remember the maximum magnification for a light microscope is around ×2000.

**2** Here are two electron micrographs labelled X and Y.

(a) Which of these cells is a prokaryote?

............................................................  **(1 mark)**

> Remember only eukaryotic cells have a nucleus. Use this to help you answer.

(b) Give **two** reasons for your choice.

This cell does not have a nucleus. It has a single chromosome, but

........................................................................................

........................................................................................

........................................................................................  **(2 marks)**

This cell is an order of magnitude smaller than cell Y.

Prokaryotic cells are ........................................................

........................................................................................

........................................................................................  **(2 marks)**

(c) Calculate the magnification used to view cell Y.

$2.5\,cm = 25\,000\,\mu m$

$\text{Magnification} = \dfrac{\text{image size}}{\text{real size}} = \dfrac{25\,000}{10} = ×2500$  **(2 marks)**

**3** The electron microscope has a much greater resolution than a light microscope.

(a) What is the resolution of a microscope? Resolution is the smallest distance

between two points that ...............................................................  **(1 mark)**

(b) Why do electron microscopes enable us to see inside a cell in a lot more detail than a light microscope?

They have a much higher magnification and ...................................  **(2 marks)**

**4** (a) A student looks at a plant cell through a light microscope using the ×5 eyepiece lens and the ×40 objective lens. What magnification are they using?

........................................................................................  **(1 mark)**

(b) Give **three** differences between a light microscope and an electron microscope.

........................................................................................

........................................................................................

........................................................................................  **(3 marks)**

# Dealing with numbers

1  Which of the following lists of units are in the correct order of decreasing size? Tick **one** box.

☐ **A**  kilogram   milligram   gram   picogram

☐ **B**  microgram   milligram   gram   kilogram

☐ **C**  milligram   gram   kilogram   tonne

☐ **D**  kilogram   gram   milligram   microgram

> You are asked for **decreasing** size so you can eliminate **B** and **C** as they give units in **increasing** size.

**(1 mark)**

2  Complete the table to give the length of a plant cell, the diameter of a cell nucleus and the diameter of a rose in micrometres in standard form.

| Structure | Measure | Measure in standard form |
|---|---|---|
| Length of plant cell | 100 µm | $1 \times 10^2$ µm |
| Diameter of cell nucleus | 10 µm | |
| Diameter of a rose | 9 cm    90 000 µm | |

**(3 marks)**

> Remember – in standard form you show numbers in the form of a number between 1 and 10 multiplied by a power of 10.

3  For each of the following, state the correct measurement for the second value:

(a)  1000 nanometres = 1 micrometre

(b)  1000 micrograms = 1 ...........................

(c)  0.000 000 000 001 metres = 1 ...........................

> pico × 1000 = nano
> nano × 1000 = micro
> micro × 1000 = milli

**(3 marks)**

4  The diagram shows a plant cell as seen under an electron microscope.

(a)  The diameter of the nucleus measures 6.0 mm. If the magnification is ×1 000 000, what is the actual diameter of the nucleus? Give your answer in metres, in standard form and to two significant figures.

nucleus

chloroplasts          5µm

.................... **(2 marks)**

(b)  A chloroplast measures 4.5 mm in an electron micrograph. The actual diameter of the chloroplast is $7.5 \times 10^{-6}$ mm. What is the magnification of the micrograph?

.................... **(2 marks)**

 **Practical skills** # Using a light microscope

**1** (a) Name the following parts.

A   the eyepiece lens

B   the ............................. lens

C   ...............................................................

> Make sure you know all of the main parts of the light microscope and what they do.

A

coarse focus

fine focus

B

C

mirror

**(3 marks)**

(b) How do you calculate the magnification you are using when you look at a specimen through a light microscope?

..................................................................................................

.................................................................................................. **(1 mark)**

> Think of the path the light must travel from your specimen to your eye to help you calculate the magnification.

(c) Give **one** precaution you should always take to protect yourself when you are using a light microscope and explain why it is important.

Never point the mirror directly at the Sun because ........................................

..................................................................................................

.................................................................................................. **(1 mark)**

(d) Give **one** precaution you should take to protect the microscope and/or slide from damage and explain why it is important.

..................................................................................................

.................................................................................................. **(2 marks)**

**2** (a) A class of students collect their own cheek cells to make slides to look at under light microscopes. They collect the cells on a swab, smear them onto a microscope slide and put a coverslip in place. Explain **two** steps that would make it easier to see the cells.

..................................................... so the cells show up more clearly.

..................................................... to avoid trapping air bubbles, which

form black circles on the slide, making it harder to see the cells. **(2 marks)**

(b) Explain how to use a light microscope safely to look at a prepared slide of human cells under low magnification.

..................................................................................................

..................................................................................................

..................................................................................................

..................................................................................................

..................................................................................................

..................................................................................................

.................................................................................................. **(4 marks)**

5

Had a go ☐ Nearly there ☐ Nailed it! ☐

## Practical skills **Drawing labelled diagrams**

**1** When you make an accurate labelled diagram of a cell based on what you can see down a microscope, you should always use a sharp HB pencil to make your drawings, not a pen. Why?

So that if you make a mistake ................................................................. **(1 mark)**

**2**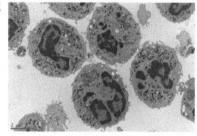

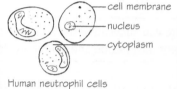
cell membrane
nucleus
cytoplasm

Human neutrophil cells

You only need to show the detailed internal structure of one of the cells in a micrograph if there is more than one of the same type.

(a) Give **three** good points about this diagram drawn from the electron micrograph of a human neutrophil.

It is drawn in pencil /............................................/........................................ **(3 marks)**

(b) Give **two** faults with this diagram.

It does not focus ........................................................./ it does not have

................................................................................................. **(2 marks)**

(c) Draw your own labelled diagram of the slide shown above.

**(4 marks)**

**3** This is a light micrograph of a plant cell. Draw and label a diagram to show what you can see.

Guided

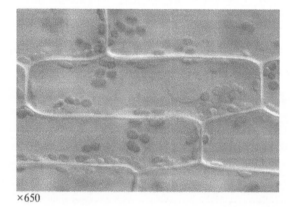

×650

**(4 marks)**

# Enzymes

**1** (a) What is an enzyme?

An enzyme is a biological catalyst which ...*speeds up rate of reaction*... **(1 mark)**

> The reactions in the body would take place without enzymes – just **very** slowly!

(b) What are enzymes made of?

.......*amino acids*....... **(1 mark)**

(c) This diagram represents the lock-and-key model of how enzymes work. What is represented by:

A .......*active site*.......

B .......*Substrate*.......

C .......*product molecule*....... **(3 marks)**

(d) Enzymes are **specific**. Use the diagram to help you explain what this means.

The ...*active site*... matches the shape of the substrate molecules and holds

them close together so ...*bonds can form*... Once the product is

formed ...*it leaves the site*. The shape of the active site of an enzyme only

...*is specific to it's Substrate*... **(3 marks)**

> Remember: it is the 3D shape of the active site that determines which substrates can bind to an enzyme.

**2** Which of the following does **not** affect the rate of an enzyme-controlled reaction?
Tick **one** box.

> Guided

☐ **A** pH        ☐ **B** temperature

☐ **C** substrate concentration      ☑ **D** humidity    **(1 mark)**

**3** In a practical, students measured the rate of reaction of a mixture containing an enzyme and a substrate, as they heated up the reacting mixture. Describe each stage of their graph.

> Consider both the free movement of the molecules and the effect of temperature on protein structure.

> When the shape of the active site of an enzyme is changed by temperature so that it no longer catalyses a specific reaction, it has been **denatured**, not 'killed'.

A At lower temperatures, molecules move more ...*slowly so substrate*...
...*takes longer to fit*...

B At the optimum temperature ...*enzyme is working at*...
...*it's fastest rates*...

C ...*Higher temperature causes the active site*...
...*to change shape*...

D ...*active site and enzyme become*...
...*denatured*... **(4 marks)**

**Practical skills** # pH and enzyme activity

You can investigate the effect of pH on the rate of enzyme activity by measuring the rate of an enzyme-controlled reaction at a known pH and then repeating the process at different pHs. By comparing the reaction rates, you can determine how pH affects the enzyme.

A group of students carried out an investigation into the effect of pH on the activity of the enzyme catalase, using the apparatus shown. Catalase catalyses (speeds up) the breakdown of hydrogen peroxide ($H_2O_2$) into water and oxygen – the oxygen is given off as a gas. By measuring the volume of gas given off in a given time, you can calculate the rate of the reaction at a given pH. Repeating the process with solutions of different pH allows you to observe the effect of pH on the activity of the enzyme.

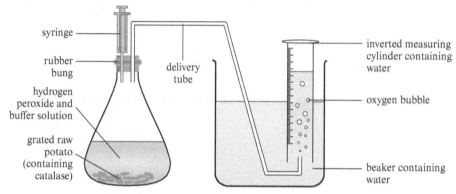

The results they achieved are shown below.

(a) Complete the table below.

| pH | Volume of gas produced in 5 min ($cm^3$) | Rate of catalase reaction ($cm^3$ oxygen/min) |
|----|----|----|
| 4 | 0 | 0 |
| 5 | 5 | 1 |
| 6 | 20 | |
| 7 | | 3 |
| 8 | 2 | |

$$\text{rate } (cm^3\backslash min) = \frac{\text{volume of gas produced}}{\text{time}}$$

**(3 marks)**

(b) Draw a suitable graph to show the effect of pH on the rate of reaction of catalase.

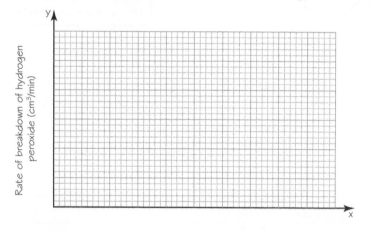

A suitable graph would be rate of breakdown of hydrogen peroxide ($cm^3$/min) against pH, or rate of reaction against pH. Include a title and label the axes.

**(4 marks)**

(c) Suggest one way in which the students could modify their experiment to make their results more reliable.

.........................................................................................................................................

......................................................................................................... **(1 mark)**

Had a go ☐   Nearly there ☐   Nailed it! ☐

# The importance of enzymes

**1** (a) What do enzymes do in the human digestive system?

Break down large, complex molecules into .................................................

.................................................................................................... **(2 marks)**

(b) Complete the following table showing three important enzymes.

| Enzyme | Where it is found in humans | Reaction catalysed |
|---|---|---|
| | | Breaking down starch into small sugars |
| catalase | | Breaking down hydrogen peroxide into water and oxygen |
| protease | | |
| lipase | | |

**(4 marks)**

> You will always be expected to know some examples of enzymes, especially digestive enzymes and catalase.

**2** (a) The enzyme DNA polymerase is an enzyme that helps DNA synthesis. What does this mean?

The enzyme catalyses (speeds up) the synthesis of large DNA molecules ............

.................................................................................................... **(2 marks)**

(b) Where do enzymes that build up large molecules from smaller molecules usually work?

> Make sure you know the difference between synthesis and digestion.

.................................................................................................... **(1 mark)**

**3** Dishwasher powders often contain enzymes as well as detergent. Explain how these enzymes help to get dishes and pans clean.

Food contains proteins (in egg, meat, etc.), lipids in fatty foods and

carbohydrates (starches). If .......................................................................

....................................................................................................

....................................................................................................

.................................................................................................... **(2 marks)**

**4** (a) Give **two** different roles for enzymes in the human body.

....................................................................................................

Guided

.................................................................................................... **(2 marks)**

(b) Normal human body temperature is 37 °C. If your internal body temperature falls below 35 °C or goes above 40 °C your body does not work properly and you may even die. Using your knowledge of enzymes, explain why your body will not function correctly if your body temperature is too hot or cold.

....................................................................................................

....................................................................................................

....................................................................................................

....................................................................................................

.................................................................................................... **(4 marks)**

# Getting in and out of cells

1 Which of these transport processes requires energy? Tick **one** box.

☐ **A** Osmosis   ☐ **C** Active transport

☐ **B** Diffusion   ☐ **D** Facilitated diffusion   **(1 mark)**

2 (a) Define diffusion.

The net movement of molecules from ...................................................... to

.................................................. down a ........................................ **(2 marks)**

(b) How does osmosis differ from diffusion?

Osmosis is ............... It involves the net movement of water molecules across

.............................................................................................. **(2 marks)**

> In both diffusion and osmosis there is **net** movement **down** a concentration gradient.

3 This diagram shows an experiment in progress. At the beginning of the experiment, the level of liquid in the beaker and in the capillary tubing were the same, and the bag contained a small volume of concentrated sucrose solution.

Name the process and explain what has happened to fill the bag and make the liquid level in the capillary tubing rise.

This process is called .................................. At the beginning there were

.............................. water molecules in the water in the beaker than in the same

volume of ............................ in the Visking tubing bag, so ..........................

This gave a net movement of water ............................ the tubing, so ...........

...............................................................................................

...............................................................................................   **(4 marks)**

4 (a) Give **one** similarity between diffusion, osmosis and active transport in cells.

They are all ........................................................................... **(1 mark)**

(b) Define osmosis.

The net movement of water molecules ..............................................

.............................................................................................. **(1 mark)**

(c) Give **one** difference between active transport and the two processes of diffusion and osmosis.

Active transport requires ........................ from respiration to move molecules

........................... The other two processes are passive and .......................

...............................................................................................   **(3 marks)**

 **Osmosis in potatoes**

 **1** This apparatus is used to demonstrate osmosis.

    (a)  Here are some of the instructions that would allow a student to carry out an investigation into osmosis using potatoes. Complete the remaining instructions.

potato

    **A**  Collect five different concentrations of solute solutions, for example, 0, 0.2, 0.4, 0.6, 0.8 mol dm$^{-3}$, and five pieces of potato, all the same length and diameter.

    **B**  Fill a boiling tube two-thirds full with one solution. Mark the value of the solute concentration on the tube. Repeat this for all of the solutions.

    **C**  Blot a piece of potato dry, .................................................................................

    ...........................................................................................................................

    **D**  After 20 minutes, remove the pieces of potato, ......................................

    ...........................................................................................................................

    ...........................................................................................................  **(4 marks)**

    (b)  Why is it important to blot the pieces of potato before measuring the mass?

    ...........................................................................................................................

    ...........................................................................................................  **(2 marks)**

 **2** The table below shows the results of an experiment to investigate osmosis in potatoes.

| Solute concentration (mol dm$^{-3}$) | Initial mass (g) | Final mass (g) | Change in mass (g) | Percentage change in mass (%) |
|---|---|---|---|---|
| 0.0 | 16.52 | 20.15 | 3.63 | 21.97 |
| 0.2 | 15.90 | 16.70 | 0.8 | 5.03 |
| 0.4 | 17.06 | 15.69 | −1.37 | |
| 0.6 | 16.88 | 14.36 | −2.52 | |
| 0.8 | 16.23 | 12.32 | −3.91 | |

    (a)  Complete the table by calculating the percentage change in mass.

> Doing lots of calculations is good practice for your exams!

    **(2 marks)**

    (b)  (i)  Draw a suitable graph to show the effect of solutions of different solute concentrations on osmosis in potato cells.

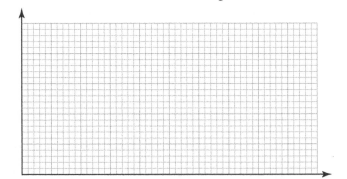

> Make sure you label the axes and give the graph a title.

    **(3 marks)**

        (ii)  Use your graph to estimate the solute concentration of the potato cells in mol dm$^{-3}$.

    ...........................................................................................................  **(1 mark)**

# Extended response – Key concepts

You are given a sweet potato and four different concentrations of sugar solution (0.2, 0.4, 0.6 and 0.8 mol dm⁻³). You also have access to all the normal laboratory equipment and distilled water.

Describe how you would use these materials to demonstrate osmosis in plants.

> Plan your answer carefully before you start writing.

> - Describe each step of the experiment you would carry out and what results you would collect.
> - How would you make sure your results were accurate?
> - How do you calculate mass increases/decreases?
> - Describe how you would present the results and explain the pattern of results you would expect to see.
> - Use your knowledge of osmosis to explain what the results should show.

......................................................................................................................

......................................................................................................................

......................................................................................................................

......................................................................................................................

......................................................................................................................

......................................................................................................................

......................................................................................................................

......................................................................................................................

......................................................................................................................

......................................................................................................................

......................................................................................................................

......................................................................................................................

......................................................................................................................

......................................................................................................................

......................................................................................................................

......................................................................................................................

......................................................................................................................

......................................................................................................................

......................................................................................................................

......................................................................................................................

......................................................................................................................

......................................................................................... **(6 marks)**

# Mitosis

1   Which of the following processes is involved in the cell cycle? Tick **one** box.

☐ **A**  meiosis      ☐ **B**  gametogenesis      ☐ **C**  mitosis      ☐ **D**  osmosis

> Be clear about the difference between mitosis and meiosis:
> **Mitosis** – the process of cell division involved in growth and repair.
> **Meiosis** – the process of cell division involved in the formation of the gametes (sex cells).

**(1 mark)**

2  (a)  Body cells are diploid. What does this mean?

They have ............................ sets of chromosomes.          **(1 mark)**

> Remember: sex cells (gametes) are haploid – they have one set of chromosomes.
>
> Body cells are diploid – they have twice as many sets of chromosomes, because the original body cell of the organism is formed when an egg from the mother, containing one set of chromosomes, is fertilised by a sperm from the father, containing another set of chromosomes.

  (b)  Why are body cells diploid?

They get one set of chromosomes from ......................................................          **(1 mark)**

  (c)  A body cell divides by mitosis. How do the daughter cells compare to the original cell?

They are both ...................................................          **(1 mark)**

3  (a)  The diagram shows the main stages that occur when an animal cell divides by mitosis. Name the **five** stages of mitosis labelled A–E.

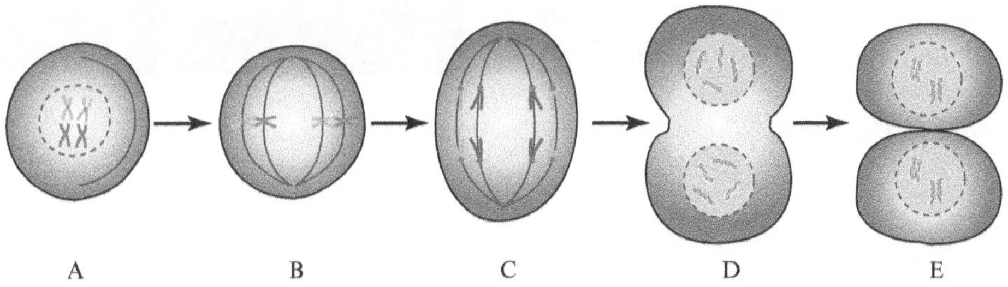

A          B          C          D          E

A  Prophase

B  ................................................................

C  ................................................................

D  ................................................................

E  ................................................................

> It is important to know the main stages of mitosis and what happens at each stage.

**(5 marks)**

  (b)  Describe what is happening in stages A, C and E.

..............................................................................................................................

..............................................................................................................................

..............................................................................................................................

..............................................................................................................................

..............................................................................................................................          **(4 marks)**

# Cell growth and differentiation

**1** Which of these processes is mitosis **not** involved in? Tick **one** box.

☐ **A** asexual reproduction

☐ **B** growth

☐ **C** repair

☐ **D** formation of the sex cells

**(1 mark)**

> Make sure you read through all the options carefully in multiple choice questions.

**2** (a) When an egg and a sperm fuse at fertilisation, the new cell that forms is called

the ............................... **(1 mark)**

(b) What type of cell division takes place as the embryo grows? Explain why this is important.

Mitosis – so all the cells of the new organism ................................................. **(2 marks)**

(c) What happens to the cells as the embryo develops? Explain why this is important.

The cells ........................... to form ........................... This is important

because ................................................................................................. **(2 marks)**

> **Growth** involves producing more cells and the cells getting bigger. **Differentiation** is the process that produces specialised cells to do particular functions in the body.

**3** Local people in Costa Rica claim the noni fruit (see photo) cures many diseases, including cancer. Scientists are testing the juice and flesh of the noni fruit to see if it has any effect on the stages of mitosis. Explain why they are doing this.

> You are not expected to know anything about the fruit in this photograph. You must use what you know about mitosis and cancer to work out the answer.

Cancer is the result of changes in cells, which lead to ...................................

........................... and the formation of ...........................

.................................................................................................

................................................................................................. **(4 marks)**

**4** (a) What is the meristem of a plant?

.................................................................................................

................................................................................................. **(1 mark)**

(b) What processes take place in meristems to produce specialised plant cells?

................................................................................................. **(2 marks)**

(c) Give **one** example of a specialised animal cell and **one** example of a specialised plant cell. For each example you choose, explain how its structure is related to its function.

.................................................................................................

.................................................................................................

.................................................................................................

................................................................................................. **(4 marks)**

# Growth and percentile charts

**1** (a) What is growth?

A permanent ............................................. **(1 mark)**

(b) Give **two** common ways in which we measure growth.

Increase in length/height; ............................................. **(2 marks)**

**2** Scientists measured the growth of two sets of 10 seedlings. Both sets of plants had lots of light, but one set were grown at 10 °C and the other set grown at 20 °C. The mean wet mass of each set of plants is shown in the table below.

| | Mass in grams week 1 | Mass in grams week 12 |
|---|---|---|
| A Plants grown at 10 °C | 245 | 1500 |
| B Plants grown at 20 °C | 250 | 1950 |

**Maths skills** (a) Calculate the increase in mass in (i) plant set A; (ii) plant set B, over the experiment.

(i) 1500 − 245 = ....................

(ii) ............................................. **(2 marks)**

**Maths skills** (b) Calculate the percentage increase in mass in (i) plant set A; (ii) plant set B. Show your working.

(i) .............................................

............................................. **(2 marks)**

$$\frac{\text{final value}}{\text{starting value}} \times 100 = \text{percentage change}$$

(ii) .............................................

............................................. **(2 marks)**

**Maths skills** (c) How big was the percentage difference between the plants in set A and set B?

............................................................................................. **(1 mark)**

(d) Explain the difference you observe.

.............................................................................................

.............................................

............................................. **(2 marks)**

**3** (a) What is a percentile chart like this one used to

record? ................................. **(1 mark)**

> **Guided**

(b) A baby boy is weighed at one year old and his weight is plotted on the chart (shown by an x). Which percentile does he belong to?

................................................. **(1 mark)**

(c) If the weight of a baby falls below the lowest line or rises above the upper line on this chart, what does it indicate?

.............................................

.............................................

............................................. **(1 mark)**

**Growth chart**

Weight-for-age percentiles: Boys, birth to 36 months

# Stem cells

1  Which of the following is **not** a type of stem cell? Tick **one** box.

☐  **A**  meristem cell

☐  **B**  epidermal cell

☐  **C**  adult stem cell

☐  **D**  embryonic stem cell

> Either knowing the three types of stem cells **or** recognising a differentiated adult cell type will help you answer this question.

**(1 mark)**

2  (a)  What is a stem cell?

> Read through the whole question before you answer. This will make sure you give the right information in the right place. And check the number of marks – you don't need to give a very long answer if you are only going to get one mark.

Unspecialised cells which ....................................................................   **(1 mark)**

(b)  Give **one** similarity and **one** difference between embryonic stem cells and meristem cells.

Embryonic stem cells and meristem cells can both ....................................

Embryonic stem cells are ......................., meristem cells are ......................   **(2 marks)**

> When asked for similarities, you only have to think of one property seen in both cell types. For differences, you need to comment on both of the cell types you are comparing.

(c)  How do adult stem cells differ from both embryonic stem cells and meristem cells?

Embryonic stem cells and meristem cells can ...........................................,

but adult stem cells can ...................................................................   **(2 marks)**

3  (a)  Give **two** medical uses of embryonic stem cells.

Replacing or ...............................................................................

...........................................................................................

Growing ..................................................................................   **(2 marks)**

(b)  Give **two** reasons why some people have concerns about using embryonic stem cells to treat human diseases.

> Give two very clearly different reasons – one scientific and one ethical.

Stem cells are good at dividing. Sometimes ............................................

...........................................................................................

An early human embryo is destroyed ....................................................

...........................................................................................   **(2 marks)**

4  In general, there are fewer objections to the use of adult stem cells in human treatment than there are about using embryonic stem cells. Discuss the reasons for this.

Guided

...........................................................................................

...........................................................................................

...........................................................................................

...........................................................................................   **(4 marks)**

# Neurones

1 (a) What is a neurone?

A specialised cell that ................................................................. **(1 mark)**

> Don't just refer to 'messages' – what physically passes through a neurone?

(b) There are three types of neurones. Explain the function of each type.

Motor neurones carry impulses .............................................................

Sensory neurones carry impulses .........................................................

Relay neurones are found ........................................................ linking

..................................................................................... **(3 marks)**

2 (a) Label the parts labelled A–D. Write your answers on the diagram.    **(2 marks)**

(b) What are the functions of (i) part B and (ii) part C?

  (i)  Part B carries ................................................... **(1 mark)**

  (ii) Part C insulates the neurone, ...................................

     .............................................................................

     ............................................................................. **(2 marks)**

D ...........

B ...........

C ...........

A ...........

3 Complete the table to compare three features of a motor neurone, a sensory neurone and a relay neurone.

> The question asks for features so you can use both structures and functions of the cells in your comparison.

| Motor neurone | Sensory neurone | Relay neurone |
|---|---|---|
| Impulse travels away from CNS | | |
| Cell body at one end | | |
| Has sensory receptor at one end | | |

**(3 marks)**

4 (a) Describe the sequence of events in your nervous system that enables you to see a piece of fruit and pick it up.

> Guided

.............................................................................................

.............................................................................................

.............................................................................................

.............................................................................................

.............................................................................................  **(3 marks)**

(b) In some inherited diseases, the myelin sheath surrounding the motor neurones is gradually destroyed. Affected children gradually lose control of their muscles and cannot move. Explain how this happens.

.............................................................................................

.............................................................................................

.............................................................................................

.............................................................................................  **(3 marks)**

**Had a go** ☐    **Nearly there** ☐    **Nailed it!** ☐

# Responding to stimuli

**1** (a) What is a synapse?

A gap between ................................... **(1 mark)**

(b) Explain what is happening in this synapse at points A, B and C.

A   An electrical impulse .......................................,

causing ...........................................................

........................................................ **(2 marks)**

B   The neurotransmitter ..........................................

and fits ..............................................................

............................................................ **(2 marks)**

C   A new .............................................................

......................................................... **(2 marks)**

> Make sure your answer gives three clear events that occur at the junction between two neurones.

**2** Synapses slow down the speed of transmission of nerve impulses, **but** they are very important for the smooth working of the nervous system. Explain **two** advantages of having synapses in the system.

> Guided

.................................................................................

................................................................... **(2 marks)**

**3** (a) What is a reflex?

Automatic, ..................................................................... **(1 mark)**

(b) Why is a reflex arc so fast?

Reflex arcs only involve .................... If the impulses went to the ...............

................................................................................. **(2 marks)**

(c) Give **two** reasons why reflexes are so important.

.................................................................................

................................................................................. **(2 marks)**

> Remember: reflexes are fast and don't involve your conscious brain.

**4** Draw a flow chart to show the sequence of events in a reflex arc from the stimulus to the response.

> Do what the question asks for and produce a flow chart – don't write sentences or produce bullet points.

**(4 marks)**

# Extended response – Cells and control

Curare is a poison. It has been used by hunters in some South American countries for centuries. A little drop of curare on the tip of an arrow means that if the arrow hits an animal, it will quickly become paralysed and stop breathing.

Scientists have discovered that curare fits into the receptors in the synapses between the motor neurones and the muscles. Use this information to explain how curare can cause paralysis, stop breathing and cause death.

---

In this question, you have to explain a situation you will not have seen before. **Don't panic!** What you have learned about the way neurones work means you know everything you need to know to give a perfect answer.

Always plan out your extended response before you start writing. It's a good idea to make a list of bullet points of the main things you want to cover and to get them in the right order before you start writing. Then, cross off each bullet point as you cover it in your answer.

Make sure you keep referring your answer to the content of the question.

Your answer should include:

- The role of motor neurones, synapses and muscles.
- How synapses work.
- How curare would block the transmission of impulses between motor neurones and muscles if it fits into the receptors of the synapses between motor neurones and muscles, and how this would cause paralysis and death.

---

| Motor neurones | What happens at junction | What curare blocks |
|---|---|---|
| CNS ↓ electrical impulses ↓ muscles | impulse causes ↓ neurotransm. chemicals ↓ stimulate muscles to contract | receptors ↓ inc. effect of specific muscles not working |

....................................................................................

....................................................................................

....................................................................................

....................................................................................

....................................................................................

....................................................................................

....................................................................................

....................................................................................

**(6 marks)**

# Meiosis

**1** Which of the following processes are involved in the formation of the gametes?
Tick **one** box.

☐ **A** meiosis

☐ **B** gametogenesis

☐ **C** mitosis

☐ **D** osmosis

> Be clear about the difference between mitosis and meiosis:
> **Mitosis** – the process of cell division involved in growth and repair.
> **Meiosis** – the process of cell division involved in the formation of the sex cells (also called ........................).

**(1 mark)**

**2 (a)** Body cells are diploid, but gametes are haploid. What do the terms diploid and haploid mean?

Diploid means a cell has ........................................ of chromosomes and haploid

means a cell has ..................................................................................... **(1 mark)**

> When gametes fuse to form a zygote, this has twice as many sets of chromosomes.

**(b)** Why are body cells diploid?

Because two gametes ............................................................................. **(1 mark)**

**(c)** Gametes are formed when a cell divides by meiosis, how do the daughter cells (formed by mitosis) compare to the original cell?

The original cell is ................., but the daughter cells are ............................ **(1 mark)**

**3** The cells that make the gametes of an animal or plant divide by meiosis. Use diagrams A–D to help you explain what happens in this process.

> Guided

A          B          C          D

> You will not be asked to name the stages of meiosis.

.........................................................................................................

.........................................................................................................

.........................................................................................................

.........................................................................................................

.........................................................................................................

.........................................................................................................

.........................................................................................................

......................................................................................... **(4 marks)**

# DNA

1 A single, long DNA molecule, tightly coiled and held together by proteins. What is this a definition of? Tick **one** box.

☐ **A**  a gene

☐ **B**  a base

☐ **C**  a chromosome

☐ **D**  a nucleus **(1 mark)**

> Make sure you are clear about the differences between DNA, genes and chromosomes.

2 Describe the difference between chromosomes, genes and DNA.

A chromosome consists of a ..................... molecule ..................................

A gene is a section ..........................................................................

DNA is the ............................................................................... **(3 marks)**

> You need to know how the base pairs are arranged: **A** pairs with ..........
> and **G** pairs with .......... Write a mnemonic to help you remember.

3 The diagram shows two models of the structure of DNA.

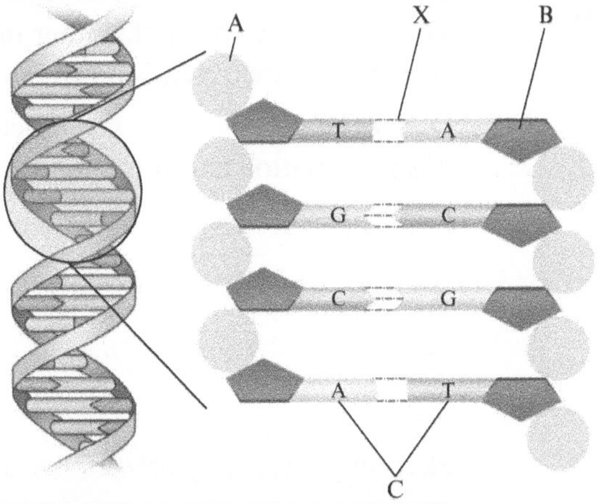

(a) The structure formed as the two strands of a DNA molecule coil around each other is known

as a ..................................... **(1 mark)**

(b) Name the parts of the DNA structure labelled:

A  phosphate group

B  .........................................

C  ......................................... **(3 marks)**

(c) Explain the importance of the structures labelled X in the diagram in a DNA molecule.

> Naming X is a good start to the answer.

X is a ..................... bond .........................................................

.................................................................................................

.................................................................................................

................................................................................................. **(3 marks)**

4 (a) DNA is a polymer. What does this mean?

............................................................................................... **(1 mark)**

(b) The bases in DNA form complementary base pairs. What does this mean?

............................................................................................... **(1 mark)**

(c) What are the complementary base pairs to adenine (A) and guanine (G)?

.................................................................................................

................................................................................................. **(2 marks)**

**Practical skills** (d) When you are extracting DNA from fruit, you add detergent to break open the membranes. Why is this such an important step?

.................................................................................................

.................................................................................................

................................................................................................. **(3 marks)**

# Genetic terms

**1** List the following genetic terms in order of size, from the smallest to the largest: genome, chromosome, gene, base.

Base, .................................................................................................... **(2 marks)**

**2 (a)** What is a gene?

A short piece ....................................................................................

which .................................................................................................... **(1 mark)**

**(b)** Explain the difference between a gene and an allele.

Alleles are ....................................................................................

which .................................................................................................... **(2 marks)**

> Make sure you know the difference between a gene and an allele and use the terms correctly. Students often lose marks by getting them muddled.

**3** This is a brown mouse. Its mother was a brown mouse and its father was a white mouse. Some of the other mice in the litter were white. The dominant allele for a brown coat is represented by **B** and the allele for a white coat by **b**.

Define the genetic terms given below. In each case illustrate your point using this information about the mouse given above.

Genotype: the alleles present in an organism for a particular ........................

Example: the mouse in the photograph will have inherited ................................

.................................................................... so its genotype is

.................................................................................................... **(3 marks)**

Phenotype: the characteristics of an individual as a result of its ......................

Example: the mouse .................................................................... **(2 marks)**

Dominant allele: the characteristic coded for appears in the phenotype ............

.......................... Example: the mouse in the photo has one brown allele and one

white allele, but .................................................................... **(3 marks)**

Recessive allele: the characteristic coded for only appears in the phenotype if ...

.................................................... Example: the mouse in the photo has one

brown allele and one white allele so ....................................................................

.................................................................................................... **(3 marks)**

**4 (a)** Define the terms homozygous and heterozygous.

....................................................................................

.................................................................................................... **(2 marks)**

**(b)** Peas can be round or wrinkled. Their shape is inherited. There is a dominant allele for round peas (represented as **R**) and a recessive allele for wrinkled peas (represented as **r**). There are three possible genotypes for the shape of peas. For each of the following, state whether the plant is homozygous or heterozygous and give the phenotype of the plant:

(i) RR ........................ **(1 mark)**    (ii) Rr ..................... **(1 mark)**

(iii) rr ........................ **(1 mark)**

# Monohybrid inheritance

1  Manx cats are born with no tails. The allele for no tail is dominant (T) over the allele (t) for having a tail. The homozygous form of the dominant allele is fatal – kittens which inherit TT die before birth.

> Read the information given to you in the question carefully. You must apply the information you are given to calculating genetic probabilities.

(a)  Complete this Punnett square to show the expected genotypes and phenotypes of the kittens born to a cross between a normal cat and a Manx cat, and calculate the percentage of the offspring which you would expect to have no tails.

|   | T |   |
|---|---|---|
| t |   |   |
|   |   |   |

> Remember: percentage probabilities in Punnett squares are always 0%, 25%, 50%, 75% or 100%.

$\frac{1}{2}$ of the kittens will have the genotype ..................... and so their phenotype will be ..................... This is $\frac{2}{4} \times 100 =$ .....................    **(3 marks)**

(b)  Complete the Punnett square to show the expected genotypes of a cross between two Manx cats.

|   | T |   |
|---|---|---|
| T |   |   |
|   |   |   |

Manx cat genotype Tt

**(1 mark)**

(c)  What ratio of Manx kittens to normal kittens would you expect from this cross (regardless of survival)?

..................... **(1 mark)**

(d)  What ratio of Manx kittens to normal kittens is actually likely to survive? Explain your answer.

.................................................................................................................

.................................................................................................................

.................................................................................................................    **(2 marks)**

2  A gardener crosses two purple flowered plants and records that the flowers of all the offspring plants are also purple. He claims that his plants will always have purple flowers. Another gardener challenges him to breed his purple plants with white flowering plants and see what happens. The allele for purple colour is dominant, represented by the letter **R**. White is recessive, indicated by the letter **r**. Use Punnett squares or genetic diagrams to show the possible genotypes and phenotypes of the crosses.

.....................................

.....................................

.....................................

.....................................

.....................................

.....................................    **(4 marks)**

# Family pedigrees

1 (a) This family pedigree shows the inheritance of albinism in a family. Albinos do not make the pigment melanin in their bodies, so they have very pale skin, white hair and pale eyes. The allele for normal pigmentation is dominant (A) and the allele for albinism is recessive (a).

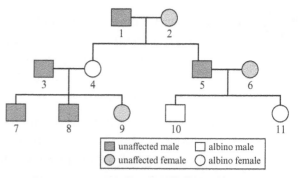

Which of the following statements is true for anyone affected by albinism? Tick **one** box.

☐   **A**   They are homozygous for allele A

☐   **B**   They are heterozygous, Aa

☐   **C**   They are homozygous for allele a

☐   **D**   Their bodies make an excess of melanin

> Read the question carefully so you know which allele represents the dominant phenotype and which represents the recessive phenotype.

**(1 mark)**

(b) State the genotypes of individuals 1 and 2 and explain how you know this.

..................................................................................................

..................................................................................................

..................................................................................................   **(3 marks)**

(c) Individual 4 is an albino, but she and her partner have three children who are not affected. Explain two different ways this may have happened (you can explain using words or draw Punnet squares or genetic diagrams).

|   | A |   |
|---|---|---|
| a |   |   |
|   |   |   |

AA × aa .....................................................

..................................................................................................

..................................................................................................

|   | A |   |
|---|---|---|
| a |   |   |
|   |   |   |

Aa × aa .....................................................

..................................................................................................   **(5 marks)**

2 This family pedigree shows the grandparents, parents and children in a family affected by Huntington's disease. This is a genetic disease that develops when people are middle-aged and it is usually fatal. The Huntington's phenotype is dominant and the allele can be represented by a capital **H**. The healthy, recessive allele is shown as **h**.

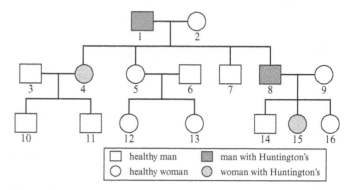

Couple 3 and 4 and couple 8 and 9 will both be affected by Huntington's. Explain how couple 3 and 4 have no affected children, but couple 8 and 9 have an affected daughter. Draw a Punnett square or genetic diagrams to help you.

|   | H |   |
|---|---|---|
| h |   |   |
|   |   |   |

Hh × hh .....................................................

..................................................................................................

..................................................................................................   **(4 marks)**

# Sex determination

**1** Which of the following is the combination of sex chromosomes you would expect to see in the cells of a human male? Tick **one** box.

☐ **A** XX

☐ **B** X

☐ **C** Y

☐ **D** XY

> Remember – chromosomes come in pairs so there will be two sex chromosomes.

**(1 mark)**

**2** When is the sex of a baby determined? Tick **one** box.

☐ **A** when the gametes are formed

☐ **B** when the baby is born

☐ **C** when the egg is fertilised by the sperm

☐ **D** as the foetus develops in the womb

> Think – the gametes are haploid so it is the moment when the two gametes fuse to form a new individual that the sex will be determined.

**(1 mark)**

**3** A couple have three little boys. They want another child. Some of their friends say that because they have three boys they are sure to have a girl if they have another child. Others say they are bound to have another boy.

(a) Complete the Punnett square below to show how the sex of the new baby is inherited.

|   | X | Y |
|---|---|---|
| X |   |   |
| X |   |   |

**(2 marks)**

(b) Are either of their sets of friends right about the sex of the baby? Explain your answer.

Each baby gets one set of chromosomes from ...............................................

Each time a baby is conceived there is a ...............................................

........................................ The outcome is not affected ...........................

........................................................................ so the new baby

has a ............................................................................... **(4 marks)**

**4** Every egg produced by a woman has a chance of becoming a baby girl. Only half of the gametes produced by a man have the chance of becoming a baby girl. Explain this statement.

..............................................................................................

..............................................................................................

..............................................................................................

..............................................................................................

..............................................................................................

..............................................................................................

..............................................................................................

..............................................................................................

.............................................................................................. **(4 marks)**

# Variation and mutation

**1** Give **one** example of genetic variation and **one** example of environmental variation between different organisms of the same species.

.................................... variation, for example, eye colour, natural hair colour:

.......................................... variation, for example, scars, being able to drive. **(1 mark)**

**2** Which of the following is an acquired characteristic? Tick **one** box.

☐ **A** brown eyes  ☐ **C** cystic fibrosis

☐ **B** a tattoo  ☐ **D** dimples

> Remember characteristics that appear during your lifetime as a result of the environment are known as **acquired characteristics**.

**(1 mark)**

**3** (a) What is a mutation?

A change ............................................................................................ **(1 mark)**

(b) Give **two** causes of mutations.

Mistakes made when ...................................................................... **(2 marks)**

(c) Most genetic mutations have no effect on the phenotype, but some do. Explain how a mutation can affect the phenotype of an organism.

The sequence of bases in the DNA codes for ............................................

............................................................... If a mutation affects the

base sequences so that different .................................................................

........................................................................................................ **(3 marks)**

**4** This bar chart shows the heights of a group of students.

(a) The *y*-axis of this bar chart shows the frequency of the characteristic. What does this mean?

..................................................................

.................................................... **(1 mark)**

(b) The bar chart is drawn with no gaps between the bars. What does this tell you?

That the characteristic measured shows ........................................... variation. **(1 mark)**

**5** This table gives you the shoe sizes of a group of Year 6 children in a UK primary school.

| Shoe size | 3 | 3.5 | 4 | 4.5 | 5 | 5.5 | 6 | 6.5 | 7 | 7.5 | 8 | 8.5 | 9 |
|---|---|---|---|---|---|---|---|---|---|---|---|---|---|
| Number of children (frequency) | 1 | 0 | 2 | 3 | 6 | 8 | 11 | 13 | 9 | 9 | 4 | 2 | 1 |

(a) Draw a bar chart to show this data in the space below.

(b) Suggest **three** factors that could have caused the variation in foot size and indicate where possible whether it is genetic, environmental or both.

.................................................................................

.................................................................................

.................................................................................

.................................................................................  **(3 marks)**

**(4 marks)**

# The Human Genome Project

**1** (a)  What is the human genome?

The human genome is ............................................................................    **(1 mark)**

(b)  What is the Human Genome Project?

A collaboration between scientists set up ............................................    **(1 mark)**

(c)  How has the Human Genome Project affected the way doctors prescribe medicines?

It enables them to look at how the genome of the person ..........................

....................................................................................................

by a particular drug.    **(2 marks)**

**2**  The results of the Human Genome Project are being used to develop new medicines and treatments for diseases.

(a)  Give **two** advantages of using the results of the Human Genome Project in medicine.

Advantage 1:

A person who is at risk from a genetic condition or ......................................

....................................................................................................

....................................................................................................

Advantage 2:

Doctors may be able to ................................................................................

....................................................................................................

....................................................................................................    **(2 marks)**

> There are more than two advantages so make sure you use two that are as different as possible.

(b)  Some people think there will be disadvantages to having all this information about the human genome. Give **one** possible **disadvantage**:

If you know you have an increased risk of developing ..................................

....................................................................................................    **(1 mark)**

**3**  Many different genes are involved in the risk of developing heart disease. Discuss the advantages and disadvantages of a genetic test, which would tell you the balance of low risk and high risk alleles in your cells.

Guided

....................................................................................................

....................................................................................................

....................................................................................................

....................................................................................................

....................................................................................................

....................................................................................................

....................................................................................................

....................................................................................................    **(5 marks)**

# Extended response – Genetics

There is a dominant mutation that results in Huntington's disease. This disease does not usually develop until the affected person is between 30 and 50 years old, although it can start much earlier or much later. The disease affects many aspects of life and there is currently no cure.

However, using the knowledge we have from the Human Genome Project, people who are at risk can be tested to see if they have the affected dominant allele. Explain how Huntington's disease is passed from one generation to the next, and discuss the advantages and disadvantages of having this test if a grandparent has been affected by the disease.

> You will always be more successful in extended response questions if you plan your answer before you start writing.
>
> You should understand how a dominant disease such as Huntington's is inherited and you should make this clear in your answer. You could sketch a genetic diagram, a Punnett square or a family tree.
>
> When you are asked to discuss, do not waffle. Identify the issues highlighted in the question and make very clear points so the examiner can see you have considered different sides of the question.
>
> In Huntington's disease you need to consider the question of having a family, as the disease usually doesn't show until middle age when children and even grandchildren can already be affected.

| include description | test advantages | test disadvantages |
|---|---|---|
| mutation | plan your life | can't change outcome |
| dominant mutation | make decisions about having kids | stress of knowing you have/will have a disease |
| HGP means it's poss. to test for faulty genes | relief if don't have faulty gene | difficult life choices |
| chances of inheriting H (Punnett) | | impact on other family members |

.......................................................................................................................

.......................................................................................................................

.......................................................................................................................

.......................................................................................................................

.......................................................................................................................

.......................................................................................................................

.......................................................................................................................

.......................................................................................................................

....................................................................................................   **(6 marks)**

# Evolution

**1** Produce a flow diagram to explain the process of natural selection.

> Adult organisms usually produce more offspring than an environment can
> support. As a result, there is ...........................................................
> between the young to survive and reproduce.

↓

> Some of the offspring inherit advantageous variations ...............................
> ..........................................................................................
> Others inherit variations ...........................................................

↓

> Individuals with the advantageous ....................................................
> ..........................................................................................

↓

> ..........................................................................................

**(4 marks)**

> Remember: **natural** selection is the process by which evolution takes place.
> **Evolution** is the emergence of a new species as a result of natural selection
> after a change in the environment or some form of isolation.

**2** Aloes and agaves look very similar. They have pointed, fleshy leaves and spines, they can both store water and they both grow in desert environments. You might think they are closely related plants, but in fact they are very different. Aloes originally come from north Africa, while agaves come from South America. DNA evidence shows that their last common ancestor lived about 93 million years ago, when there were dinosaurs on the Earth. Explain the similarities between these two very different groups of plants using Darwin's theory of evolution.

Aloe

Agave

> You are not expected to know anything about aloes and agaves: in this question, you have to apply your knowledge about natural selection and evolution to an unfamiliar example.

..........................................................................................
..........................................................................................
..........................................................................................
..........................................................................................
..........................................................................................
..........................................................................................

**(5 marks)**

# Human evolution

 **1**

| Species | Age (millions of years) | Skull volume (cm³) |
|---|---|---|
| Ardi (*Ardipithecus ramidus*) | 4.4 | 350 |
| Lucy (*Australopithecus afarensis*) | 3.2 | 400 |
| Modern human (*Homo sapiens*) | current | 1450 |

The table gives you some information about two famous ancestral human-like species and modern human beings.

(a) What is our main source of information about early human ancestors?

............................................................                     **(1 mark)**

(b) What is the main limitation to our understanding of human evolution?

The lack of ...............................................                     **(1 mark)**

(c) Why is measuring the skull volume of early human fossils so important in helping us to understand the progress of human evolution?

The volume of the skull ................................................., and the big increase

..............................................................................................................

..............................................................................................................     **(2 marks)**

**2** Explain how scientists use stone tools as evidence for human evolution.

The layers of rock where stone tools were found have been dated. The earliest stone tools found are relatively simple, because those human ancestors had

relatively small brains. ...................................................................................

..............................................................................................................     **(2 marks)**

**3**

Guided

Ardipithecus          Australopithecus      Homo habilis       Homo erectus       Homo sapiens
   ramidus                afarensis         Skull volume:      Skull volume:      Skull volume:
    ('Ardi')               ('Lucy')          500–600 cm³          850 cm³           1450 cm³
Skull volume:         Skull volume:
   350 cm³               400 cm³

This diagram shows some of our early ancestors, although this is **not** a direct line of evolution from Ardi to modern humans. Using this diagram and your own knowledge, give four ways in which human-like species and humans have evolved over time, with evidence where possible.

..............................................................................................................

..............................................................................................................

..............................................................................................................

..............................................................................................................     **(4 marks)**

# Classification

1  Which of these groups of organisms is a classification domain? Tick **one** box.

☐ **A** mammals

☐ **B** flowering plants

☐ **C** animals

☐ **D** bacteria                                                                                   **(1 mark)**

2  Complete the table giving **three** characteristics of each kingdom of organisms listed.

| Kingdom | Characteristics |
|---|---|
| Animals | 1 multicellular<br>2<br>3 |
| Plants | 1 multicellular/cells have nuclei<br>2<br>3 |
| Fungi | 1 multicellular (apart from yeasts)/cells have nuclei<br>2<br>3 |
| Protists | 1 mostly unicellular<br>2<br>3 |
| Prokaryotes | 1 unicellular<br>2<br>3 |

**(5 marks)**

> Learn the key features of the five kingdoms and the three domains.

3  The three domain system of classification was suggested relatively recently.

(a) What is the three domain system?

...................................................................................................................   **(1 mark)**

(b) Name and describe the three domains.

...................................................................................................................

...................................................................................................................

...................................................................................................................   **(3 marks)**

(c) Explain why the three domain classification system has only been developed relatively recently.

...................................................................................................................

...................................................................................................................

...................................................................................................................

...................................................................................................................

...................................................................................................................

...................................................................................................................   **(3 marks)**

# Selective breeding

**1** Which of the following organisms are **not** the result of selective breeding? Tick **one** box.

☐ **A** Jersey cows

☐ **B** golden labrador dogs

☐ **C** garden roses

☐ **D** red squirrels

> Almost all animals kept by people – both farm animals and pets – are the result of **many years** of selective breeding.

**(1 mark)**

**2 (a)** What is meant by selective breeding?

It is when plants or animals with .............................................................................

so the offspring produced ................................................................................ **(1 mark)**

**(b)** Farmers have carried out selective breeding on plants and animals for centuries. Give **three** possible characteristics they might try to improve.

Disease resistance/.............................................................................................

........................................................................................................................... **(3 marks)**

**3** Some people love cats, but are allergic to cat hair. Explain how a breeder might produce a breed of cats with very little fur, so that people allergic to cats can enjoy having them as pets.

First, the breeder would choose two cats – male and female – with very little hair.

Then, ..................................................................................................................

........................................................................................................................... **(3 marks)**

**4 (a)** Describe the change in the yields of wheat in the UK since 1887.

.................................................................

.................................................................

.................................................................

.................................................................

................................................ **(3 marks)**

> This answer is worth three marks – so just saying the yields increased isn't enough!

UK wheat yields 1885–2020

(graph: Tonnes per hectare vs years 1885–2020, showing yield roughly constant around 2 until ~1945 then rising to about 8)

**(b)** Suggest **two** factors that might have brought about this increase in yield.

.................................................................................................................................

......................................................................................................................... **(2 marks)**

**(c)** Suggest **one** problem that might arise from changing yields like this, and explain how such problems might be overcome.

.................................................................................................................................

.................................................................................................................................

......................................................................................................................... **(3 marks)**

# Genetic engineering

1 (a) What is genetic engineering?

Genetic engineering is changing ...................................................................

.................................................................................................... **(1 mark)**

(b) Summarise the three main steps in the process of genetic engineering.

The gene for ...........................................................................................

The gene is inserted .................................................................................

The cell of the ................................................................. **(3 marks)**

2 In America, parents can buy glowing fish for their children. These fish are bred from genetically modified organisms – fish that have had genes added from jelly fish or sea anemones, which make them fluoresce bright colours. Glowing fish were originally developed to help scientists monitor pollution in waterways.

(a) What is a genetically modified organism?

An organism which has ................................................................. **(1 mark)**

(b) Give **one** advantage of producing genetically modified organisms such as glowing fish and **one** disadvantage.

> Glowing fish are only being used as an example – think of all the different advantages and disadvantages of genetically modifying organisms you have considered.

Advantage: they can be .............................................................................

....................................................................................................

Disadvantage: some people feel ...................................................................

.................................................................................................... **(2 marks)**

3 People with diabetes cannot live without insulin injections. In the past, they had to use insulin extracted from cows and pigs. The supply was limited and some people reacted to the insulin from other animals, because it was not quite the same as human insulin. Scientists then discovered how to genetically modify bacteria to produce human insulin. They grow the bacteria in huge containers and now there is plenty of human insulin for everyone who needs it.

(a) Why did the scientists use genetic engineering rather than selective breeding to make insulin-producing bacteria?

....................................................................................................

....................................................................................................

.................................................................................................... **(2 marks)**

(b) Describe how the GM bacteria which make human insulin are produced, and why scientists do not need to keep repeating the process.

....................................................................................................

....................................................................................................

.................................................................................................... **(3 marks)**

# Stages in genetic engineering

1  In genetic engineering, what is the term for anything that carries a new gene into the host cell? Tick **one** box.

☐ **A** plasmid

☐ **B** enzyme

☐ **C** virus

☐ **D** vector

> Learn the key terms in genetic engineering including plasmids, vector, sticky ends, restriction enzymes and DNA ligase.

**(1 mark)**

2  Human growth hormone is made in the pituitary gland in the brain. Children need human growth hormone to grow properly. Some children cannot make their own growth hormone. For many years it was very difficult to get enough growth hormone to treat affected children. Now scientists have genetically modified bacteria to make human growth hormone. Now there is plenty of the hormone to treat everyone affected by this condition.

(a)  How is the required gene for making growth hormone removed from a human cell?

Specific enzymes called ............................................................................................

They leave ............................................................................................  **(2 marks)**

(b)  How is the bacterial cell prepared for the new gene?

The same .................................... are used to ........................................

............................................................................................................  **(2 marks)**

(c)  Describe how the new gene is inserted into the bacterial DNA.

The pieces of DNA containing the human growth hormone gene are ....................

............................................................................................................

............................................................................................................

............................................................................................................

............................................................................................................  **(4 marks)**

(d)  A relatively small number of bacteria are modified. How can this small number of bacteria fill huge tanks and make enough human growth hormone for everyone who needs it?

The bacteria ......................................................................................

.................................... so they can make a lot of human growth hormone.  **(1 mark)**

3  Compare the roles of restriction enzymes and DNA ligase in genetic engineering.

............................................................................................................

............................................................................................................

............................................................................................................

............................................................................................................

............................................................................................................

............................................................................................................

............................................................................................................

............................................................................................................  **(5 marks)**

# Extended response – Genetic modification

The Light Sussex cockerel on the left is the result of hundreds of years of selective breeding, while the scarlet macaw on the right is the result of millions of years of evolution. Bacteria that have been genetically engineered to produce human proteins have been developed over a matter of months and years.

Compare and contrast evolution, selective breeding and genetic engineering, and evaluate the usefulness of selective breeding and genetic engineering to people.

> To be successful in extended response questions, plan your answer before you start writing.
>
> When you are asked to compare and contrast processes, look for similarities **and** differences.
>
> There are two command terms here: 'compare and contrast', and 'evaluate'. Both mean you need to look for pros and cons, advantages and disadvantages, but when you evaluate you must make some judgement on the advantages and disadvantages of the processes. Your answer could explain the following points:
>
> - similarities between the three processes of evolution, selective breeding and genetic engineering
> - differences between the processes of evolution, selective breeding and genetic engineering
> - consider the usefulness to people of selective breeding compared with genetic engineering
> - any other sensible, thoughtful points.

| Evolution | Selective breeding | Genetic engineering |
|---|---|---|
| Huge periods of time | Decades/centuries | Relatively fast |
| Environmental factors selected | Desired and undesired characteristics selected | Only chosen characteristics selected |
| | Same species only | Genes from different species can be used |

..................................................................................................................

..................................................................................................................

..................................................................................................................

..................................................................................................................

..................................................................................................................

..................................................................................................................

..................................................................................................................

..................................................................................................................

..................................................................................................................

**(6 marks)**

# Health and disease

1 (a) What is a communicable disease?

A disease which ............................................................................................................

.......................................................................................................................... **(1 mark)**

(b) What causes communicable diseases?

................................................................. **(1 mark)**

(c) Which of the following diseases is non-communicable? Tick **one** box.

☐ **A** influenza                    ☐ **C** tuberculosis

☐ **B** lung cancer                  ☐ **D** common cold      **(1 mark)**

> Remember the difference!
> Communicable diseases can be passed from one person to another and are caused by pathogens.
> Non-communicable diseases cannot be passed from one person to another **and** are not caused by pathogens.

2 The World Health Organization defines good health as a state of 'complete physical, social and mental well-being'. What is meant by:

(a) physical well-being?

Being free .......................................................................................... **(1 mark)**

(b) Social well-being?

Getting on well ................................................................................... **(1 mark)**

(c) Mental well-being?

.......................................................................................................... **(1 mark)**

3 (a) What is a pathogen?

A microorganism which ..................................................................... **(1 mark)**

(b) Complete the following table showing the four main types of pathogens.

| Pathogen | How do they make you ill? |
|---|---|
| Bacteria | May release ........................................ |
| Viruses | Take over ...........................................  ............................................................ |
| ............................. | Eukaryotic organisms that dissolve and damage cells |
| ............................. | Eukaryotic organisms that can live in the body and damage cells |

**(4 marks)**

> Learn how the different types of pathogens cause the symptoms of disease.

4 Explain why having a non-communicable disease makes you more likely to become ill from other diseases.

Guided

..........................................................................................................

..........................................................................................................

.......................................................................................................... **(2 marks)**

# Common infections

**1** Which of the following is a communicable disease only affecting plants? Tick **one** box.

Guided

☐ **A** tuberculosis

☐ **B** cholera

☐ **C** chalara

☐ **D** malaria

**(1 mark)**

**2** Botswana is an African country with a population of just over 2.26 million. The data in the graph shows the relationship between HIV infection and the numbers of people infected with TB each year.

Maths skills

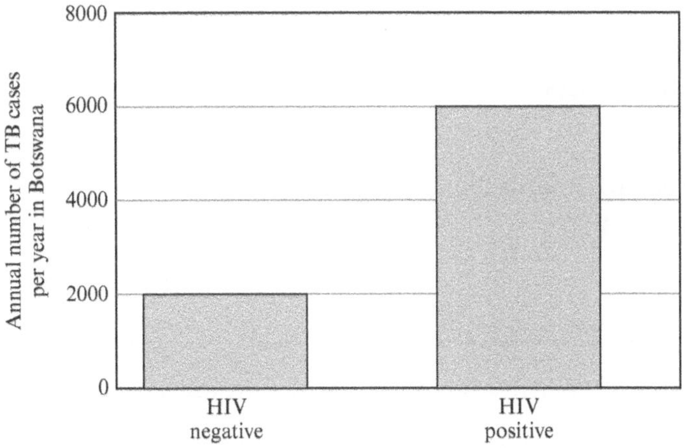

(a) Give the total number of people infected each year with TB in Botswana.

....................................... **(1 mark)**

Maths skills

(b) What percentage of the people infected with TB are also infected with HIV?

$\frac{6000}{8000}$ × ............................. **(2 marks)**

(c) Explain why people infected with HIV are so much more likely to also become infected with TB.

.......................................................................................................................

.......................................................................................................................

.......................................................................................................................

....................................................................................................................... **(3 marks)**

**3** Complete the table to give three common human infections, with the symptoms of each.

Guided

| Pathogen | Disease | Symptoms |
|---|---|---|
| Bacterium | .................................... | ..........................................<br>.......................................... |
| Virus | .................................... | ..........................................<br>.......................................... |
| Protist | .................................... | ..........................................<br>.......................................... |

**(6 marks)**

# How pathogens spread

1  How do the viruses that cause colds and flu spread from one person to another?
   Tick **one** box.

   ☐  **A**  through a cut in the skin

   ☐  **B**  through insect bites

   ☐  **C**  through the mouth in food or water

   ☐  **D**  by droplet infection from the air

> Think carefully about the different ways pathogens can get into your body and which part of the body is affected by the pathogen.

**(1 mark)**

2  Cholera is an infection that kills thousands of people

   (a)  What type of pathogen causes cholera?

   ........................................................................................................................  **(1 mark)**

   (b)  Describe the main symptoms of cholera.

   Large amounts ................................................................................................  **(1 mark)**

   (c)  Cholera is a particular problem after natural disasters, such as floods and
        earthquakes. Explain this observation.

   The bacteria that cause cholera ............................................. If there is a good

   sewage system, they ........................................................................................

   After natural disasters.................................... so diarrhoea gets into water

   used for ...........................................................................................................  **(3 marks)**

3  Describe the difference between a pathogen and a vector.

   A pathogen is ..................................................................................................

   A vector is a living ..........................................................................................  **(2 marks)**

> Mosquitoes are the vectors for the protist that causes malaria, carrying it from host to host in their bodies.

4  Here are **three** ways of reducing the spread of pathogens and so reducing infectious
   diseases. Explain how each way works:

   **Guided**

   (a)  Washing hands thoroughly after using the toilet.

   ........................................................................................................................

   ........................................................................................................................  **(2 marks)**

   (b)  Boiling water before using it to drink or wash salads in hot countries with poor
        sanitation.

   ........................................................................................................................

   ........................................................................................................................  **(2 marks)**

   (c)  Using tissues when you cough, sneeze or blow your nose, putting the used tissue in
        a bin and then washing your hands.

   ........................................................................................................................

   ........................................................................................................................

   ........................................................................................................................  **(2 marks)**

# STIs

1 Which of the following statements about STIs is **not** correct? Tick **one** box.

☐ **A** An STI is a sexually transmitted infection.

☐ **B** STIs are usually transmitted through sexual activity.

☐ **C** Many people with STIs do not know they are infected.

☐ **D** STIs are always incurable.

**(1 mark)**

> STIs caused by bacteria such as *Chlamydia*, gonorrhoea and syphilis can all be cured using antibiotics if they are picked up early, before they cause permanent damage.
>
> STIs caused by viruses such as herpes and HIV can be treated to greatly reduce the symptoms.

2 Explain the following statements about STIs.

(a) The spread of many STIs can be prevented if men wear condoms when having sex.

STIs are spread ......................................................................

If a man wears a condom, ............................................................

..............................................................................................

.............................................................................................. **(3 marks)**

(b) All pregnant women are routinely screened for STIs including *Chlamydia* and HIV.

A woman can have these STIs without knowing. The pathogens can be passed

from ......................................................................................

If the infection is picked up by screening ............................................

.............................................................................................. **(3 marks)**

3 There are a number of ways in which we can reduce the incidence, and prevent the spread, of STIs. For each of the methods given below, explain how they have their effect.

**Guided**

Using condoms during sexual intercourse.

..............................................................................................

.............................................................................................. **(1 mark)**

Screening blood transfusions for STIs.

..............................................................................................

.............................................................................................. **(2 marks)**

Increasing sex education for young people.

..............................................................................................

..............................................................................................

..............................................................................................

.............................................................................................. **(3 marks)**

Supplying intravenous drug users with sterile needles.

..............................................................................................

.............................................................................................. **(2 marks)**

# Human defences

1  Which of the following acts as both a physical and a chemical barrier to the entry of pathogens into your body? Tick **one** box.

☐  **A**  tears

☐  **B**  saliva

☐  **C**  mucus

☐  **D**  skin

> Many chemical barriers contain enzymes or acids to kill pathogens whereas a physical barrier stops pathogens entering your body. This question is asking you to identify a barrier that does both.

**(1 mark)**

2  The human body is surrounded by microorganisms all the time and some of them are pathogens. Explain how each of the following helps to defend the body against these pathogens.

> The command word here is 'explain' and you get 2 marks – so just saying the skin acts as a barrier isn't enough to get full marks – that is just a description!

(a)  The skin

Unbroken skin forms ....................................................................................

because it is ....................................................................................  **(2 marks)**

(b)  The acid in the stomach

The acid in the stomach acts as ....................................................................

................................................................................................................  **(2 marks)**

(c)  The tears

Tears act as ................................................................................................

................................................................................................................  **(2 marks)**

3  Children in households where one or both of their parents smoke are much more likely to get infections, especially chest infections.

(a)  Name the structures labelled A, B and C.

A .................................................................

B .................................................................

C .................................................................  **(3 marks)**

(b)  Suggest how these structures protect our lungs.

> The air you breathe contains lots of dirt and pathogens. Think about how your body keeps your lungs clean.

................................................................................................................

................................................................................................................  **(2 marks)**

(c)  Explain how breathing in second-hand smoke can increase the risk of children getting chest infections.

................................................................................................................

................................................................................................................

................................................................................................................

................................................................................................................

................................................................................................................  **(3 marks)**

# The immune system

1 The immune system uses chemicals found on the outside of cells and viruses to identify if something is a cell of the body or if it has come from outside the body. What are these special identifying chemicals called? Tick **one** box.

☐ **A** antigens

☐ **B** antibodies

☐ **C** antivirals

☐ **D** antibiotics

> **Antigens** are chemicals on the outside surface of **all** cells. White blood cells produce **antibodies** that match the shape of specific antigens on the pathogen cells or viruses so that the body can recognise its own cells from foreign cells or viruses. Make sure you learn the difference between these two similar sounding words.

**(1 mark)**

2 When you get a disease, your immune system will attack and destroy the pathogens causing your illness.

(a) Describe how your immune system recognises the pathogens.

White blood cells called .......................................... have ..............................

on their surfaces. The shape ..................................................................

.............................. If the pathogen is present ......................................

.................................................

**(3 marks)**

(b) Explain how your immune system destroys the pathogens so that you recover from the disease.

A l........................ is activated when an .......................... from a ..............

................ fits into ........................................................ It then divides

.................................................... These ............................................

which ................................ and destroy them.

**(3 marks)**

(c) Once you have had a disease once, you are unlikely to get it again because you will develop natural immunity. Explain how this works.

Some of the activated ....................... form .......................... When you meet

the same ........................... again, they can .............................................

........................... before you develop symptoms of the disease.

**(3 marks)**

3 (a) What event has happened at point X?

.................................................

................................. **(1 mark)**

(b) What events are indicated by the letters A and B?

A .................................................

B .................................................

first infection with pathogen

**(2 marks)**

(c) The antibody numbers per cm³ of blood climb faster and get much higher in response B than in response A. Explain both of these differences.

.................................................................................................

.................................................................................................

.................................................................................................

.................................................................................................

**(3 marks)**

# Immunisation

1 Define the following terms.

(a) Immunisation

Immunisation is ..............................................................................

.......................................................................... in the future.  **(1 mark)**

(b) Vaccine

A vaccine is ........................................................................................,

to produce ...................................................................................  **(2 marks)**

2 If you are immunised against a disease, you should never get it. This is known as artificial immunity. Compare natural immunity and artificial immunity.

Natural immunity results from your exposure to a ............................................

In artificial immunity, ............................ pathogens are injected into the body

(or taken by mouth/nose), so you never get ............................

In both natural and artificial immunity, the ................................ on the

pathogens trigger ...................................................................

........................ If you then meet the live pathogen, ............................

.............................................................................................

.............................................................................................  **(4 marks)**

> This question carries a lot of marks. Plan your answer carefully to make sure you cover all the main points. Make sure you compare the processes, highlighting the similarities as well as the differences.

3 In the UK, babies are given a single injection at eight, 12 and 16 weeks of age to immunise them against diphtheria, tetanus, whooping cough, polio and Hib.

Guided

(a) What does this tell you about the vaccine the babies are given?

.............................................................................................

.............................................................................................

.............................................................................................  **(1 mark)**

(b) Immunisation only protects babies from specific diseases. Explain why immunisation against one pathogen does not give immunity to other diseases.

.............................................................................................

.............................................................................................

.............................................................................................

.............................................................................................

.............................................................................................

.............................................................................................

.............................................................................................

.............................................................................................  **(5 marks)**

# Treating infections

1 Which of the following is a type of medicine that can kill bacteria and so cure bacterial diseases? Tick **one** box.

☐ **A** antigens

☐ **B** anti-inflammatories

☐ **C** antibodies

☐ **D** antibiotics

> Don't get muddled between words linked to the immune response and the drugs that cure bacterial diseases.

**(1 mark)**

2 (a) Why are antibiotics so useful at treating bacterial infections in humans?

Because they ..........................., but do not affect ...................................... **(1 mark)**

(b) Give **two** ways antibiotics can affect bacteria.

They can ............................... or they can .............................................

............................................................................................................... **(2 marks)**

(c) A worried mother goes to the doctor with her toddler, who has a bad cold. She wants some antibiotics to make the child better. The doctor does not give any antibiotics. Suggest why this decision was made.

Colds are caused ........................... Antibiotics do not ...............................

so they would ............................................ **(2 marks)**

3 In the early years of the 20th century, many women died from infection shortly after they gave birth.

(a) What was the highest rate of maternal deaths recorded in the United States between 1900 and 2010?

.................................................... **(2 marks)**

(b) Suggest a reason for the rapid fall in maternal deaths observed in the shaded area of the graph.

....................................................

.................................................... **(1 mark)**

Maternal death rates in the US 1900–2010

(c) The rate of maternal deaths from infection has remained very low for many years. Scientists now fear that, as a result of the over-use of antibiotics, the number of women dying from these infections may increase again in the future. Discuss this statement.

...............................................................................................................

...............................................................................................................

...............................................................................................................

...............................................................................................................

...............................................................................................................

...............................................................................................................

...............................................................................................................

............................................................................................................... **(4 marks)**

# New medicines

1 Which of the following processes is **not** involved in the development of new medicines? Tick **one** box.

☐ **A**  discovery

☐ **B**  clinical testing

☐ **C**  immunisation

☐ **D**  development

> The four stages of drug development are discovery, development, pre-clinical testing and clinical testing.

**(1 mark)**

2 Scientists have discovered a new chemical in the fruit of a tree from the rain forests of South America. Local people use the fruit to cure many types of disease, including some cancers. Scientists observe that people who take the fruit do seem to recover from some of their illnesses.

(a) Suggest **two** reasons why the scientists don't bring the fruit back to the UK and start using it to treat ill people immediately.

Because they don't know ..................................................... There may be

.............................................................................................. **(2 marks)**

(b) Once the chemicals have been isolated from the fruit, they will have to go through several stages of pre-clinical testing.

(i) What is pre-clinical testing?

Testing new medicines .......................................................................

.............................................................................................. **(2 marks)**

(ii) Describe **three** different stages of pre-clinical testing.

Testing on ...............................................

Testing on ...............................................

Testing on ............................................... **(3 marks)**

(c) Describe what happens if the pre-clinical testing of the new medicine is successful.

It goes into ......................... First it is tried on ...................................

..................................., and then it is tried on ................................... **(3 marks)**

3 New drugs are being developed all the time. It takes many years and costs enormous amounts of money to bring new medicines into your doctor's surgery.

(a) Give **one** reason new medicines are tested so carefully before they are used on patients.

.............................................................................................. **(1 mark)**

(b) What is the efficacy of a drug?

.............................................................................................. **(1 mark)**

(c) What is meant by the optimum dose of a drug?

.............................................................................................. **(1 mark)**

(d) What does it mean if a drug is found to be toxic during pre-clinical or clinical trials?

.............................................................................................. **(1 mark)**

(e) When a medicine has passed the stages of development, doctors will report any problems when they use it. Suggest a reason why this constant testing is important.

..............................................................................................

.............................................................................................. **(3 marks)**

# Non-communicable diseases

1 (a)  What is the one thing all non-communicable diseases have in common?

They cannot be ............................................................................... **(1 mark)**

(b)  Many non-communicable diseases are caused by the interaction of a number of factors. List **four** of the factors that can affect your risk of developing a non-communicable disease.

Genes, ..............................., ..............................., ..................... **(4 marks)**

2  A mutation in the BRCA gene affects the risk of developing both breast and ovarian cancer in women. It also affects the risk of developing some other cancers in men. The data in this bar chart looks at the effect of the BRCA allele in women.

> Bar chart to show the impact of the BRCA
> mutation on cancer risk

Always look carefully at any data you are given – you will be expected to use it in your answers.

**Maths skills**

(a)  What is the increased percentage risk of developing breast cancer for a woman before the age of 50?

........................................................... **(1 mark)**

**Maths skills**

(b)  How does the risk of developing breast cancer by the age of 70 compare with the risk of developing ovarian cancer by the age of 70 for a woman who has inherited the BRCA mutation?

.............................. for breast cancer compared with ........................... **(1 mark)**

(c)  Breast cancer and ovarian cancers are examples of non-communicable disease. From the data in the bar chart:

(i)  give **one** factor which increases the risk of developing breast cancer other than genetics.

................................................................................................ **(1 mark)**

(ii)  describe the effect this factor has on the risk.

It ........................ the risk – from around ........................................

to around ........................... Over those 20 years ...........................

................................................................................................ **(3 marks)**

Use data from the graph where you can to support your answer and get all of the marks.

3  Here are four factors that increase your risk of developing a non-communicable disease. For each factor, give an example of how it affects your risk.

Age: ..................................................................................................

Lifestyle factors: ....................................................................................

................................................................................................

Environmental factors: ..............................................................................

................................................................................................

Sex: ............................................................................................... **(4 marks)**

# Alcohol and smoking

1 One of these diseases is often caused by drinking a lot of alcoholic drinks over a long period of time. Which one? Tick **one** box.

☐ **A** heart disease

☐ **B** cirrhosis of the liver

☐ **C** lung cancer

☐ **D** heart failure

> Remember: ethanol, the drug found in alcoholic drinks, is processed in the liver, so liver cells are more likely to be damaged by excess drinking than any other body cells.

**(1 mark)**

2 The table below gives the amount of alcohol drunk per person per year and the incidence of liver disease per 100 000 of the population in several countries, listed alphabetically.

| Country | Alcohol drunk per person per year (dm³) | Deaths from liver disease (per 100 000 people) |
|---|---|---|
| Australia | 10.00–12.49 | 6.8 |
| Brazil | 7.5–9.99 | 28.8 |
| Russia | ⩾12.50 | 48.7 |
| UK | ⩾12.50 | 16.0 |
| USA | 7.5–9.99 | 14.9 |

**Maths skills**

(a) List the countries in order of amounts of alcohol drunk per year, from the least to the most.

Brazil, USA, ............................, ............................, ............................  **(1 mark)**

**Maths skills**

(b) List the countries in order of the number of deaths from liver disease per year.

Australia, USA, ............................, ............................, ............................  **(1 mark)**

(c) Here are two statements about non-communicable diseases:

A Non-communicable diseases may be caused by a single lifestyle factor.

B Non-communicable diseases are often the result of several different factors.

Using the data from the table, give examples that illustrate both of these points.

A Russia is one of the countries ............................................................

and also has ............................................, which is ............................

B The UK appears to drink ............................................, but ............................

............................, Australia drinks ............................, but ............................

............................ – facts like these suggest ............................  **(3 marks)**

3 (a) What is meant by a lifestyle disease?

............................................................................................................

............................................................................................................

............................................................................................................  **(1 mark)**

(b) Cigarette smoke contains many substances that have negative effects on health. List **four** of them and describe how they affect the body.

............................................................................................................

............................................................................................................

............................................................................................................

............................................................................................................  **(4 marks)**

# Malnutrition and obesity

**1** (a)  What is malnutrition?

When someone eats too ......................... or too ...................................... **(1 mark)**

(b)  Give an example of a lifestyle disease caused by eating too little of a named nutrient.

.................................................................................................................... **(1 mark)**

> Learn a few examples of diseases caused by lack of specific nutrients or by excess food/fat.

**2** (a)  A woman visits her doctor and is told her BMI is too high. What does BMI stand for?

Body ............................................................................................................... **(1 mark)**

(b)  How do you calculate the BMI of a person?

BMI = $\dfrac{.........................}{.........................}$ **(1 mark)**

(c)  A man has a health check for his job. He weighs 70 kg and he is 1.6 m tall. Is he obese? Explain your answer.

BMI = 70 ......................... = ............................... = ...............................

A BMI of over ............................... is obese, so ...................................... **(3 marks)**

**3** (a)  What is waist : hip ratio?

..............................................................................................................

.............................................................................................................. **(2 marks)**

Charts to show the relationships between BMI and
waist : hip ratio with death from cardiovascular
disease in over 4000 Australian men

(b)  What do both of the charts tell us about the relationship between obesity and cardiovascular disease?

..............................................................................................................

..............................................................................................................

.............................................................................................................. **(2 marks)**

(c)  Suggest why your waist : hip ratio is a better predictor of your risk of cardiovascular disease than your BMI.

..............................................................................................................

..............................................................................................................

.............................................................................................................. **(3 marks)**

# Cardiovascular disease

1 Explain how blood vessels can be damaged as a result of smoking, leading to cardiovascular disease.

> The question refers to smoking, so make sure you relate your answer to the damage caused by smoking.

Substances from tobacco smoke damage ...................................................... **(1 mark)**

Fat builds up on the artery wall at the site of ................................................,

making the artery ....................................................................................... **(2 marks)**

A blood clot may block the artery where ................................................., or

..............................................................................., causing a heart

attack or ....................................................................................... **(3 marks)**

2 (a) Give **four** lifestyle changes a doctor might suggest to treat early signs of cardiovascular disease or to prevent cardiovascular disease from developing.

Lose ....................; give up .........................; take .........................;

eat ....................................... **(4 marks)**

(b) Give **two** advantages and **one** disadvantage of these treatments.

Advantages: no side effects/ ...................................................................

Disadvantages: ....................................................................... **(3 marks)**

3 If lifestyle changes do not reverse cardiovascular disease the patient they will be given medication. Heart medication drugs can lower the level of fat in the blood, lower the blood pressure, or make the heart beat more strongly, more slowly or more rapidly. Complete this table to show **two** advantages and **two** disadvantages of taking drugs to treat cardiovascular disease.

| Advantages | Disadvantages |
|---|---|
| Have an immediate ...... | |
| | |

**(4 marks)**

4 If a patient has a narrowed coronary artery which does not respond well to lifestyle changes or medication, they may be offered surgery. One option is to insert a stent. Another is bypass surgery.

> Guided

(a) Why is it so important to treat a narrowed coronary artery successfully?

..............................................................................................................

....................................................................................................... **(3 marks)**

(b) What is a stent?

....................................................................................................... **(1 mark)**

(c) Describe what happens during bypass surgery.

....................................................................................................... **(1 mark)**

(d) Surgery offers a long-term solution to the problems of cardiovascular disease. Explain why it is not the first choice of treatment.

..............................................................................................................

..............................................................................................................

....................................................................................................... **(5 marks)**

# Extended response – Health and disease

In 2010, UK newspapers reported a woman who had just turned 100 years old – and had been a regular smoker for 70 years, as well as enjoying a regular drink of whisky and beer. She was quoted as saying 'I've been smoking since I was 30 and have had no problems at all!'

Scientists often describe non-communicable diseases such as lung cancer and heart disease as multi-factorial.

Discuss how this story confirms that view of disease.

> You will always be more successful in extended response questions if you plan your answer before you start writing.
>
> When you are asked to discuss, do not waffle. Identify the issues highlighted in the question and make very clear points so the examiner can see you have considered different sides of the question.
>
> In this question, you have to cover factors that can affect multifactorial diseases, the expected results of long term smoking and the other factors which mean some people remain healthy in spite of smoking.
>
> Your answer could explain the following points:
>
> - factors affecting health and the development of non-communicable diseases
> - the known impacts of smoking on health
> - the known impacts of drinking on health
> - the factors that would make you expect this lady to have some type of serious non-communicable disease
> - the factors that might have protected her from diseases such as lung cancer and heart disease
> - any other sensible, thoughtful points.
>
> Make sure you refer to scientific evidence about links between lifestyle factors and disease – but emphasise that statistics refer to populations, not individuals.

.................................................................................................

.................................................................................................

.................................................................................................

.................................................................................................

.................................................................................................

.................................................................................................

.................................................................................................

.................................................................................................

.................................................................................................

.................................................................................................

.................................................................................................

.................................................................................................

.................................................................................................

................................................................................................. **(6 marks)**

# Photosynthesis

**1** (a) Which of the following is **not** needed for photosynthesis to take place? Tick **one** box.

☐ **A** carbon dioxide

☐ **B** water

☐ **C** oxygen

☐ **D** light

> Remember: oxygen is one of the products of photosynthesis.

**(1 mark)**

(b) Complete this word summary to show the reactants and products of photosynthesis.

carbon dioxide + ..................... → ..................... + oxygen          **(2 marks)**

(c) Where does photosynthesis take place in the plant cells?

...............................................          **(1 mark)**

> **Chloroplasts** are the organelles where photosynthesis takes place.
> **Chlorophyll** is the green pigment in the chloroplasts which traps the light needed for the process.

(d) Photosynthesis is an endothermic reaction. What does this mean?

.................................................................................................................

.................................................................................................................          **(2 marks)**

**2** A student investigated the importance of light to plants. They left a plant in the dark for 48 hours. Then they completely covered one leaf in black card and another leaf in black card with a circle cut out of it. One leaf was left uncovered. The plant was placed in the light for the day. Then three leaves (A, B and C in the diagram) were removed from the plant and tested for starch using iodine solution.

> Guided
>
> Practical skills

leaf A          leaf B          black card

black card with circle cut out          leaf C

(a) Why is the plant left in the dark for 48 hours before the investigation?

.................................................................................................................

.................................................................................................................          **(2 marks)**

(b) What would you expect the result to be on leaf A? Explain your answer.

.................................................................................................................

.................................................................................................................          **(2 marks)**

(c) What would you expect the result to be on leaf B? Explain your answer.

.................................................................................................................

.................................................................................................................          **(2 marks)**

(d) What would you expect the result to be on leaf C? Explain your answer.

.................................................................................................................

.................................................................................................................          **(2 marks)**

(e) Suggest one way in which the student could make their results more reliable.

.................................................................................................................          **(1 mark)**

# Limiting factors

**1** Give **three** factors that can limit the rate of photosynthesis if they are in short supply.

..................................................................................................................... **(3 marks)**

> Quantify where you can – light **intensity**, not just light, carbon dioxide **concentration**, not just carbon dioxide.

**2** This graph shows the results of an investigation into the effect of light intensity on the rate of photosynthesis.

(a) What is happening at point A on the graph?

.......................................................................

....................................................... **(2 marks)**

(b) What is happening at point B on the graph?

.....................................................................................................................

..................................................................................................................... **(3 marks)**

> Looking at the marks gives you an idea of how much information you need to give in your answer.

**3** (a) Explain why carbon dioxide concentration affects the rate of photosynthesis.

..................................................................................................................... **(2 marks)**

(b) Explain how temperature affects the rate of photosynthesis.

.....................................................................................................................

.....................................................................................................................

..................................................................................................................... **(3 marks)**

> The effect of temperature on the rate of photosynthesis differs from the effect of carbon dioxide or light intensity because very high temperatures denature enzymes and stop photosynthesis permanently.

**4** This graph shows the interaction of light intensity and carbon dioxide concentration on the rate of photosynthesis.

(a) What are the limiting factors at points A, B and C?

A .............................................................................................

B .............................................................................................

C ....................................................................... **(3 marks)**

(b) Sketch on the graph what you would expect to happen at 0.2% $CO_2$ concentration if the temperature increases by 10 °C. **(1 mark)**

(c) Explain which factors might be limiting the rate of photosynthesis in a field of wheat:

(i) early in the morning. ......................................................................

..................................................................................................................... **(2 marks)**

(ii) at midday. ..........................................................................................

..................................................................................................................... **(2 marks)**

# Light intensity

**Practical skills**

1 (a) What is this apparatus often used to investigate?

..................................................................................... **(1 mark)**

(b) How do you measure the rate of photosynthesis?

...............................................................................

.........................................................................**(2 marks)**

(c) Give **two** steps you must take to make sure your results are as reliable as possible.

...............................................................................

...............................................................................

............................................................................... **(1 mark)**

oxygen

oxygen bubbles

water

pondweed

> This question is testing your practical skills so make sure you give practical answers.

**Guided**

**Practical skills**

2 In an investigation into the effect of light intensity, students placed a lamp at different distances from some Cabomba (pondweed) in water. They measured the volume of the gas produced.

| Distance from lamp (cm) | 5 | 10 | 15 | 20 | 25 | 30 |
|---|---|---|---|---|---|---|
| Volume of gas produced (mm³) | 83 | 57 | 43 | 28 | 19 | 11 |

(a) Plot a graph of the results of this investigation.

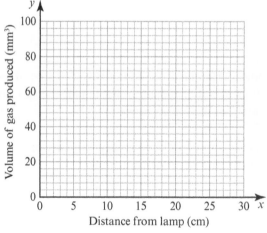

**(2 marks)**

(b) Use your graph to find the volume of gas likely to be given off if you moved the lamp to 18 cm from the pondweed.

............................................................................... **(1 mark)**

(c) Explain the difference between the distance of the light from the lamp and light intensity.

...............................................................................

...............................................................................

...............................................................................

...............................................................................

............................................................................... **(2 marks)**

# Specialised plant cells

1   The diagram shows some cells from a plant tissue specialised for transport.

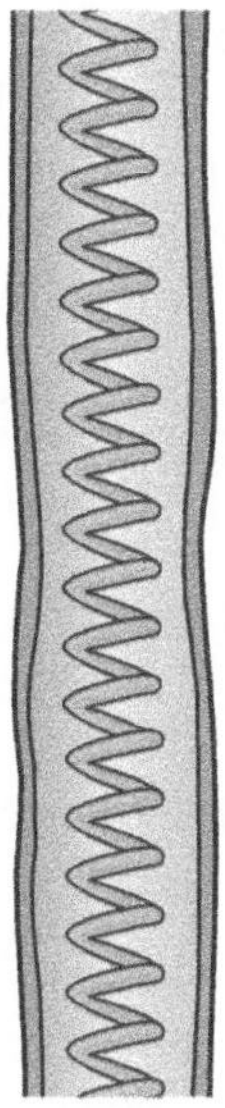

   (a)   State the name of this plant transport tissue.

   ..................................................................

   ..................................................................

                                                           **(1 mark)**

   (b)   What does it transport?

   ..................................................................

   ..................................................................   **(1 mark)**

   (c)   Give **two** features of this tissue and explain the importance of each.

   ..................................................................

   ..................................................................

   ..................................................................

   ..................................................................   **(4 marks)**

> Make sure you can recognise xylem and phloem cells – and know what they do.

2   The diagram shows a root hair cell.

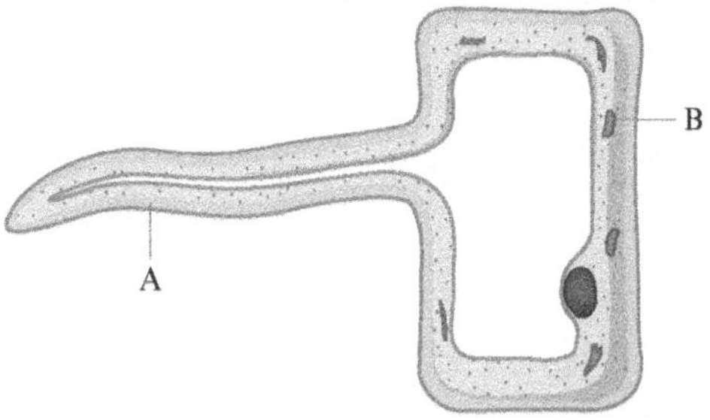

   (a)   What is the function of a root hair cell?

   ............................................................

   ............................................................

   ............................................................   **(1 mark)**

   (b)   Give **two** ways in which the structure labelled A is adapted for the functions of the root hair cell.

   ..................................................................

   ..................................................................

   ..................................................................

   ..................................................................   **(4 marks)**

   (c)   Explain why structure B is so important in the cytoplasm of the root hair cell.

   ..................................................................

   ..................................................................   **(2 marks)**

> Think about what organelle B provides to the cell and what it is used for.

3   (a)   State the name of the tissue that transports sucrose around a plant.

   ..................................................................   **(1 mark)**

> Guided

   (b)   Give **two** ways in which phloem tissue is adapted for its function.

   ..................................................................

   ..................................................................   **(2 marks)**

# Transpiration

1  What is the loss of water from a plant by evaporation and diffusion through the leaves known as? Tick **one** box.

☐  **A**  translocation

☐  **B**  transportation

☐  **C**  respiration

> Be clear about the difference between **transpiration** and **translocation**.

☐  **D**  transpiration                                                        **(1 mark)**

2  (a)  What is the transpiration stream?

.................................................................................................... **(1 mark)**

(b)  Complete this flow chart of the transpiration stream.

> Name the plant structures involved in transpiration as well as the processes.

Water ............................................................................................

↓

Water ............................................................................................

↓

Water ............................................................................................

↓

Water ............................................................................................                **(4 marks)**

3  (a)  Describe the role of stomata in plants.

............................................................

............................................................

.......................................... **(2 marks)**

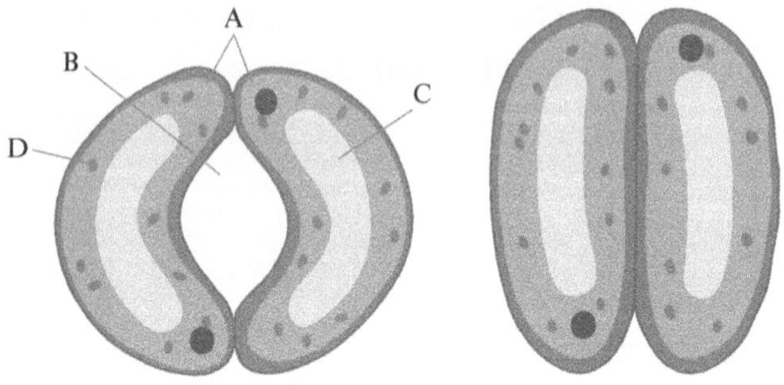

(b)  Name the structures labelled A, B, C and D in the diagrams showing an open and a closed stoma.

..............................................................

..............................................................

..............................................................                                    **(2 marks)**

stoma open                    stoma closed

(c)  Explain how stomata open when it is light and close when it is dark.

....................................................................................................

....................................................................................................

....................................................................................................

....................................................................................................

.................................................................................................... **(4 marks)**

# Translocation

1  Which plant tissue is involved in translocation? Tick **one** box.

☐ **A** xylem

☐ **B** phloem

☐ **C** mesophyll

☐ **D** meristem

> **Phloem** carries **food**. They are spelled differently, but both words sound as if they start with an F. Use this to help you remember the difference between the roles of phloem and xylem.

**(1 mark)**

2 (a) State what is meant by translocation.

............................................................................................................................. **(1 mark)**

(b) A poison that inhibits active transport is applied to the leaves of a plant in an experiment. Explain the effect this would have on translocation.

.............................................................................................................................

.............................................................................................................................

............................................................................................................................. **(2 marks)**

> To answer this question you need to apply what you know about translocation, the structure of phloem and active transport.

3  Complete the table below to show the **two** main differences between transpiration and translocation.

| | Transpiration | Translocation |
|---|---|---|
| **Tissue where it takes place** | | |
| **Substances transported** | | Sucrose dissolved in ... |
| **Direction of transport** | | |

**(3 marks)**

4 (a) Give **two** ways in which the sucrose transported in the phloem may be used by the plant.

> Guided

.............................................................................................................................

.............................................................................................................................

............................................................................................................................. **(2 marks)**

(b) Scientists supply a plant with radioactive water. They also supply the lower leaves with carbon dioxide containing radioactive carbon. They kill a ring of stem tissue with a jet of steam. They find radioactive water in the leaves of the plant from the top to the bottom of the plant, but they only find radioactively labelled sucrose below the ring of dead tissue. Explain these observations in terms of the properties of xylem and phloem.

.............................................................................................................................

.............................................................................................................................

.............................................................................................................................

.............................................................................................................................

.............................................................................................................................

.............................................................................................................................

............................................................................................................................. **(5 marks)**

##  Practical skills **Water uptake in plants**

**1** (a)  What does this apparatus measure?

..................................................... **(1 mark)**

(b)  Explain what happens to the air bubble:

(i)  if the stem is placed next to a table fan.

.............................................

.............................................

............................................. **(3 marks)**

(ii)  if the underside of the leaves is covered with petroleum jelly.

............................................................................

............................................................................

**(3 marks)**

rubber stopper

reservoir for pushing air bubble to right-hand end of capillary tube

air bubble

capillary tube with scale

> Think your answers through clearly a step at a time to get all the marks.

**2**  Students placed a leafy shoot in a potometer. They observed how far the air bubble moved in 5-minute intervals. They altered the conditions and repeated their observations. They recorded their observations each time and used them to calculate the mean rate of water uptake in mm/min, using the distance moved by the bubble to indicate water uptake by the shoot.

**Maths skills**

(a)  Complete the table below.

| Movement of air bubble in 5-minute intervals (mm) | Plant A at 15 °C | Plant B at 25 °C | Plant C at 25 °C with a fan blowing at the leaves |
|---|---|---|---|
| Reading 1 | 50 | 80 | 105 |
| Reading 2 | 45 | 84 | 106 |
| Reading 3 | 55 | 91 | 104 |
| Mean result | 50 | | |
| Mean rate of water uptake (mm/min) | $\frac{50}{5} = 10$ | | |

**(4 marks)**

(b)  Why did the students take three readings under each set of conditions?

.................................................................................................... **(1 mark)**

(c)  Explain the differences between the results seen for:

(i)  plant A and plant B.

............................................................................

............................................................................

............................................................................ **(4 marks)**

(ii)  plant B and plant C.

............................................................................

............................................................................

............................................................................ **(4 marks)**

# Extended response – Plant structures and functions

A farmer grows lettuces in nutrient-rich water in a specially designed greenhouse. This allows an extra crop to be fitted in each year. The hours of light, the concentration of carbon dioxide in the air, and the temperature can all be controlled using sensors and computers. The computer data shows that in the early morning the greenhouse needs to be heated and sometimes requires extra lighting. As the day goes on, more carbon dioxide is pumped into the greenhouse, but the heating is often switched off and sometimes cooling fans operate. By late afternoon, the fans are switched off, but the carbon dioxide is still being pumped in – and sometimes the lights and heating come on again.

Explain what is happening in the greenhouse and why the conditions change during the day.

> You may not know much about farming lettuces in huge greenhouses, but you know a lot about photosynthesis and limiting factors and this will allow you to answer the question.
>
> Always plan out your extended response before you start writing. Make sure you keep referring your answer to the content of the question.
>
> Your answer should include:
> - the process of photosynthesis
> - the principles of limiting factors
> - the need to have the maximum rate of photosynthesis for maximum plant growth
> - the changing conditions through the day, the changing limiting factors and how they are overcome.

.......................................................................................................................

.......................................................................................................................

.......................................................................................................................

.......................................................................................................................

.......................................................................................................................

.......................................................................................................................

.......................................................................................................................

.......................................................................................................................

.......................................................................................................................

.......................................................................................................................

.......................................................................................................................

.......................................................................................................................

.......................................................................................................................

.......................................................................................................................

.......................................................................................................................

**(6 marks)**

# Hormones

1  Which of the following endocrine glands releases the hormone ADH? Tick **one** box.

☐ **A** adrenal glands

☐ **B** pituitary gland

☐ **C** ovaries

☐ **D** thyroid gland

> The pituitary gland produces several different hormones and it's important to remember what they are and what they do

**(1 mark)**

2  Define a hormone.

> Make three clear points to get the three marks here.

..............................................................................................................................................

..............................................................................................................................................

..............................................................................................................................................  **(3 marks)**

3

Guided

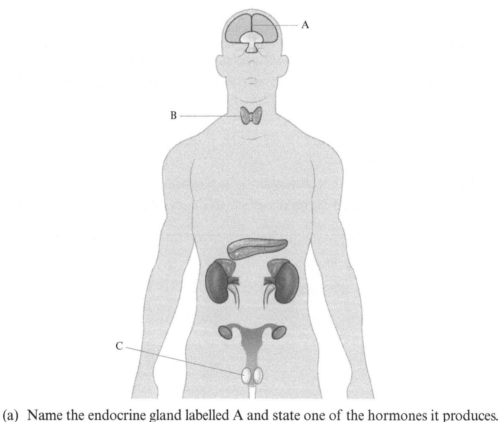

(a)  Name the endocrine gland labelled A and state one of the hormones it produces.

..............................................................................................................................................  **(2 marks)**

(b)  Name the endocrine gland labelled B and state one of the hormones it produces.

..............................................................................................................................................  **(2 marks)**

(c)  Name the endocrine gland labelled C and state one of the hormones it produces.

..............................................................................................................................................  **(2 marks)**

4  Complete the table below stating where each of the hormones is produced and the main target organ/organs for each hormone.

| Hormone | Produced in | Target organ/s and tissues |
|---|---|---|
| **TSH** | | Thyroid gland |
| **Insulin** | | Liver, muscles and fatty tissue |
| **Adrenaline** | Adrenal glands | .........., .........., skin, other organs |
| **Oestrogen** | | |

**(4 marks)**

# Adrenaline and thyroxine

**1** The production of thyroxine is an example of control by negative feedback.

(a) What is the role of thyroxine in the body?

...................................................................................................................... **(1 mark)**

(b) Explain what is meant by negative feedback.

......................................................................................................................

...................................................................................................................... **(2 marks)**

(c) Describe how the production of thyroxine is controlled by negative feedback.

......................................................................................................................

......................................................................................................................

......................................................................................................................

...................................................................................................................... **(5 marks)**

> Take note: part (b) asks you about the general principles of negative feedback, but part (c) asks for details of the control of thyroxine levels in the blood. Make sure you apply the general principles from (b) to your answer in (c).

**2** (a) Adrenaline is often described as the 'fight or flight' hormone. Suggest reasons for this description.

......................................................................................................................

...................................................................................................................... **(2 marks)**

(b) Describe the effects of adrenaline on the heart and explain how they help in the 'fight or flight' response of the body.

......................................................................................................................

...................................................................................................................... **(2 marks)**

(c) Complete the table below to describe and explain the effect of adrenaline on the blood vessels of the body.

| Type of blood vessel | Effect on the blood vessel | Impact on the body |
|---|---|---|
| Supplying blood to the skeletal muscles | | |
| Supplying blood to organs such as the gut | | |

**(4 marks)**

> The second column of the table tests your knowledge, the third column tests your understanding.

**3** The thyroid gland needs iodine from the diet to make thyroxine. If people lack iodine in their diet, their thyroid gland may grow and swell to form a goitre. Suggest a reason for this.

......................................................................................................................

......................................................................................................................

...................................................................................................................... **(3 marks)**

> You aren't expected to know this – you are expected to apply your knowledge and work out a possible answer.

# The menstrual cycle

**1** What is the mean length of menstrual cycles in women? Tick **one** box.

☐ **A** 14 days

☐ **B** 21 days

☐ **C** 9 months

☐ **D** 28 days

> On average, a menstrual cycle lasts 28 days, but in fact they are very variable. Pregnancy lasts nine months.

**(1 mark)**

**2** Define the following terms.

(a) Ovulation

> When describing menstruation, don't forget to say what happens to the egg/ovule. When describing fertilisation, include where/when it usually occurs.

...................................................................................................................................... **(1 mark)**

(b) Menstruation

...................................................................................................................................... **(1 mark)**

(c) Fertilisation

...................................................................................................................................... **(1 mark)**

**3** This diagram represents the menstrual cycle. Explain what happens:

(a) On days 1–5.

................................................................

.................................................... **(1 mark)**

(b) On approximately day 14.

................................................................

.................................................... **(1 mark)**

(c) Through weeks 2, 3 and 4.

................................................................

.................................................... **(1 mark)**

The menstrual cycle

lining thickens
28 1 2 3 4 5 6 7 8 9 10 11 12 13 14 15 16 17 18 19 20 21 22 23 24 25 26 27
period
week 4   week 1
week 3   week 2
ovulation

**4** (a) What is contraception?

...................................................................................................................................... **(1 mark)**

(b) If a couple do not use contraception, when during the menstrual cycle is pregnancy most likely to occur? Explain your answer.

...................................................................................................................................... **(2 marks)**

(c) Give one example of a barrier method of contraception and explain how it works.

................................................................................................................................

...................................................................................................................................... **(2 marks)**

(d) Explain how hormonal methods of contraception work.

................................................................................................................................

...................................................................................................................................... **(2 marks)**

(e) Discuss the advantages and disadvantages of using barrier and hormonal contraception.

................................................................................................................................

................................................................................................................................

...................................................................................................................................... **(4 marks)**

# Control of the menstrual cycle

1   Which of the following hormones is not involved in the menstrual cycle? Tick **one** box.

   ☐   **A**   oestrogen

   ☐   **B**   FSH

   ☐   **C**   progesterone

   ☐   **D**   TSH

> There are four hormones involved in the menstrual cycle. FSH and LH are produced by the pituitary gland. Oestrogen and progesterone are produced in the ovaries.

**(1 mark)**

2   The following hormones are all involved in the menstrual cycle. For each hormone, state where it is made and its target organ/organs.

   (a)   FSH .................................................................................   **(2 marks)**

   (b)   Oestrogen ........................................................................   **(2 marks)**

   (c)   Progesterone ...................................................................   **(2 marks)**

3   Four hormones – FSH, LH, oestrogen and progesterone – interact to control the menstrual cycle in women.

   (a)   Explain the relationship between FSH and oestrogen in the menstrual cycle.

   ........................................................................................................

   ........................................................................................................

   ........................................................................................................

   ........................................................................................................   **(4 marks)**

   (b)   Explain the relationship between LH and oestrogen in the menstrual cycle.

   ........................................................................................................   **(1 mark)**

   (c)   Explain the relationship between LH and progesterone in the menstrual cycle.

   ........................................................................................................

   ........................................................................................................

   ........................................................................................................

   ........................................................................................................   **(3 marks)**

   (d)   If a relatively young woman appears to be in the menopause, her doctor may carry out blood tests to look at her FSH and oestrogen levels.

     (i)   What is the menopause?

   ........................................................................................................   **(1 mark)**

     (ii)   Why would doctors test for the levels of FSH and oestrogen?

   ........................................................................................................

   ........................................................................................................

   ........................................................................................................

   ........................................................................................................   **(3 marks)**

# Assisted Reproductive Therapy

1  What is infertility? Tick **one** box.

☐  **A**  the inability to have a child

☐  **B**  the ability to have a child

☐  **C**  the process of conceiving a child

☐  **D**  the artificial prevention of pregnancy

> Remember: there are many different causes of infertility. Make sure you understand which types of infertility are treated by which forms of Assisted Reproductive Therapy (ART).

**(1 mark)**

2  Two women are infertile. Neither of them appears to be ovulating. The results of blood tests show that woman A has low levels of FSH and LH in her system. Woman B has normal levels of FSH and LH, but doctors discover she has no eggs in her ovaries.

**Guided**

(a)  What is ovulation?

..................................................................................................................  **(1 mark)**

(b)  Doctors suggest using clomifene therapy for one of these patients. State which one and explain how the therapy will work.

..................................................................................................................

..................................................................................................................

..................................................................................................................

..................................................................................................................  **(4 marks)**

(c)  Explain why clomifene therapy is not suggested for the other patient.

..................................................................................................................

..................................................................................................................  **(2 marks)**

3  A couple have infertility problems. Doctors discover that the woman has blocked oviducts.

**Guided**

(a)  State which Assisted Reproductive Therapy might be used to help the couple become pregnant.

..................................................................................................................  **(1 mark)**

(b)  Describe **five** stages in this process.

..................................................................................................................

..................................................................................................................

..................................................................................................................

..................................................................................................................

..................................................................................................................

..................................................................................................................  **(5 marks)**

# Blood glucose regulation

1  Which of the following is a hormone produced in the pancreas and released when
blood glucose levels fall? Tick **one** box.

☐  **A**   insulin

☐  **B**   glycogen

☐  **C**   glucose

☐  **D**   glucagon

> Read the question carefully – the hormone released
> when blood glucose levels **fall** is not the same as the
> hormone released when blood glucose levels **rise**.

**(1 mark)**

2  (a)  Why is glucose so important for the body?

...............................................................................................................................   **(1 mark)**

(b)  Which organ secretes the hormones that control blood glucose levels?

...............................................................................................................................   **(1 mark)**

(c)  Why do blood glucose levels rise after a meal?

...............................................................................................................................

...............................................................................................................................   **(2 marks)**

(d)  Name the **two** hormones involved in controlling blood glucose levels?

...............................................................................................................................   **(1 mark)**

(e)  Explain why it is so important that blood glucose levels are maintained within a
narrow range of concentrations.

...............................................................................................................................

...............................................................................................................................

...............................................................................................................................   **(2 marks)**

3

This diagram shows how blood glucose concentration is controlled by hormones
made and released by the pancreas. Explain what is happening in each of the boxes
labelled A–F.

A  ...........................................................................................................   **(1 mark)**

B  ...........................................................................................................   **(2 marks)**

C  ...........................................................................................................   **(2 marks)**

D  ...........................................................................................................   **(1 mark)**

E  ...........................................................................................................   **(2 marks)**

F  ...........................................................................................................   **(2 marks)**

# Diabetes

1 (a) This graph shows the changes in blood glucose concentration of a person who has just had a meal. Describe what is happening at points A and B.

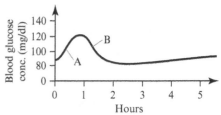

> Remember to refer to the graph in your answer.

At A ........................................................................................................

.............................................................................................................

At B ........................................................................................................

............................................................................................................. **(4 marks)**

(b) Describe what you would expect to see if the person had untreated type 1 diabetes.

............................................................................................................. **(1 mark)**

> For (b) no explanation is needed for the 1 mark, just a description.

(c) Explain your answer to (b).

.............................................................................................................

.............................................................................................................

............................................................................................................. **(4 marks)**

(d) How can this be treated?

............................................................................................................. **(2 marks)**

2 Complete this table comparing type 1 diabetes and type 2 diabetes.

Guided

|  | Type 1 diabetes | Type 2 diabetes |
|---|---|---|
| Cause |  |  |
| Control |  |  |

**(6 marks)**

3 This data shows the percentage of UK adults in three BMI categories with type 2 diabetes.

Guided

(a) Using the data, what can you say about the relationship between BMI category and obesity?

..................................................................

..................................................................

..................................................................

.................................................... **(3 marks)**

Percentage of adults in each BMI category with type 2 diabetes

(b) A student looks at the data and makes the following claim 'Men are more likely to develop type 2 diabetes than women'. Evaluate this claim.

.........................................................................................................................

.........................................................................................................................

.........................................................................................................................

......................................................................................................... **(4 marks)**

# Extended response – Control and coordination

When people want to have sex, but do not want to get pregnant, it is important to use contraception. The following data is taken from the National Health Service website about the effectiveness of different types of contraception. Describe and evaluate the different methods of contraception shown in the bar chart below.

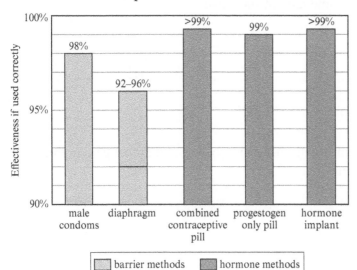

You will always be more successful in extended response questions if you plan your answer before you start writing.

When you are asked to evaluate you need to refer to data. Your answer could explain the following points:

- how the different methods of contraception work
- which types of contraception appear most effective from the data
- what it means if a contraceptive method is described as 98% effective
- what 'if used correctly' means and why it is so important when considering the data
- pros and cons of the different methods beyond statistical effectiveness
- any other sensible, thoughtful points.

.......................................................................................................

.......................................................................................................

.......................................................................................................

.......................................................................................................

.......................................................................................................

.......................................................................................................

.......................................................................................................

.......................................................................................................

.......................................................................................................

.......................................................................................................

.......................................................................................................

.......................................................................................................

.......................................................................................................

.......................................................................................................

.......................................................................................................

.......................................................................................................

.......................................................................................................

.......................................................................................................  **(6 marks)**

Had a go ☐    Nearly there ☐    Nailed it! ☐

# Exchanging materials

1 Which of the following substances needs to be transported **out** of multicellular organisms? Tick **one** box.

☐ **A**   oxygen

☐ **B**   glucose

☐ **C**   carbon dioxide

☐ **D**   lipids

> Remember: carbon dioxide is a toxic waste product of cellular respiration.

**(1 mark)**

**Maths skills**

2 (a) Calculate the surface area to volume ratio of these two model organisms.

Smaller organism SA = 6 × 1μm² ............................

.........................................................................

.........................................................................

.........................................................................

**(2 marks)**

(b) Explain why larger, multicellular organisms need transport and exchange systems, but small single-celled organisms do not.

.........................................................................

.........................................................................

.........................................................................

.........................................................................

**(3 marks)**

> It is the surface area : volume ratio of an organism that is important when you discuss the need for exchange and transport systems – not just the surface area.

3 (a) Name **two** human organs which are adapted for exchange of materials.

......................................................................... **(2 marks)**

**Guided**

(b) Name **one** human system which is involved in transport of materials around the body.

......................................................................... **(1 mark)**

(c) Give **two** features which are important in specialised exchange surfaces.

......................................................................... **(2 marks)**

4 A mammal is too large for simple diffusion to supply its needs. Complete this table showing the main substances which need to be exchanged and the site where the exchange takes place.

**Guided**

| Substance | Site of exchange | Reason for exchange |
|---|---|---|
| Oxygen | | |
| Carbon dioxide | | |
| Dissolved food molecules | | |
| Mineral ions | | |
| Urea | | |

**(5 marks)**

# Alveoli

**1** (a) Define breathing.

The movement of air in and out of the ..................................................... **(1 mark)**

(b) Describe gas exchange in the lungs.

.........................................................................................................

......................................................................................................... **(2 marks)**

(c) Explain how breathing affects gas exchange.

.........................................................................................................

.........................................................................................................

......................................................................................................... **(3 marks)**

**2** State **three** ways in which the alveoli of the lungs are adapted for gas exchange and explain how each of the features makes gas exchange in the lungs more efficient.

Large surface area – .....................................................

.........................................................................

.........................................................................

.........................................................................

.........................................................................

.........................................................................

......................................................................................................... **(4 marks)**

**3** Here are brief descriptions of three diseases of the lungs. They can all cause breathlessness and low levels of oxygen in the blood. In each case, explain how the problems are caused in terms of the structures and adaptations of the exchange surfaces of the lungs.

Guided

(a) COPD is a family of lung diseases where the structure of the alveoli breaks down, forming a few large air sacs instead of many small ones.

.........................................................................................................

......................................................................................................... **(2 marks)**

(b) In lung cancer, a solid tumour grows into the lung tissue taking up space where the alveoli should be.

.........................................................................................................

......................................................................................................... **(2 marks)**

(c) In a pulmonary embolism, a blood clot blocks the artery leading to the lungs.

.........................................................................................................

......................................................................................................... **(2 marks)**

# Blood

1 What is the yellow liquid that makes up around 55% of the blood called?
Tick **one** box.

☐ **A** phloem

> Learn the main components of the blood and their relative proportions.

☐ **B** lymph

☐ **C** pus

☐ **D** plasma **(1 mark)**

2 (a) Name the **four** main components of the blood shown in this diagram.

A ..................... B ................. C ................. D ..................... **(2 marks)**

> **Guided**

(b) Give **one** function of each component you named in (a).

A ...........................................................................................

B ...........................................................................................

C ...........................................................................................

D ........................................................................................... **(4 marks)**

3 Explain **three** ways in which erythrocytes are adapted for their role in the body.

> Remember: 'erythrocytes' is the proper name for red blood cells.
> The question says 'Explain...' so your answer needs to refer specifically to how the different features of the red blood cell enable it to carry out its function of transporting oxygen.

.....................................................................................................

.....................................................................................................

.....................................................................................................

.....................................................................................................

..................................................................................................... **(3 marks)**

4 Children born with a genetic condition called SCID do not have functioning white blood cells. The affected children get many infections, one after the other.

> **Guided**

(a) Describe **two** ways in which white blood cells prevent infection in healthy people.

.....................................................................................................

.....................................................................................................

.....................................................................................................

.....................................................................................................

..................................................................................................... **(4 marks)**

(b) Explain why children affected by SCID get many repeated infections which may kill them.

.....................................................................................................

.....................................................................................................

.....................................................................................................

.....................................................................................................

..................................................................................................... **(3 marks)**

# Blood vessels

**1** (a) Name the types of vessels labelled A, B and C.

network of fine capillaries in the lungs

.................................................................

**(2 marks)**

(b) In which type of blood vessel – A, B or C – is the blood pressure highest? Explain your answer.

A

B

heart

C

.................................................................

.................................................................

.................................................................

.................................................................

**(2 marks)**

**2** All veins, except for the pulmonary vein, carry blood towards the heart.

(a) Describe the structure of a vein.

Walls thinner than arterial walls, ...............................................

You do not need to explain in (a), just describe.

.................................................................

**(2 marks)**

(b) Explain how the structure of a vein is adapted for its function.

.................................................................

.................................................................

**(3 marks)**

**3** (a) Arteries have thick layers of elastic and muscle fibres in their walls. Explain how this is related to their function in the body.

Blood is squeezed into the arteries by the heart at high pressure. The elastic walls

.................................................................

**(3 marks)**

(b) Veins have thin walls and blood flows through them at low pressure. Explain how blood is returned to the heart in the veins.

.................................................................

.................................................................

**(2 marks)**

**4** Almost every cell in the body is close to a capillary.

(a) What is a capillary?

.................................................................

.................................................................

**(1 mark)**

(b) Why is it important that every cell in the body is close to a capillary?

.................................................................

.................................................................

**(2 marks)**

(c) How are capillaries adapted for their functions in the body?

.................................................................

.................................................................

.................................................................

.................................................................

**(3 marks)**

# The heart

1  Which of the following blood vessels carries oxygenated blood from the lungs to the heart? Tick **one** box.

☐ **A** aorta

☐ **B** pulmonary artery

☐ **C** pulmonary vein

☐ **D** vena cava

> Remember: arteries carry **oxygenated blood away** from the heart – except for the **pulmonary artery**. Veins carry **deoxygenated blood towards** the heart – except for the **pulmonary vein**.

**(1 mark)**

2  This diagram shows a section through a human heart.

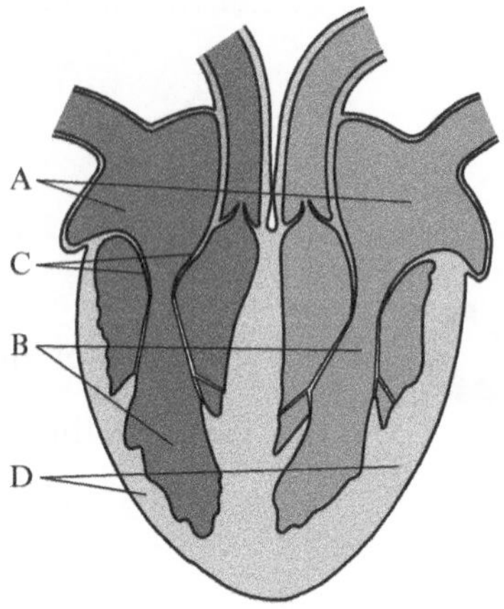

(a) Name the chambers of the heart labelled A and B.

............................................................. **(2 marks)**

(b) Name the structures labelled C and describe their role in the heart.

............................................................. **(2 marks)**

(c) Explain the difference you can observe in the structures labelled D on the left- and right-hand sides of the heart.

.............................................................

.............................................................

............................................................................................ **(2 marks)**

> Remember! The sides of the heart are labelled as if you are looking at the person so the left-hand side of the heart is on the right-hand side of the diagram.

3  (a) Complete this simple flow diagram to show the movement of blood through the heart.

Guided

| Blood returns to the heart from ............................. in ....................... |

↓

| the ............................. contract, forcing ....................................... |

↓

| the ........... close, preventing ................................... through the heart |

↓

| the ............................. contract, forcing ............................... into ................................... which carry it to the organs. |

**(4 marks)**

(b) Some babies are born with a gap in the wall of muscle that divides the right and left side of the heart. This is known as a 'hole in the heart'. These children are often weak and breathless, and may even die if the hole is not mended. Surgeons can mend the hole, allowing the children to live active, healthy lives. Give a biological explanation for why affected children have these symptoms.

.............................................................................................

.............................................................................................

.............................................................................................

............................................................................................ **(5 marks)**

# Aerobic respiration

**1** (a)  Define aerobic respiration.

It is a process that .................. energy from ..................... for use in ...........

.............................., using. ....................................    **(2 marks)**

(b)  Write a simple word summary for this process.

Glucose + ............................. → ............................. + water    **(2 marks)**

(c)  Where do the chemical reactions of aerobic respiration take place?

Mainly in the ....................................................................................    **(1 mark)**

(d)  Explain where the glucose and oxygen used in aerobic respiration come from.

Glucose comes from .............................., oxygen from .............................

.................................................................. in the lungs.    **(2 marks)**

**2** (a)  Describe **three** ways in which the energy released in aerobic respiration is used
    in animals.

For .......................... processes.

To enable .................................... contraction.

In mammals to help ..........................................................................    **(3 marks)**

(b)  Plants also use energy from aerobic respiration. Give one example from plant cells.

Building ............... molecules from ............... molecules. For example, ...............

..................................................................................................

..................................................................................................    **(2 marks)**

**3** (a)  The reactions of respiration are all controlled by enzymes. The body temperature
    of the human body and the pH of the cells are carefully controlled. Suggest an
    explanation for these observations.

..................................................................................................

..................................................................................................

..................................................................................................

..................................................................................................

..................................................................................................    **(4 marks)**

(b)  If a culture of cells are given the poison curare, all of the reactions of metabolism
    fail and the cells die. If the cells are provided with energy in a useable form, they
    can survive. Suggest an explanation for the way the poison works.

..................................................................................................

..................................................................................................

..................................................................................................

..................................................................................................

..................................................................................................    **(3 marks)**

# Anaerobic respiration

1  Which of the following substances is produced in humans during anaerobic respiration, but not in aerobic respiration? Tick **one** box.

☐ **A**  carbon dioxide

☐ **B**  lactic acid

☐ **C**  oxygen

☐ **D**  water

> In aerobic respiration in people, glucose is fully broken down into carbon dioxide and water using oxygen. In anaerobic respiration, glucose is not fully broken down.

**(1 mark)**

2  (a)  What is anaerobic respiration?

..................................................................................................................................

.............................................................................................................................. **(2 marks)**

(b)  Complete the following table to show some of the advantages and disadvantages of anaerobic respiration in humans.

| Advantages of anaerobic respiration | Disadvantages of anaerobic respiration |
|---|---|
| | |
| | |

**(4 marks)**

3  The graph shows the breathing rate and heart rate of a student during and after exercise.

(a)  What type of respiration takes place at the start of a period of exercise?

...................................................................

................................................... **(1 mark)**

(b)  Explain what happens in the muscles as the period of exercise continues, and the heart and lungs cannot supply all the glucose and oxygen needed.

..................................................................................................................................

.............................................................................................................................. **(3 marks)**

(c)  Describe, from the graph, what happens to the breathing rate and heart rate after exercise stops.

..................................................................................................................................

.............................................................................................................................. **(2 marks)**

(d)  Explain the observations you described in (c).

..................................................................................................................................

..................................................................................................................................

..................................................................................................................................

.............................................................................................................................. **(4 marks)**

##  Practical skills **Rate of respiration**

1 The diagram shows a respirometer used to investigate the rate of respiration in germinating peas.

> You need to be able to answer questions about the apparatus in core practicals as well as understand the science and make deductions about unknown situations.

screw clip – closed after 10 minutes

coloured liquid – this liquid moves as oxygen is taken up by the germinating seeds during respiration

clamp

soda lime – absorbs carbon dioxide

germinating seeds

stand

(a) Describe the function of the soda lime in the respirometer.

....................................................................................

....................................................................................

**(1 mark)**

(b) Explain how this respirometer could be used to measure the respiration rate of the seeds.

....................................................................................

....................................................................................

**(2 marks)**

> Make clear that you are measuring the rate of respiration indirectly by measuring the movement of the liquid, not directly by measuring the volume of oxygen taken in by the organisms.

(c) If the peas were boiled and cooled before they were put in the respirometer, what results would you expect? Explain why.

....................................................................................

....................................................................................

**(2 marks)**

2 A student set up a respirometer to measure the rate of respiration of mealworms.

(a) What gas will be produced as the mealworms respire aerobically?

....................................................................................

**(1 mark)**

Guided

(b) Suggest **two** ethical issues you would have to consider when using mealworms in this experiment.

....................................................................................

....................................................................................

....................................................................................

**(2 marks)**

(c) Describe the differences you might expect to see in the rate of respiration of mealworms measured in a respirometer compared with that of germinating peas measured in a respirometer.

....................................................................................

**(1 mark)**

(d) Explain why these differences might appear.

....................................................................................

....................................................................................

....................................................................................

....................................................................................

**(4 marks)**

# Changes in heart rate

1 If a student has a stroke volume of 0.09 litres and at rest their heart beats 70 times a minute. Their cardiac output is:

   ☐ **A**   6.3 centilitres/s

   ☐ **B**   6.3 litres/min

   ☐ **C**   6.3 litres/s

   ☐ **D**   6.3 millilitres/min        **(1 mark)**

> Make sure you know the units of different measurements.

2 One way of measuring the fitness of an individual is to measure how well their heart is pumping blood. Define each of the following and state the units in which they are measured.

> Guided

  (a) Stroke volume ................................................................................

................................................................................................ **(2 marks)**

  (b) Heart rate ....................................................................................

................................................................................................ **(2 marks)**

  (c) Cardiac output ..............................................................................

................................................................................................ **(2 marks)**

  (d) Give the formula for measuring the cardiac output of an individual.

................................................................................................ **(1 mark)**

3 This bar chart shows the effect of moderate exercise on the cardiac output of three people labelled A, B and C.

> Guided

  (a) Which of these people is the fittest? Explain your answer.

.......................................................................

.......................................................................

.......................................................................

................................................... **(2 marks)**

  (b) Which person would you expect to have the highest recorded heart rate during the period of exercise? Explain your answer.

................................................................................................

................................................................................................ **(2 marks)**

  (c) During the period of exercise, person B had a stroke volume of 0.095 litres and a heart rate of 120 beats per minute. Person C had a stroke volume of 0.15 litres and a heart rate of 100 beats per minute. What was the cardiac output of each individual?

................................................................................................

................................................................................................ **(2 marks)**

  (d) How much more blood, in percentage terms, did person C pump each minute than person B?

................................................................................................

................................................................................................ **(1 mark)**

# Extended response – Exchange

 These images show Tom taking part in an endurance race. The first image is from the beginning of the race, the second is much later on. Apart from the fact that he is much muddier, Tom's muscles are working hard later in the race and they start to ache. Explain why Tom's muscles are aching, and what happens to his heart and breathing as the race progresses.

> To be successful in extended response questions, plan your answer before you start writing.
>
> When you are asked to explain, you need to think carefully about what is happening and why. Here you are asked about three different systems in the body – for a good answer you must cover each of them in turn. Make sure you refer to the context of the question. Your answer could explain the following points:
>
> • what the muscles need to keep working effectively in a race
> • why Tom's muscles are aching
> • the changes you would expect in his breathing and why they are needed
> • the changes you would expect in his heart rate and why they are needed

.........................................................................................................................
.........................................................................................................................
.........................................................................................................................
.........................................................................................................................
.........................................................................................................................
.........................................................................................................................
.........................................................................................................................
.........................................................................................................................
.........................................................................................................................
.........................................................................................................................
.........................................................................................................................
.........................................................................................................................
.........................................................................................................................
.........................................................................................................................

**(6 marks)**

# Ecosystems and abiotic factors

1  Which of the following is **not** an abiotic factor affecting the distribution of organisms in an ecosystem? Tick **one** box.

☐ **A**  rainfall

☐ **B**  light levels

☐ **C**  nitrate levels in the soil

☐ **D**  predator numbers

> Remember the difference! Abiotic means non-living; biotic means living.

**(1 mark)**

2  Define the following terms, which are all important in the study of ecology:

Guided

(a) Organism

................................................................................................................................. **(1 mark)**

(b) Population

................................................................................................................................. **(1 mark)**

(c) Community

................................................................................................................................. **(1 mark)**

(d) Ecosystem

................................................................................................................................. **(1 mark)**

3  (a) List **three** abiotic factors which can affect the organisms in an ecosystem.

Guided

................................................................................................................................. **(3 marks)**

(b) This sundew is a carnivorous plant. It captures insects on the sticky drops on its leaves and digests them. It grows on bogs, where very few other plants can survive. Suggest an explanation for these observations in terms of abiotic factors.

........................................................................

........................................................................

........................................................................

........................................................................

................................................................................................................................. **(3 marks)**

(c) Great tits feed their babies on tiny caterpillars and other insects. When the weather is particularly cold, when there are late frosts or there is a lot of very heavy rain, these birds raise fewer chicks than in warm, dry years. Suggest how these abiotic factors may affect the success of the breeding birds.

.................................................................................................................................

.................................................................................................................................

.................................................................................................................................

.................................................................................................................................

.................................................................................................................................

**(3 marks)**

# Biotic factors

1  Which of the following is a biotic factor affecting the distribution of organisms in an area? Tick **one** box.

☐ **A**  temperature

☐ **B**  rainfall

☐ **C**  competition

☐ **D**  oxygen levels in water

> Biotic factors have **bio**logical causes.

**(1 mark)**

2  Red deer stags grow large antlers each year and fight each other.

(a)  What are they fighting for?

..................................................................................................................... **(2 marks)**

(b)  What is this process called?

..................................................................................................................... **(1 mark)**

(c)  Male deer of the same species fight against each other. Give an example of competition between two different species.

> Learn three examples of interspecific competition for resources.

.....................................................................................................................

..................................................................................................................... **(2 marks)**

3  In a UK oak woodland, lots of small plants, such as primroses and bluebells, grow and flower early in the year. By the summer, the ground is mainly bare. Explain why plants on the ground grow so early and then disappear until the next spring.

> You won't always be familiar with the example you are given, but you should be able to apply your knowledge and work it out.

.....................................................................................................................

.....................................................................................................................

..................................................................................................................... **(3 marks)**

4  This graph shows the numbers of snowshoe hares and the lynx, which are their predators, over a period of years in Canada.

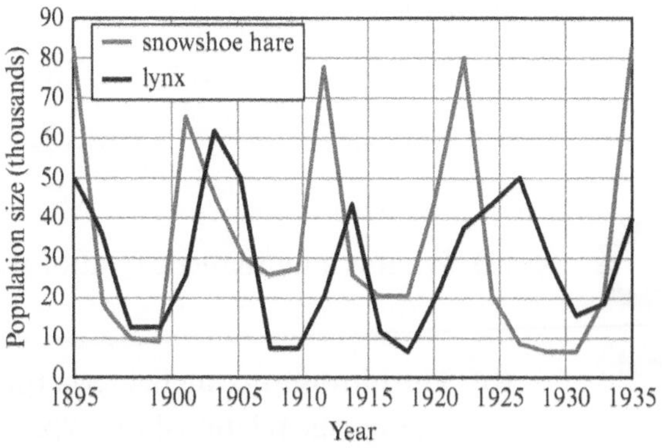

> Guided

(a)  Define the term predator.

............................................................... **(1 mark)**

(b)  The snowshoe hare is a prey animal. What does this mean?

............................................................... **(1 mark)**

(c)  Look at the graph. Describe how the hare and the lynx numbers are correlated.

.....................................................................................................................

..................................................................................................................... **(2 marks)**

(d)  Suggest an explanation for the pattern you can see.

.....................................................................................................................

.....................................................................................................................

..................................................................................................................... **(4 marks)**

# Parasitism and mutualism

1  Which of the following organisms is **not** a parasite? Tick **one** box.

☐  **A**  flea

☐  **B**  tapeworm

> Make sure you know the difference between parasitic organisms and mutualistic organisms.

☐  **C**  louse

☐  **D**  clownfish

**(1 mark)**

2  (a)  What is a parasite?

.................................................................................................... **(2 marks)**

(b)  Complete this table about three different parasites.

| Parasite | How it feeds |
|----------|--------------|
| flea |  |
| tapeworm |  |
| mistletoe |  |

**(3 marks)**

> You will be expected to be able to recall examples of parasitism and mutualism. Make sure you learn three examples of each.

> Different parasites feed in different ways – learn some examples.

3  A tapeworm is a parasite that can live in the gut of mammals.

Give **three** adaptations shown by tapeworms and explain how these benefit their parasitic lifestyle.

....................................................................................................

....................................................................................................

.................................................................................................... **(3 marks)**

4  (a)  What is a mutualistic relationship?

.................................................................................................... **(1 mark)**

(b)  The nitrogen-fixing bacteria that live in the root nodules of legumes are in a mutualistic relationship. Explain what this means for the bacteria and the plant.

....................................................................................................

.................................................................................................... **(2 marks)**

(c)  Clown fish live among the stinging tentacles of large sea anemones. Suggest and explain the benefits of this mutualistic relationship for each of the organisms.

....................................................................................................

.................................................................................................... **(2 marks)**

 **Fieldwork techniques**

**1** In a long-running investigation into the numbers of penguin nests on a beach in Argentina, scientists recorded the results shown in the table below.

| Quadrat number along transect | 1 | 2 | 3 | 4 | 5 | 6 | 7 | 8 | 9 |
|---|---|---|---|---|---|---|---|---|---|
| Number of nests/100 m² | 10 | 2 | 15 | 9 | 3 | 22 | 14 | 12 | 20 |

In the previous two years there was a mean nest density of 5.6 nests/100 m² and 8.4 nests/100 m².

(a) Calculate the mean number of nests per 100 m² for the data in the table.

........................ **(3 marks)**

(b) Do you think this was a good breeding year or a bad one? Explain your answer.

........................................................................................................

........................................................................................................ **(2 marks)**

(c) Suggest **one** biotic factor and **one** abiotic factor which might affect the success of penguins breeding in any given year.

biotic ........................................ abiotic................................................ **(2 marks)**

**2** A student measures the abundance of slugs in a garden. They take five random samples of the garden using a 1 m² quadrat. The number of slugs in the quadrats was 10, 6, 5, 9 and 2. The garden has an area of 100 m².

(a) What does abundance measure?

........................................................................................................ **(1 mark)**

(b) Estimate the total population of slugs in the garden.

........................ **(3 marks)**

**3** A class is going to investigate the effect of abiotic factors on the distribution of plants in a local park. One group suggests looking at random quadrats. Another group suggests taking a belt transect across the park. Both groups plan to record the conditions at each quadrat recorded.

(a) Explain what the term 'the distribution of plants' means.

........................................................................................................ **(1 mark)**

(b) Describe a quadrat.

........................................................................................................ **(1 mark)**

(c) Which method would ensure they sampled different environments?

........................................................................................................

........................................................................................................

........................................................................................................

........................................................................................................ **(4 marks)**

79

# Organisms and their environment

**1** A scientist is looking at the distribution of sundew plants in the New Forest in the UK. Sundews are found in bogs and they capture and digest insects to get the nitrates they need. The scientist is investigating an area of heathland which has some very boggy parts and she begins by doing two belt transects. She uses a 0.25 m² quadrat and places the quadrat at two-metre intervals along the transect. Her data is shown in the table.

| Transects | Number of sundew plants | | | | | | | | Mean |
| --- | --- | --- | --- | --- | --- | --- | --- | --- | --- |
| | Quadrat 1 | Quadrat 2 | Quadrat 3 | Quadrat 4 | Quadrat 5 | Quadrat 6 | Quadrat 7 | Quadrat 8 | |
| **A** | 0 | 0 | 1 | 3 | 1 | 4 | 0 | 0 | |
| **B** | 0 | 4 | 6 | 8 | 10 | 10 | 5 | 3 | |

(a) Calculate the mean number of sundew plants in transect A and transect B (to the nearest whole number).

> In this example, the mean is the **sum** of the numbers of organisms **divided** by the number of quadrats taken.

.................... **(2 marks)**

(b) Suggest what these results tell you about the ecosystems covered by the two transects.

.......................................................................................................................

.......................................................................................................................

.......................................................................................................................

....................................................................................................................... **(3 marks)**

> Think carefully about what you are told in the question and the data you are given. Work out as much detail as you can from the data about how boggy the ground is in the different transects.

(c) Suggest **two** ways in which the scientist could improve her method in future.

1 ....................................................................................................................

2 .................................................................................................................... **(2 marks)**

**2** A student wants to investigate the distribution of shellfish called mussels across a rocky shore. Describe how they might do this.

.......................................................................................................................

.......................................................................................................................

.......................................................................................................................

.......................................................................................................................

.......................................................................................................................

.......................................................................................................................

....................................................................................................................... **(5 marks)**

# Human effects on ecosystems

1  When too many nutrients are added to a water ecosystem, eventually resulting in a lack of oxygen in the water, this is known as:

☐ **A**  fertilising the soil     ☐ **C**  pollution

☐ **B**  eutrophication          ☐ **D**  conservation          **(1 mark)**

2  When the prickly pear cactus was introduced to Australia, it rapidly became a pest species. By 1920 it had covered 58 million hectares, ruining lots of good farmland. In the late 1920s, the caterpillars of a moth that feeds only on prickly pear cactus were released onto the cacti in some of the worst hit areas. In a matter of years it had brought the plague of cacti under control.

> In questions like this, you will be given information about a new situation. You are not expected to know about prickly pear cacti or cacti-eating moths, **but** you are expected to be able to show you understand the basic principles behind species interactions.

(a)  What process is illustrated in the story of the prickly pear cactus and the cactus moth?

..................................................................................................................... **(1 mark)**

(b)  Using the prickly pear cactus as an example, explain the dangers of introducing new species to an ecosystem.

.....................................................................................................................

..................................................................................................................... **(2 marks)**

(c)  Using the cactus moth as an example, explain how the introduction of non-indigenous species can have benefits.

.....................................................................................................................

..................................................................................................................... **(2 marks)**

3  (a)  What is fish farming?

.....................................................................................................................

..................................................................................................................... **(2 marks)**

(b)  Explain how farming fish can be a better way of providing fish for people to eat than catching wild fish.

.....................................................................................................................

.....................................................................................................................

..................................................................................................................... **(3 marks)**

(c)  Suggest **two** harmful effects fish farming can have on the environment.

.....................................................................................................................

..................................................................................................................... **(2 marks)**

4  Some fishermen reported many dead fish in a local lake. Scientists discovered a local farmer had increased the amount of fertiliser spread on the fields in an effort to get more crops. Produce a flow diagram to show how this could have killed the fish.

**(5 marks)**

# Biodiversity

**1** (a) What is biodiversity?

The variety of .................................................................................. **(1 mark)**

(b) Give **three** reasons why it is important to maintain biodiversity both at local and global levels.

.......................................................................................................

.......................................................................................................

.......................................................................................................

....................................................................................................... **(3 marks)**

**2** (a) Explain the effect of deforestation on biodiversity.

Deforestation removes ..................... from an area. This also removes the .........

....................................................................................................... **(2 marks)**

(b) State what is meant by reforestation and suggest **two** ways it can be carried out.

.......................................................................................................

....................................................................................................... **(2 marks)**

(c) Rainforests are thought to contain around 500 species per hectare and UK woodlands around 12 species per hectare. Some people claim deforestation of a rainforest is more damaging to biodiversity than deforestation in the UK. Discuss this claim.

.......................................................................................................

.......................................................................................................

.......................................................................................................

.......................................................................................................

....................................................................................................... **(3 marks)**

**3** Red squirrels are indigenous to the UK. Their numbers have been declining for centuries. They do best in coniferous woodlands. Climate change means coniferous woodlands now do best in the cooler north. Millions of acres of woodland have been destroyed by people for housing, agriculture, etc. and many people have planted deciduous woodlands rather than conifers. Grey squirrels, introduced in the late 19th century, are more effective at converting food to biomass and so can out-compete red squirrels. Squirrelpox is a disease which can kill red squirrels fast, but many grey squirrels are immune to it.

Suggest how red squirrels might be conserved in the UK.

.......................................................................................................

.......................................................................................................

.......................................................................................................

.......................................................................................................

....................................................................................................... **(4 marks)**

# The carbon cycle

1 Which of the following processes takes carbon dioxide out of the air during the carbon cycle? Tick **one** box.

☐ **A** photosynthesis

☐ **B** combustion

☐ **C** respiration

☐ **D** decomposition

> Make sure you know which of the processes of the carbon cycle put carbon dioxide into the atmosphere and which remove it.

**(1 mark)**

2 (a) Describe the role of decomposers in the carbon cycle.

..............................................................................................................................

..............................................................................................................................  **(1 mark)**

(b) Describe how burning forests affect the levels of carbon dioxide in **two** ways.

..............................................................................................................................

..............................................................................................................................

..............................................................................................................................

..............................................................................................................................  **(4 marks)**

3 This diagram represents the carbon cycle.

(a) Define the carbon cycle.

...............................................................

...............................................................

...............................................................

...............................................  **(1 mark)**

(b) Name the processes listed on the diagram of the carbon cycle. For each one, explain the part it plays in the carbon cycle:

(i) Process A

..............................................................................................................................

..............................................................................................................................

..............................................................................................................................  **(4 marks)**

(ii) Process B

..............................................................................................................................

..............................................................................................................................  **(3 marks)**

(iii) Process C

..............................................................................................................................

..............................................................................................................................

..............................................................................................................................  **(3 marks)**

(iv) Process D

..............................................................................................................................

..............................................................................................................................

..............................................................................................................................  **(3 marks)**

# The water cycle

**1**

(a) Define the water cycle.

.................................................................................................................... **(1 mark)**

(b) Give **two** reasons why water is so important to living organisms.

....................................................................................................................

....................................................................................................................

.................................................................................................................... **(2 marks)**

(c) Name each of the processes labelled A–D on the diagram of the water cycle.

....................................................................................................................

.................................................................................................................... **(2 marks)**

**2** Clean drinking water (potable water) is in short supply in many places. In some areas, people are using sea water to make drinking water.

(a) Explain why we can't drink sea water.

Sea water contains lots of ............ and this would upset the ...........................

.................................................................................................................... **(1 mark)**

(b) Name the process used to turn sea water into potable water.

.................................................................................................................... **(1 mark)**

(c) Explain how sea water can be distilled to give potable water.

Seawater is heated until the water evaporates forming steam ...........................

....................................................................................................................

.................................................................................................................... **(3 marks)**

**3** Describe how water cycles through the **abiotic** parts of an ecosystem.

....................................................................................................................

....................................................................................................................

....................................................................................................................

....................................................................................................................

.................................................................................................................... **(5 marks)**

# The nitrogen cycle

**1** Which of the following processes involves the release of nitrogen back into the air?
Tick **one** box.

☐ **A** nitrogen fixation

☐ **B** decomposition

☐ **C** combustion

☐ **D** denitrification

**(1 mark)**

**2** Farmers have many ways to make their soil more fertile and to help them grow the biggest, healthiest crops possible. Explain the science behind these three farming methods:

(a) Adding nitrate fertiliser to fields.

Plants need nitrates to make ....................................................................................

....................................................................................................................

.................................................................................................................... **(3 marks)**

(b) Rotating crops every year.

Different species of plants ...................................................................................

.................................................................................................................... **(2 marks)**

(c) Planting a crop of peas or clover at regular intervals in their crop rotation.

Peas and clover have root nodules containing bacteria that can ........................

....................................................................................................................

....................................................................................................................

....................................................................................................................

.................................................................................................................... **(4 marks)**

**3** This diagram represents the nitrogen cycle in nature. Nitrogen compounds are very important as they are needed to form proteins and DNA.

(a) What are the key organisms in the nitrogen cycle?

...............................................

(b) Explain what is happening at the stages of the nitrogen cycle labelled A–E.

....................................................................................................................

....................................................................................................................

....................................................................................................................

....................................................................................................................

.................................................................................................................... **(5 marks)**

**(1 mark)**

# Extended response – Ecosystems and material cycles

Pandas are well-known animals which are at risk of becoming extinct. In the past they have been extensively hunted for their body parts to be used in traditional medicine and their habitat of bamboo forests has been destroyed. The following data shows the recorded panda populations in China since 1974.

| Date of survey | Estimated wild panda population |
|---|---|
| 1974–7 | 2459 |
| 1985–8 | 1114 |
| 2003–4 | 1596 |
| 2014 | 1864 |

Discuss possible reasons why panda numbers have decreased and are now on the rise again, using recorded data where possible to support your comments. Suggest any other possible benefits from the rise in panda numbers.

> You will always be more successful in extended response questions if you plan your answer before you start writing.
>
> When you are asked to discuss, do not waffle. Identify the issues highlighted in the question and make very clear points so the examiner can see you have considered different sides of the question.
>
> In this question you need to think about:
>
> - the causes of the decline in pandas
> - when it appeared to be halted
> - the current state of the population (using percentage increases taken from the data)
> - the sort of measures which can be taken to increase the numbers of a threatened species
> - any implications for other species.

.................................................................................................

.................................................................................................

.................................................................................................

.................................................................................................

.................................................................................................

.................................................................................................

.................................................................................................

.................................................................................................

.................................................................................................

.................................................................................................

.................................................................................................

.................................................................................................

.................................................................................................

.................................................................................................  **(6 marks)**

# Formulae

**1** Which formula contains the greatest number of oxygen atoms? Tick **one** box.

☐ **A** NaOH

☐ **B** $Mg(OH)_2$

☐ **C** $H_2O_2$

☐ **D** $Ca(NO_3)_2$

> Don't forget: when you have brackets, everything inside is multiplied by the number outside the bracket.

**(1 mark)**

**2** Draw lines to match the formula with the name.

| water | magnesium sulfate | sodium hydroxide | potassium chloride | methane | iron oxide | sodium carbonate |

$Na_2CO_3$   $CH_4$        $H_2O$        $Fe_2O_3$        KCl        $MgSO_4$   NaOH    **(7 marks)**

**3** Name the elements present in the following compounds.

(a) copper sulfate, $CuSO_4$

copper, sulfur, ...................................................

(b) lithium oxide, $Li_2O$

...................................................................

(c) hydrochloric acid, HCl

hydrogen, ...................................................    **(3 marks)**

**4** What are the names of the compounds formed by combining the following elements?

(a) magnesium and oxygen ....................................

(b) chlorine and sodium ....................................

(c) hydrogen and fluorine ....................................    **(3 marks)**

> When you have a metal and a non-metal forming a compound name the metal first.

**5** How many atoms are present in the following molecules?

(a) aluminium oxide, $Al_2O_3$ ....................................

(b) calcium oxide, CaO ....................................

(c) potassium nitrate, $KNO_3$ ....................................    **(3 marks)**

**6** Ammonia, $NH_3$, is a very important molecule used for making fertilisers. Ammonia is made by combining nitrogen, $N_2$, and hydrogen, $H_2$. Explain why nitrogen and hydrogen are elements, but ammonia is a compound.

> Elements contain only one **type** of atom. They can, however, contain more than one atom of the **same type**, bonded together. For example, molecules of hydrogen, which are made up of pairs of hydrogen atoms.

........................................................................................

........................................................................................

........................................................................................    **(2 marks)**

# Equations

1  Are the following equations correctly or incorrectly balanced?

> Check the number of each type of atom is the same on both sides. Remember that you need to multiply by the subscript number. For example, $N_2$ means two lots of nitrogen atoms.

| | Correct or incorrect? |
|---|---|
| $Mg + O_2 \rightarrow 2MgO$ | |
| $HCl + NaOH \rightarrow NaCl + 2H_2O$ | |
| $CaCO_3 \rightarrow CaO + CO_2$ | |
| $2Na + 2H_2O \rightarrow NaOH + H_2$ | |

**(4 marks)**

2  Write word equations for the following reactions.

(a)  When lead chloride is heated with magnesium powder a violent reaction produces magnesium oxide and lead.

lead chloride + magnesium → ................... + ..................   **(2 marks)**

(b)  Sulfuric acid will also react with magnesium to make the new products magnesium sulfate and hydrogen.

.................... + magnesium → ..................... + ....................   **(2 marks)**

3  In the reaction between calcium carbonate and hydrochloric acid three products are formed.

$$CaCO_3(s) + 2HCl(aq) \rightarrow CaCl_2(aq) + H_2O(1) + CO_2(g)$$

Name the substances that are:

solid ...............................

aqueous hydrochloric acid and .......................................

liquid .............................

gas ...................................   **(4 marks)**

4  In an experiment a student mixes together sulfuric acid, $H_2SO_4$, and copper carbonate, $CuCO_3$. A blue solution forms and bubbles are produced.

(a)  In the experiment what were the reactants? ...............................................   **(1 mark)**

> Reactants are the chemicals that are mixed at the start of a reaction.

(b)  Name the gas that was produced. ...........................................   **(1 mark)**

(c)  Write a word equation for the reaction.

sulfuric acid + ..................... → copper sulfate + water + ....................   **(2 marks)**

(d)  Write a balanced symbol equation for the reaction. Include state symbols.

................. + $CuCO_3$ → $CuSO_4$ + ................. + .................   **(3 marks)**

> The question has asked for state symbols so you must use them. You will gain a mark for including the correct state symbols.

# Ionic equations

1  $MgCl_2$ is an ionic solid. When dissolved in water the ions dissociate (split apart). Identify the two ions produced. Tick **one** box.

☐  **A**  $Mg^+$ and $2Cl^-$

☐  **B**  $Mg^{2+}$ and $2Cl^-$

☐  **C**  $Mg^+$ and $Cl^{2-}$

☐  **D**  $2Mg^+$ and $Cl^{2-}$                                             **(1 mark)**

2  Substances that form ions are compounds that contain a metal ion and a non-metal ion, are acids or are ammonium compounds. State the ions present in the following compounds.

> Remember to write the charges on the ions.

(a)  NaCl

................ and ...............  **(1 mark)**

(b)  $H_2SO_4$

................ and ...............  **(1 mark)**

(c)  $Cu(OH)_2$

................ and ...............  **(1 mark)**

(d)  $NH_4NO_3$

................ and ...............  **(1 mark)**

3  A barium meal is a liquid given to a patient before X-rays are taken to help image their digestive system. It contains the compound barium sulfate. Barium sulfate can be made by reacting barium chloride and sodium sulfate.

$$BaCl_2(aq) + Na_2SO_4(aq) \rightarrow BaSO_4(s) + 2NaCl(aq)$$

(a)  Write down symbols and charges for the ions in the reactants.

$Ba^{2+}$, ...............................................................................................................  **(2 marks)**

(b)  Which product will not split into ions when put into water? .........................  **(1 mark)**

(c)  What ions are present in sodium chloride?

...................... and ......................

> A precipitate is formed that will not dissolve in water.

**(1 mark)**

(d)  Name the ions that appear as both reactants and products.

...................... and ......................                                              **(2 marks)**

(e)  Complete the ionic equation for this reaction.

$Ba^{2+}(aq) + $ ............ $(aq) \rightarrow BaSO_4(s)$

> In your final exam you need to know how to write balanced ionic equations.

**(1 mark)**

4  In neutralisation reactions a hydrogen ion reacts with a hydroxide ion to form water.

(a)  Write the formula of hydroxide ions.

......................................                                                            **(1 mark)**

(b)  Write the formula of a hydrogen ion.

......................................                                                            **(1 mark)**

(c)  Write the ionic equation for the reaction.

................ + ................ $\rightarrow H_2O$                                     **(1 mark)**

# Hazards, risk and precautions

1 Before any experiment is carried out in a laboratory, a risk assessment must take place. It must include all hazards and associated risks with the experiment.

(a) Name **two** hazards associated with using a Bunsen burner.

The Bunsen burner could topple over and cause a fire.

............................................................................................ **(2 marks)**

(b) Identify **two** risks associated with using a Bunsen burner.

............................................................................................

............................................................................................ **(2 marks)**

(c) Give **two** precautions that should be taken when using a Bunsen burner.

............................................................................................

............................................................................................ **(2 marks)**

> A hazard is something that could cause harm, a risk is the chance of the hazard causing harm and a precaution is what action you can take to prevent harm.

2 Hazard labels are used on bottles of chemicals so people can quickly identify the hazards of the chemical. Describe the following hazard warning symbols.

....................... ....................... oxidising ....................... **(4 marks)**

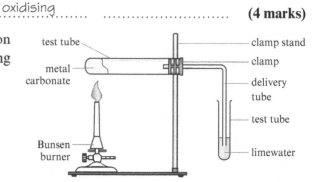

3 A student is planning to carry out an investigation into the decomposition of metal carbonates, using the equipment in the diagram.

Identify **two** hazards, associated risks and the precautions that should be taken.

| Hazard | Risk | Precaution |
|---|---|---|
| Cold limewater sucks back into hot test tube and smashes the glass | | |
| | | |

**(9 marks)**

90

# Atomic structure

1 Draw a diagram of a helium atom, clearly showing the different particles present in the nucleus and the shells of the atom.

> The nucleus of an atom contains protons and neutrons. Electrons are placed in shells around the nucleus.

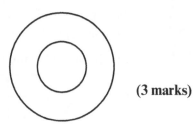

**(3 marks)**

2 Atoms are made up of subatomic particles.

(a) Complete the following table.

| Particle | Relative mass | Relative charge |
|---|---|---|
| neutron | | |
| | $\frac{1}{1835}$ | |
| | | $+1$ |

**(3 marks)**

(b) Explain why atoms contain charged particles, but have no overall charge.

Atoms contain positive protons and negative electrons in equal numbers therefore

...................................................................................................... **(1 mark)**

3 If an atom was the size of the Earth the nucleus would be the size of a football stadium. A carbon atom has a nucleus with a radius of $2.7 \times 10^{-15}$ m and an atomic radius of $9 \times 10^{-11}$ m. How many times smaller is the nucleus compared with the size of the atom?

> To type $2 \times 10^{-5}$ into your calculator it would be 2 EXP –5.

$\frac{9 \times 10^{-11}}{2.7 \times 10^{-15}} =$ .............................  **(1 mark)**

4 John Dalton developed atomic theory in the 1800s. He said, 'the atom was the smallest thing that existed and they could not be broken down'. Given what we know now, why is this wrong?

......................................................................................................

...................................................................................................... **(1 mark)**

> Consider what has been discovered since the 1800s.

5 Ernest Rutherford added to the development of atomic theory. While investigating the plum pudding model he fired positive alpha particles at a sheet of gold foil. Explain the following observations.

> You should be familiar with how this experiment was carried out and be able to explain the three different ways the particles behave.

(a) Most alpha particles went straight through.

These particles did not hit anything because ...............................................

...................................................................................................... **(1 mark)**

(b) Some were deflected from their path.

......................................................................................................

...................................................................................................... **(1 mark)**

(c) A few bounced straight back.

......................................................................................................

...................................................................................................... **(1 mark)**

# Isotopes

**1** Isotopes of different elements can be very useful. Carbon-14, $^{14}_{6}C$ is used to date archaeological artefacts.

(a) In the following table, which line shows an isotope of Carbon-12, $^{12}_{6}C$?

|   | Protons | Electrons | Neutrons |
|---|---------|-----------|----------|
| X | 6 | 6 | 6 |
| Y | 12 | 6 | 6 |
| Z | 13 | 12 | 12 |

..................................... **(1 mark)**

(b) Carbon has three main isotopes: carbon-12, $^{12}_{6}C$, carbon-13, $^{13}_{6}C$ and carbon-14, $^{14}_{6}C$.

(i) What does the number 6 represent?

.................................................................................... **(1 mark)**

(ii) 12, 13 and 14 are the ................................................. **(1 mark)**

(iii) Which isotope has the most neutrons?

.................................................................................... **(1 mark)**

**2** Boron has two main isotopes: boron-10, $^{10}_{5}B$, and boron-11, $^{11}_{5}B$.

(a) Complete the diagrams to show the protons, electrons and neutrons for each isotope.

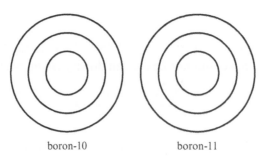

boron-10                boron-11                **(3 marks)**

(b) Boron-10 and boron-11 have similar chemical properties. Use the information above to explain why.

> Chemical properties of an element are determined by the arrangement of electrons – the number of electrons in the outer shell and the number of shells.

.................................................................................................

.................................................................................... **(1 mark)**

(c) Boron is made up of 20% boron-10 and 80% boron-11. What is the exact relative atomic mass of boron to one decimal place?

$\left(\frac{20}{100} \times 10\right) + \left(\frac{80}{100} \times 11\right) =$ ................................... **(2 marks)**

# Mendeleev's table

**1** Mendeleev constructed his version of the periodic table in 1869. What was the main way in which he ordered the elements? Tick **one** box.

☐ **A** reactivity with water

☐ **B** increasing atomic mass

☐ **C** physical appearance

☐ **D** decreasing atomic number

**(1 mark)**

**2** A version of Mendeleev's 1869 table is shown in the diagram.

Group

| 1 | 2 | 3 | 4 | 5 | 6 | 7 |
|-----|--------|-------|-------|-------|-------|-------|
| Li | Be | B | C | N | O | F |
| Na | Mg | Al | Si | P | S | Cl |
| K | Ca Zn | * * | Ti * | V As | Cr Se | Mn Br |
| Rb Ag | Sr Cd | Y In | Zr Sn | Nb Sb | Mo Te | Tc I |

(a) Mendeleev initially put hydrogen into group 1 of the periodic table. Why does this element not belong in group 1?

Hydrogen is a gas not a metal ...............................................................

.................................................................................................... **(1 mark)**

(b) Mendeleev put lithium, sodium and potassium in the same group. What evidence did he use to do this?

....................................................................................................

.................................................................................................... **(2 marks)**

(c) Why did Mendeleev leave gaps in his periodic table?

....................................................................................................

.................................................................................................... **(1 mark)**

(d) Iodine has a mass of 127 and tellurium has a mass of 128. Suggest a reason why Mendeleev reversed these elements in his periodic table

> Look to see where iodine would have been if it had not been reversed. Would the properties match the other elements in that group?

....................................................................................................

.................................................................................................... **(1 mark)**

**3** What group of the periodic table is missing from Mendeleev's version? Explain why Mendeleev might have left it out.

....................................................................................................

....................................................................................................

....................................................................................................

.................................................................................................... **(2 marks)**

# The periodic table

**1** In the lists below circle the odd one out.

(a)  Na  K  Rb  Cl

(b)  Ca  Fe  N  Br

(c)  O  Al  Ni  Ag

(d)  S  Mg  Ne  C

> Look at where these elements are in the periodic table, paying attention to their groups and periods. (Partial table shown below.)

**(1 mark)**

**2** The diagram shows the first part of the periodic table with their atomic numbers.

> Guided

| | | | | | | | | | | | | | H 1 | | | | | | 0 |
|---|---|---|---|---|---|---|---|---|---|---|---|---|---|---|---|---|---|---|---|
| I | II | | | | | | | | | | | III | IV | V | VI | VII | | | He 2 |
| Li 3 | Be 4 | | | | | | | | | | | B 5 | C 6 | N 7 | O 8 | F 9 | Ne 10 |
| Na 11 | Mg 12 | | | | | | | | | | | Al 13 | Si 14 | P 15 | S 16 | Cl 17 | Ar 18 |
| K 19 | Ca 20 | Sc 21 | Ti 22 | V 23 | Cr 24 | Mn 25 | Fe 26 | Co 27 | Ni 28 | Cu 29 | Zn 30 | Ga 31 | Ge 32 | As 33 | Se 34 | Br 35 | Kr 36 |

(a)  What is the name of the group that contains the elements with atomic numbers 9, 17 and 35?

............................................................  **(1 mark)**

(b)  What name is given to the group of elements between atomic number 21 and 30?

............................................................  **(1 mark)**

(c)  Give the atomic numbers of three alkali metals.

............................................................  **(1 mark)**

(d)  Complete the following table

| Atomic number | Group number | Period number |
|---|---|---|
| 12 | | 3 |
| 14 | 4 | |
| | 7 | 2 |
| 17 | | 3 |
| 19 | 1 | |

**(5 marks)**

**3** The modern periodic table is arranged by atomic number.

(a)  What does atomic number mean?

..........................................................................................................................  **(1 mark)**

(b)  New elements are still being discovered. Why are scientists certain that no new elements will be found that belong between hydrogen and lawrencium in the periodic table?

*Between hydrogen and lawrencium the atomic numbers increase by 1 each time ...*

..........................................................................................................................

..........................................................................................................................  **(2 marks)**

**4** In the modern periodic table argon-40 and potassium-39 are not in order of increasing atomic weight. Why is this?

> Guided

..........................................................................................................................

..........................................................................................................................  **(2 marks)**

# Electronic configurations

1 Which of the following statements correctly describes how electrons are arranged in atoms? Tick **one** box.

☐ **A**  The first shell contains eight electrons.

☐ **B**  The outer shell is always filled first.

☐ **C**  The first shell is filled first.

☐ **D**  Electrons must be shared evenly between shells.    **(1 mark)**

2 Sodium (atomic number 11) and lithium (atomic number 3) are in the same group of the periodic table and behave similarly when added to water.

(a) State the electron configuration for sodium and lithium.

Sodium: ................................

Lithium: ................................    **(2 marks)**

> The atomic number tells you the number of protons in an atom. In **neutral atoms** the number of protons is the same as the number of electrons. In **ions**, the numbers of protons and electrons are not equal.

(b) Draw diagrams to show the arrangement of electrons in sodium and lithium.

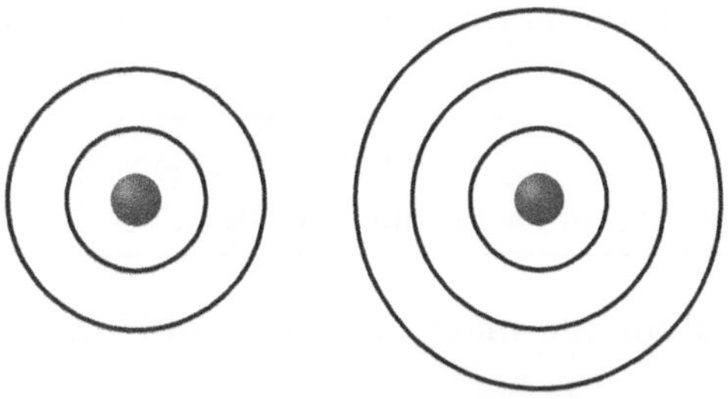

   **(3 marks)**

(c) Use the diagrams above to explain why sodium and lithium are in the same group.

> You must refer to something you can see in the diagrams when you answer the question.

................................................................................................

................................................................................................    **(2 marks)**

3 The atomic number of boron is 5. In terms of electron configuration explain why carbon (atomic number 6) is in the same period as boron, but aluminium (atomic number 13) is not.

Boron has the electronic configuration 2,3. Carbon is 2,4, but aluminium is 2,8,3.

This means that aluminium has .............................................................

................................................................................................    **(2 marks)**

4 Deduce the electron configurations of the following elements.

Magnesium, Mg (atomic number 12) ................................

Sulfur, S (atomic number 16) ................................

Neon, Ne (atomic number 10) ................................    **(3 marks)**

# Ions

**1** Atoms that have lost or gained electrons are called ions. Sodium has the atomic number 11 and forms $Na^+$ ions.

  (a) Calculate how many electrons a sodium ion contains.

11 – 1 = ..................................... **(1 mark)**

  (b) Write the electronic configuration of a sodium ion.

.....................................

> If an ion is negative it has gained electrons. If it is positive, it has lost electrons.

**(1 mark)**

  (c) State the general name given to positive ions.

.....................................

**(1 mark)**

**2** The following table contains a mixture of elements, positive ions and negative ions.

  (a) State and explain which letter is a positive ion.

C because ...............................................

  (b) State and explain which letter is a negative ion.

B because ...............................................

|   | Protons | Electrons | Neutrons |
|---|---------|-----------|----------|
| A | 19 | 19 | 20 |
| B | 9 | 10 | 10 |
| C | 13 | 10 | 14 |

**(2 marks)**

**(2 marks)**

  (c) State the general name given to negative ions.

.....................................................

**(1 mark)**

**3** The diagram shows the electron arrangement of an unknown substance.

> Remember: each electron has a negative charge, so gaining an electron makes the charge of the ion more negative.

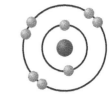

  (a) If this is a neutral atom how many protons would it have?

.................................................................................................... **(1 mark)**

  (b) How many protons and electrons would it have if it became a 2+ ion?

.................................................................................................... **(1 mark)**

  (c) How many protons and electrons would it have if it became a 1– ion?

.................................................................................................... **(1 mark)**

**4** Complete the following table to show the number of protons, electrons and neutrons of the following ions.

|   | Atomic number | Mass number | Protons | Electrons | Neutrons |
|---|---------------|-------------|---------|-----------|----------|
| $Mg^{2+}$ | 12 | 24 | 12 |  | 12 |
| $F^-$ | 9 | 19 | 9 | 10 |  |
| $O^{2-}$ | 8 | 16 | 8 | 10 |  |
| $Li^+$ | 3 | 7 |  |  | 4 |
| $Al^{3+}$ | 13 | 27 | 13 |  |  |

**(5 marks)**

# Formulae of ionic compounds

**1** Magnesium phosphide contains the ions $Mg^{2+}$ and $P^{3-}$.

(a) Which statement below is incorrect? Tick **one** box.

☐   **A**   When the ions combine the compound formed will be neutral.

☐   **B**   Two magnesium ions and three phosphate ions will combine to make magnesium phosphide.

☐   **C**   Magnesium is the cation and phosphate is the anion.

☐   **D**   The formula of magnesium phosphide is $Mg_3P_2$.    **(1 mark)**

(b) What is the difference between a phosphide ion and a phosphate ion?

....................................................................................................................

.................................................................................................................... **(2 marks)**

**2** Complete the table to write the formula of the compounds.

> Make sure the + and – charges balance in each compound. Use brackets around any complex ion you want to multiply. For example, $Be(OH)_2$ shows there is one beryllium atom to two hydroxide ions.

| | $Cl^-$ | $NO_3^-$ | $SO_4^{2-}$ | $CO_3^{2-}$ | $OH^-$ |
|---|---|---|---|---|---|
| $Na^+$ | | | | | |
| $Ca^{2+}$ | | | | | |
| $Al^{3+}$ | | | | | |
| $NH_4^+$ | | | | | |

**(20 marks)**

**3** Zinc sulfide, ZnS, is an ionic compound. The sulfide ion is $S^{2-}$.

(a) Using this information, deduce the charge on the zinc ion. .............................. **(1 mark)**

(b) Explain how you worked this out.

.................................................................................................................... **(1 mark)**

**4** Sodium chloride, NaCl, is used to flavour foods, whereas sodium chlorate is highly toxic and is used in bleach. The chlorate ion has the formula $ClO_3^-$.

(a) What is similar about the two compounds?

.................................................................................................................... **(1 mark)**

(b) What is different about the two compounds?

.................................................................................................................... **(1 mark)**

**5** An inorganic chemist produces a compound that has the formula $Mg_3(PO_4)_2$. From this formula what three pieces of information can you deduce about the compound and its structure?

It is made up of 3 ..................... ions and 2 ..................... ions. These ions

bond together by ................... bonding.    **(3 marks)**

# Properties of ionic compounds

1   The diagram shows the structure of sodium chloride.

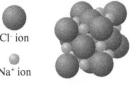

Cl⁻ ion

Na⁺ ion

> Make sure you include information about both the structure **and** the bonding to get both marks.

(a)  Describe the structure and bonding present.

Ionic bonding .............................................................................................

.........................................................................................................

......................................................................................................... **(2 marks)**

(b)  Sodium chloride has a melting point of 801 °C. Explain why the melting point is so high.

Electrostatic ...................................................................................... **(3 marks)**

2   A student uses the circuit shown to investigate the electrical conductivity of different substances.

(a)  State and explain what would happen if solid sodium chloride was used.

No reading on ammeter ....................

.................................................

therefore ......................................

.................................................

battery

ammeter (A)

test substance

X

crocodile clip

**(3 marks)**

> The circuit contains an ammeter. Make sure you mention what would happen to the reading in your answer. An exact value is not required.

(b)  The student then dissolves the sodium chloride in water and repeats the experiment. Explain how the results would be different.

.........................................................................................................

......................................................................................................... **(2 marks)**

3   The table shows several properties of three different substances.

Guided

| | Melting point | Conductivity of solid | Conductivity of liquid |
|---|---|---|---|
| **A** | 2340 | high | high |
| **B** | 322 | zero | zero |
| **C** | 1026 | zero | high |

State and explain which substance is ionic.

.........................................................................................................

......................................................................................................... **(2 marks)**

4   Molten potassium bromide and aqueous potassium bromide both conduct electricity. Explain how both of these compounds are able to conduct electricity.

> Ionic compounds dissociate when added to water.

.........................................................................................................

......................................................................................................... **(2 marks)**

# Covalent bonds

**1** (a) Covalent bonds form between which type of elements? ................................. **(1 mark)**

 (b) For a covalent bond to form what needs to happen with the electrons? .............. **(1 mark)**

(c) How many electrons are involved in each single covalent bond? ........................ **(1 mark)**

(d) What is the name given to a bond where four electrons are present? .................. **(1 mark)**

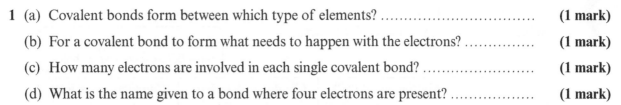

**2** Water, $H_2O$, is a covalent molecule and has a radius of $2.75 \times 10^{-10}$ m. An oxygen atom has an atomic radius of $4.8 \times 10^{-11}$ m.

(a) Calculate how many times bigger the molecule is compared with the atom.

$\dfrac{2.75 \times 10^{-10}}{4.8 \times 10^{-11}} =$ ......................................... **(1 mark)**

(b) Draw the dot cross diagram of water showing only the outer electrons.

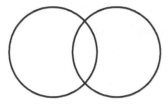

**(2 marks)**

**3** Many of the gases in the periodic table form diatomic molecules. A diatomic molecule is a molecule where two atoms of the same type have joined together.

(a) Explain, in terms of electrons, why it may be favourable for atoms to make diatomic molecules.

..................................................................................................... **(1 mark)**

(b) $H_2$ and $O_2$ are two different diatomic molecules. Draw dot cross diagrams showing only the outer electrons for the molecules.

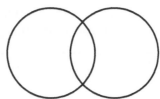

> If you cannot make a full outer shell using a single bond try using a double bond.

**(2 marks)**

(c) Explain the similarities and differences between the bonding in the elements hydrogen and oxygen.

.....................................................................................................
..................................................................................................... **(2 marks)**

**4** Carbon atoms have a valency of four and hydrogen atoms have a valency of one. Use this information to determine the formula of methane, a hydrocarbon composed of only carbon and hydrogen, and draw a diagram of the bonding showing only the outer electrons.

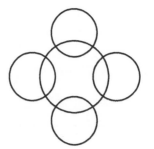

Formula: ...............................

**(3 marks)**

# Simple molecular substances

**1** The table shows physical properties of four different substances (A–D). Which one has a simple molecular structure?

.................................................

> Consider all of the data in the table before you make a choice.

**(1 mark)**

|   | Melting point (°C) | Conducts electricity when solid | Conducts electricity when molten |
|---|---|---|---|
| **A** | 2389 | yes | yes |
| **B** | 951 | no | yes |
| **C** | 42 | no | no |
| **D** | 3982 | yes | yes |

Explain your choice of substance.

......................................................................................................................... **(1 mark)**

**2** Ammonia is a gas at room temperature. It has the formula $NH_3$.

(a) Complete the dot cross diagram for ammonia.

**(1 mark)**

(b) Using the dot cross diagram describe the bonding that occurs in the molecule.

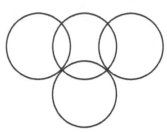

..............................................................................

**(1 mark)**

> Are electrons shared between atoms or passed between ions?

(c) Ammonia has a boiling point of –33 °C so is a gas at room temperature. Explain why the boiling point is so low.

There are weak intermolecular forces between ................................................

so ........................................................................................................... **(2 marks)**

**3** The bar chart shows the melting points of the four halogens fluorine, chlorine, bromine and iodine. Use the bar chart to describe how the melting points of the halogens change as you go down the group and suggest a reason why this might happen.

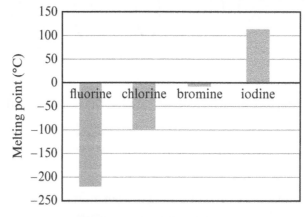

.........................................................................................................................

.........................................................................................................................

.........................................................................................................................

......................................................................................................................... **(2 marks)**

100

# Giant molecular substances

1 Which of the following can be described as having the following properties?

'High melting point, conducts electricity, not soluble in water'. Tick **one** box.

☐ **A** $NH_3$

☐ **B** Diamond

☐ **C** Graphite

☐ **D** NaCl

> You need to know the physical properties of both ionic and covalent substances.

**(1 mark)**

2 Diamond and graphite are allotropes of each other. An allotrope is when the same element takes on a different shape when bonding. A diagram to show the shapes that diamond and graphite make can be seen below.

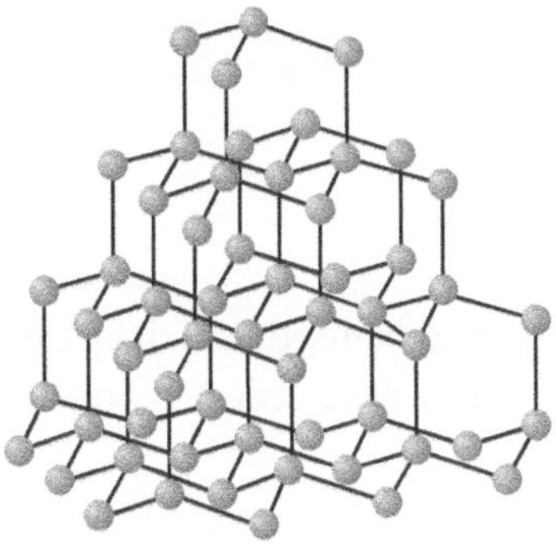

diamond 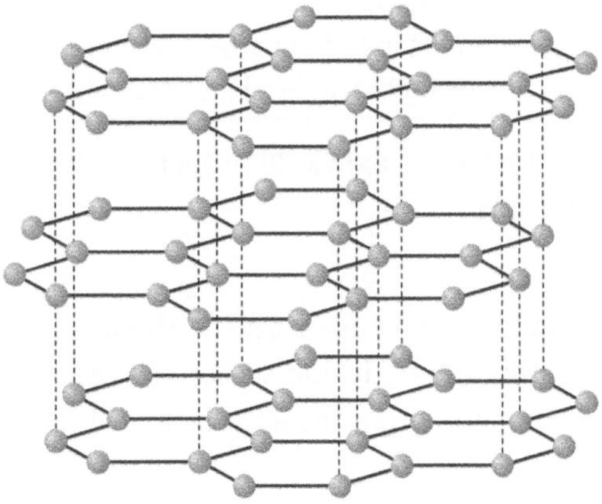             graphite

(a) Name **one** feature that is similar. ............................... ............................... **(1 mark)**

(b) Name **one** feature that is different. ............................... **(1 mark)**

(c) What name is given to describe these large structures?

Giant ........................... **(1 mark)**

(d) Graphite is often used as a lubricant. Using the diagram, and referring to structure and bonding, explain why graphite has these features.

There are weak intermolecular forces between ...............................

............................... **(2 marks)**

3 Silicon has similar structure and bonding properties to diamond. When bonded to oxygen it can form the giant structure silicon oxide.

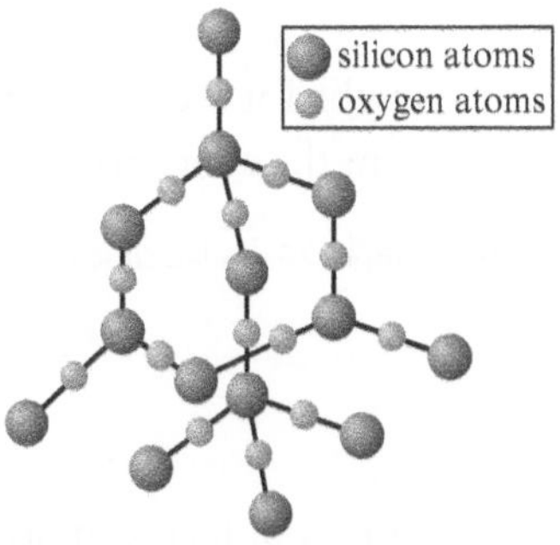

⬤ silicon atoms
● oxygen atoms

(a) Explain why carbon and silicon are both able to form four bonds.

............................... **(1 mark)**

> Look at the periodic table to see the group that carbon and silicon belong in.

(b) Using your knowledge of diamond predict two physical properties of silicon oxide.

............................... **(2 marks)**

(c) Name a physical property of diamond and name a use based on that property.

Hard so can be used for ...............................

............................... **(2 marks)**

Had a go ☐    Nearly there ☐    Nailed it! ☐

# Other large molecules

1 The plastic poly(propene) has many uses ranging from car bumpers to carpets.

(a) Name the monomer used to make poly(propene). ..................................... **(1 mark)**

(b) When the monomers join together what type of bond is formed? .................... **(1 mark)**

2 Buckminster fullerenes are made entirely of carbon. Sixty carbon atoms are arranged in a football shape.

(a) Explain why buckminster fullerenes have a low melting point.

There are weak ..............................................

.......................................................... **(2 marks)**

> Despite their size, fullerenes are simple molecular substances.

(b) State why they have a physical property of being 'soft and slippery'.

.......................................................................... **(1 mark)**

(c) Fullerenes have many uses: one of them is that they can be used as a drug delivery system within the body and so deposit drugs where they are needed. Name another use for fullerenes given the description in part (b).

.......................................................................... **(1 mark)**

3 Graphene is made from honeycomb sheets of carbon just one atom thick.

(a) Looking at the diagram, how is the bonding similar to graphite?

..............................................

..............................................

..........................................................

.......................................................... **(2 marks)**

> This question is asking about the bonding, not the structure.

(b) Weight-for-weight, graphene is 200 times stronger than steel. Explain graphene's strength in terms of bonding.

Each carbon is bonded to three others ...........................................

..........................................................

.......................................................... **(3 marks)**

(c) Explain in terms of structure and bonding why graphene is able to conduct electricity.

..........................................................

.......................................................... **(2 marks)**

> Use your knowledge of graphite to help you answer this question.

# Metals

1 Metallic bonding is described as the electrostatic attraction between which of the following? Tick **one** box.

☐   **A**   positive metal ions and negative delocalised electrons.

☐   **B**   positive ions and negative ions.

☐   **C**   negative electrons shared between two positive ions.

☐   **D**   negative ions and delocalised electrons.    **(1 mark)**

2 Gold has been used for jewellery for thousands of years. Gold can be hit with a hammer and shaped into many complicated designs.

(a) What is the name given to metals to describe that they can be hit with a hammer without shattering?

...................................................................................................................... **(1 mark)**

(b) Complete the diagram below to show how the structure would look after being hit by a hammer.

> You only need to draw a rough diagram of the atoms: do not try to redraw the hammer.

**(1 mark)**

3 The bar chart shows the electrical conductivity of different metals and the ions that they form.

(a) What is the relationship between the electrical conductivity and the ions the metal forms?

The greater the charge on the metal ion .........

...................................................................

...................................................................

**(2 marks)**

(b) Explain this relationship in terms of the structure and bonding of metals.

The greater the charge on a metal ion the more delocalised electrons it produces

......................................................................................................................

...................................................................................................................... **(2 marks)**

# Limitations of models

**1** Chemicals can be modelled in lots of different ways. Four different models for the molecule water are shown below. Draw lines to match the disadvantages and advantages to the correct type of model.

**(4 marks)**

| Advantage | Type of model | Disadvantage |
|---|---|---|
| Shows three-dimensional arrangement as well as size relationships between atoms. | Structure | Identification of atoms requires a key of colour representations. |
| Shows three-dimensional arrangement of atoms and bonds. | Dot cross | Only shows two-dimensional shape and no indication about type of bonding. |
| Shows how electrons are shared between atoms. | Ball and stick | Bonding between atoms can sometimes be difficult to distinguish. |
| Shows all the bonds that are present. | Space fill | Only shows two-dimensional shape and gets very crowded with larger molecules. |

**2** A scientist wants to show how the outer electrons are bonded in a molecule. Which model should they use and why?

..........................................................................................................................

.......................................................................................................................... **(2 marks)**

**3** In general, why are models important when studying elements and compounds?

..........................................................................................................................

.......................................................................................................................... **(2 marks)**

**4** In most text books the model used to illustrate metallic bonding will use the following diagram. Use your knowledge of metallic bonding to describe the limitations of this model.

The positive metal ions are not fixed in place, they vibrate on the spot and the model can not show them vibrating.

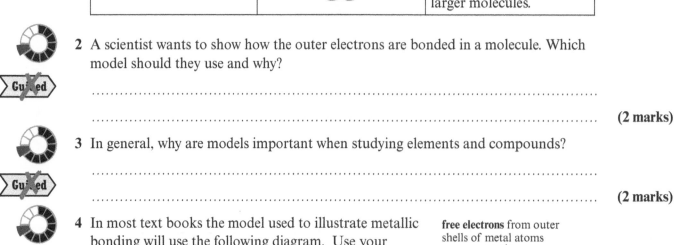

free electrons from outer shells of metal atoms

metal ions

.....................................................................................

..................................................................... **(2 marks)**

# Relative formula mass

1  Helium atoms have a mass number of 4. That means three helium atoms will have the same mass as one atom of carbon. ($A_r = 12$)

   (a)  What element has atoms with a mass twice that of carbon?

   $A_r$ of carbon is 12 so 2 × 12 = 24 ........................................   **(1 mark)**

   (b)  How many helium atoms would have the same mass as one atom of oxygen?

   $A_r$ of oxygen is 16 and the $A_r$ of helium is 2 so 16 ÷ 2 = .........................   **(1 mark)**

   (c)  What element has atoms with a mass twice that of lithium?

   2 × 7 .......................................   **(1 mark)**

> Once you have calculated the values, you need to use the periodic table to find the answers. You will be given a periodic table in the exam.

2  When atoms join together to form molecules, the relative formula mass of the molecule is found by adding together the masses of the individual atoms. Calculate the relative formula masses of the following molecules:

   (a)  $O_2$ ..................   **(1 mark)**

   > Pay attention to the number of each type of atom in the molecules. For example there are two oxygen atoms in carbon dioxide.

   (b)  $CO_2$ ..................   **(1 mark)**

   (c)  $NH_3$ ..................   **(1 mark)**

   > In a formula, the subscript number after an element tells you how many atoms of that element are present.

   (d)  $H_2O$ ..................   **(1 mark)**

3  The relative formula mass of a compound is the sum of the relative atomic masses of each of the atoms in the compound. Calculate the relative formula masses for the following compounds.

   (a)  $Li_2O$

   ...............................................   **(1 mark)**

   (b)  $BaCl_2$

   ...............................................   **(1 mark)**

   (c)  $Al(OH)_3$

   27 + (16 + 1) + (16 + 1) + (16 + 1) ......

   > If you find brackets confusing, write out the contents of the brackets to help you calculate the relative formula mass. For example, $Al(OH)_3$ could be written as AlOHOHOH.

   ...............................................   **(1 mark)**

   (d)  $Na_2SO_4$

   ...............................................   **(1 mark)**

   (e)  $(NH_4)_3PO_4$

   14 + (1 × 4) = 18 then 18 × 3 as there are three lots of $NH_4$

   ...............................................   **(1 mark)**

   (f)  $Mg(NO_3)_2$

   ...............................................

   > The little 2 tells you there are two lots of $NO_3$. The little 3 belongs only to the oxygen.

   ...............................................   **(1 mark)**

   (g)  $CH_3CH_2OH$

   ...............................................   **(1 mark)**

Had a go ☐   Nearly there ☐   Nailed it! ☐

# Empirical formulae

1  Mass spectroscopy has found a compound to have a relative formula mass of 84. Its empirical formula is $CH_2$. Calculate its molecular formula. ($A_r$ C = 12, $A_r$ H = 1)

Calculate the mass of the $CH_2$ = 12 + (1 × 2) = 14. Then divide the formula mass by 14 to calculate the factor to multiply the empirical formula by = 6

84 ÷ 14 = 6. .................................................................................... **(2 marks)**

2  Calculate the empirical formula for the following compounds.

(a)  $H_2O_2$ ........................... **(1 mark)**   (b)  $C_6H_{12}O_6$ ........................... **(1 mark)**

(c)  $C_3H_6O_3$ ........................... **(1 mark)**   (d)  $P_4O_{10}$ ........................... **(1 mark)**

> Write the simplest ratio of the elements.

3  Calculate the empirical formula for when the following elements combine.

(a)  2.8 g nitrogen and 1.6 g oxygen. ($A_r$ N = 14, $A_r$ O = 16).

Divide the mass of the elements by their atomic masses. Then find the ratio between these values 2.8 ÷ 14 = 0.2, 1.6 ÷ 16 = 0.1. There are twice as many

nitrogen atoms as oxygen atoms. ................................................... **(1 mark)**

(b)  20 g carbon and 5 g of hydrogen. ($A_r$ C = 12, $A_r$ H = 1).

Divide mass by atomic number:     20 ÷ 12 = 1.66     5 ÷ 1 = 5

Divide by lowest value:          1.66 ÷ 1.66 = 1     5 ÷ 1.66 = 2.99 so
                                                    ratio is 1:3, C:H.

.................................................................................................. **(1 mark)**

4  In an experiment, students used the equipment in the diagram to reduce copper oxide, CuO, to copper, Cu, in an attempt to calculate the empirical formula of copper oxide. They recorded the following information.

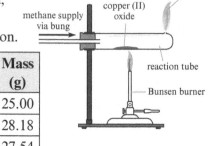

|   |                                                | Mass (g) |
|---|------------------------------------------------|----------|
| 1 | Test tube + bung                               | 25.00    |
| 2 | Test tube + bung + copper oxide (reactant)     | 28.18    |
| 3 | Test tube + bung + copper (product)            | 27.54    |

(a)  Calculate the mass of copper produced in the experiment.

Line 3 − line 1 ................................................................ **(1 mark)**

(b)  What was the mass of oxygen, $A_r$ = 16, removed from the copper oxide?

Line 2 − line 3 ................................................................ **(1 mark)**

(c)  Using the student's results calculate the empirical formula of copper oxide. ($A_r$ Cu = 63.5, $A_r$ O = 16).

Divide mass by atomic number .....................................................

Divide by lowest value ............................................................ **(2 marks)**

# Conservation of mass

**1** A student investigated the reaction between calcium carbonate and hydrochloric acid, using the equipment shown, and obtained the set of data shown.

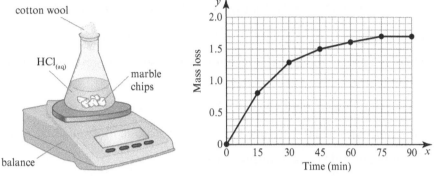

(a) State and explain if this system is closed or open.   Remember, gases have a mass.

The system is open ..................................................................

.................................................................................. **(2 marks)**

(b) Name **one** safety precaution when carrying out this experiment.

.................................................................................. **(1 mark)**

(c) At what time was the reaction completed? Explain why.

..................................................................................

.................................................................................. **(2 marks)**

Look at the reagents being used: are any of them hazardous?

**2** Chemists often want to calculate exactly how much of one reactant to add to another in reactions to prevent any waste.

(a) Calculate the mass of oxygen needed to react with 24 g of magnesium. ($A_r$ Mg = 24, $A_r$ O = 16.)

$$2Mg + O_2 \rightarrow 2MgO$$

Moles of magnesium = mass / relative molecular mass = 24 ÷ 24 = 1 mol.
Magnesium and oxygen molecules react in a 2 : 1 ratio, so
Moles of $O_2$ = 0.5 mol
Mass of oxygen = moles of $O_2$ × $M_r$ $O_2$ (= 32) ..................... **(3 marks)**

(b) Calculate the mass of zinc needed to react with 7.3 g of hydrochloric acid. ($A_r$ Zn = 65, $A_r$ H = 1, $A_r$ Cl = 35.5.)

$$Zn + 2HCl \rightarrow ZnCl_2 + H_2$$

Moles of hydrochloric acid .............................................

Moles of zinc ...............................................................

Mass of zinc ................................................................ **(3 marks)**

There are 2 moles of HCl to every 1 mole of Zn, so to calculate moles of zinc, the moles of hydrochloric acid must be halved.

Had a go ☐   Nearly there ☐   Nailed it! ☐

# Reacting mass calculations

1. Limestone statues are eroded by acid rain. Students decided to investigate the effect of acid on calcium carbonate using the following reaction.

$$CaCO_3(s) + 2HCl(aq) \rightarrow CaCl_2(aq) + CO_2(g) + H_2O(l)$$

(a) Which statement is incorrect about this reaction? Tick **one** box.

☐ **A**   There is a loss in mass as the reaction progresses, as gas escapes from the reaction vessel.

☐ **B**   If HCl is in excess, all of the $CaCO_3$ will be used up.

☐ **C**   Two molecules of HCl are needed to react with one molecule of $CaCO_3$.

☐ **D**   Calcium chloride is the limiting reagent.     **(1 mark)**

> Look at the state symbols and the moles of each substance in the equation to help you.

(b) The students reacted equal numbers of moles of both calcium carbonate and hydrochloric acid. Using the stoichiometry of the equation explain which reagent is the limiting reagent.

*For every one molecule of calcium carbonate that reacts, two molecules of hydrochloric acid must react. Therefore, if the students started with equal*

*numbers of both, the reactant that will run out first will be* ............................ **(2 marks)**

2. 'Fools gold' is another name for the mineral pyrite. Pyrite is made from the compound iron(II) sulfide. In the laboratory, iron powder can be mixed with sulfur and heated to produce iron sulfide.

(a) In an experiment, 5.6 g of iron, $A_r$ 56, and 6.4 g of sulfur, $A_r$ 32, are mixed together and heated strongly to produce iron sulfide. $Fe + S \rightarrow FeS$. Which reagent is in excess and why?

*Moles of iron $= \frac{5.6}{56} = 0.1$; mol of sulfur $= \frac{6.4}{32} = 0.2$. So there are more moles of*

*sulfur than iron. The excess reagent is* .......................................................

.......................................................................................................... **(3 marks)**

(b) Calculate the maximum amount, in grams, of iron sulfide that can be made in the reaction.

*Mass $=$ number of mol x $M_r = 0.1 \times (56 + 32)$* ........................................ **(2 marks)**

> The limiting factor determines the number of moles of product that can be made.

3. In an experiment, solid calcium hydroxide is mixed with aqueous sulfuric acid to form aqueous calcium sulfate and water.

(a) Balance the equation for the reaction:

$$...Ca(OH)_2 + ...H_2SO_4 \rightarrow ...CaSO_4 + ...H_2O \qquad \textbf{(1 mark)}$$

(b) How many grams of calcium sulfate, $CaSO_4$ will be formed if 130 g of calcium hydroxide, $Ca(OH)_2$, is reacted with excess sulfuric acid, $H_2SO_4$?

*Moles of $Ca(OH)_2 = \frac{130}{40 + (17 \times 2)} = 1.76$ mol*

*Mass of $CaSO_4 = 1.76 \times (40 + 32 + (16 \times 4)) =$* .....................................

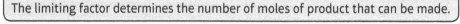

.................................................................................................. **(2 marks)**

# Concentration of solution

1  Convert the following volumes into $dm^3$.

$$1 \, dm^3 = 1000 \, cm^3. \ 1 \, cm^3 = 0.001 \, dm^3.$$

(a)  $4000 \, cm^3$

$\frac{4000}{1000}$ = ................  **(1 mark)**

(b)  $100 \, cm^3$

$\frac{100}{1000}$ = ................  **(1 mark)**

2  Convert the following into $cm^3$.

(a)  $0.25 \, dm^3$

$0.25 \times 1000$ = ................  **(1 mark)**

(b)  $2.125 \, dm^3$

$2.125 \times 1000$ = ...............  **(1 mark)**

In an exam it is always worth checking answers using your calculator.

3  For the following solutions, calculate the concentration in $g \, dm^{-3}$.

(a)  15 g copper sulfate $CuSO_4$ dissolved in $2000 \, cm^3$.

$\left(\frac{15}{2000}\right) \times 1000$ = ................................  **(1 mark)**

(b)  0.1 g potassium iodide dissolved in $500 \, cm^3$.

$\left(\frac{0.1}{500}\right) \times 1000$  **(1 mark)**

(c)  2 g sodium chloride dissolved in $0.2 \, dm^3$.

................................................................................  **(1 mark)**

(d)  3 kg sodium chloride dissolved in $10 \, dm^3$.

Tip 1 kg = 1000 g.

................................................................................  **(1 mark)**

4  A student takes $200 \, cm^3$ of a $2 \, g \, dm^{-3}$ solution of sodium chloride. She adds this to $200 \, cm^3$ of water. She says that the concentration of solution is now half what it used to be. Show, using calculations, that the student is correct.

The original mass of sodium chloride used to make the solution was

$2 \times \frac{200}{1000} = XX$ ................................

This mass is now in $400 \, cm^3$ so the new concentration is $\left(\frac{XX}{400}\right) \times 1000$ ...........

.......................................  **(2 marks)**

5  A research scientist is trying to prepare $500 \, cm^3$ of a $25 \, g \, dm^{-3}$ solution of potassium nitrate. She takes the powdered potassium nitrate and stirs it into the necessary amount of water.

Guided

(a)  What mass of potassium nitrate did she need to use?

................................................................................  **(1 mark)**

(b)  Why was it important to stir the solution?

................................................................................  **(1 mark)**

(c)  She accidently drops 5 g of the powdered potassium nitrate before she adds it to the water. She continues to make the solution. What happens to the concentration of the solution she makes?

................................................................................

................................................................................

................................................................................  **(2 marks)**

Had a go ☐   Nearly there ☐   Nailed it! ☐

# Avogadro's constant and moles

**Guided**

1  Avogadro's number, $6.02 \times 10^{23}$, is an important number in chemical calculations. Which statement below is correct? Tick **one** box.

☐  **A**  The amount of substance with the Avogadro number of particles in is called the mole.

☐  **B**  The Avogadro number can only be used with pure atoms.

☐  **C**  One mole of Cl contains as many atoms as one mole of $Cl_2$ molecules.

☐  **D**  Avogadro's number tells you how many atoms there are in 1g of a substance.   **(1 mark)**

2  Calculate the number of particles in:

(a)  1 mol of magnesium, Mg ($A_r$ Mg = 24).

........................................................

> In this question you are given the $A_r$ values for the elements, but you do not need to use them as you are given the number of moles.

**(1 mark)**

(b)  0.5 mol of water, $H_2O$ ($A_r$ H = 1, $A_r$ O = 16).

$0.5 \times 6.02 \times 10^{23} =$ ........................................   **(1 mark)**

(c)  3 mol of sulfur dioxide, $SO_2$ ($A_r$ S = 32, $A_r$ O = 16).

........................................................   **(1 mark)**

3  Calculate the number of moles in:

(a)  100 g of calcium hydroxide, $Ca(OH)_2$ ($A_r$ Ca = 40, $A_r$ O = 16, $A_r$ H = 1).

$\dfrac{100}{40 + (16 + 1) \times 2} =$ ........................................   **(1 mark)**

(b)  19.2 g of sulfate ions, $SO_4^{2-}$ ($A_r$ S = 32, $A_r$ O = 16).

........................................................   **(1 mark)**

(c)  51 g of ammonia, $NH_3$ ($A_r$ N = 14, $A_r$ H = 1).

........................................................   **(1 mark)**

4  Calculate the number of particles in 0.2 mol of iron.

> 1 mole contains $6.02 \times 10^{23}$ so multiply this by the number of moles of the substance you want to calculate.

..................................................................................................   **(2 marks)**

5  Calculate the number of moles in $1.8 \times 10^{24}$ molecules of hydrogen.

> Divide the number of particles you have by Avagadro's number.

..................................................................................................   **(2 marks)**

6  What mass of zinc contains $2 \times 10^{23}$ atoms? ($A_r$ of zinc = 65)

> This needs to be done in two steps.

First calculate moles of zinc by dividing the number of atoms of zinc by Avagadro's number.

..................................................................................................

The second step finds the mass of zinc by multiplying the number of moles of zinc by the $A_r$ of zinc.

..................................................................................................   **(2 marks)**

# Extended response – Types of substance

 Molten sodium chloride, graphite and iron all conduct electricity. Describe the structure and bonding for each material, and explain how each substance conducts electricity.

> For your exam, you need to be able to draw simple diagrams of ionic compounds, covalent compounds, metals, graphite and diamond.

> Planning your answer helps you get your ideas down in a logical and clear way. If it helps, you can use headings use to help you structure your answer.

### Molten sodium chloride

Draw a diagram to show how, when molten, the ions that were stuck together in a lattice can now move. Then describe how the molten sodium chloride can now conduct electricity.

### Graphite

Draw a diagram of graphite and describe how each carbon makes three bonds to three other carbon atoms, leaving one electron to become delocalised. Explain how it can conduct electricity.

### Iron

Iron is a metal so draw a diagram to show that iron has metallic bonding. Use the diagram to explain how iron conducts electricity.

...................................................................................................................................

...................................................................................................................................

...................................................................................................................................

...................................................................................................................................

...................................................................................................................................

...................................................................................................................................

...................................................................................................................................

...................................................................................................................................

...................................................................................................................................

...................................................................................................................................

...................................................................................................................................

...................................................................................................................................

...................................................................................................................................

...................................................................................................................................

...................................................................................................................................

...................................................................................................................................

...................................................................................................................................   **(6 marks)**

> Continue your answer on your own paper. You should aim to write half a side of A4.

# States of matter

1 Which of the following has a regular arrangement of atoms? Tick **one** box.

☐ **A** hydrogen gas inside a balloon

☐ **B** molten lead

☐ **C** a salt solution used to clean contact lenses

> Think about whether the substance is a solid, liquid or gas.

☐ **D** aluminium used in an aircraft wing                    **(1 mark)**

2 'Solids and liquids cannot be compressed, but gases can'. Explain this statement in terms of atoms.

Atoms in solids are fixed in place. Atoms in liquids are ...................................

............................................................................................................................

............................................................................................................................

............................................................................................................................

............................................................................................................................ **(3 marks)**

3 (a) Solids, liquids and gases have different arrangements and movements of their atoms. Complete the table to show the arrangement and movement of the atoms.

| A – Gas | B – Liquid | C – Solid |
|---------|-----------|-----------|
| Movement = | Movement = | Movement = vibrates on the spot |

**(4 marks)**

(b) Name the process of moving from A to C. ...............................................  **(1 mark)**

(c) Describe the change in energy moving from B to A. ...................................  **(1 mark)**

(d) A substance has a melting point of –22 °C and a boiling point of +45 °C. What state will it be in at room temperature (25 °C)? .......................................  **(1 mark)**

4 The density of an element changes depending upon the state it is in. The table shows the density of copper in different states.

| | g/cm³ |
|---|---|
| **Solid** | 8.96 |
| **Liquid** | 8.02 |

> Density is a measure of the mass of something in a fixed volume. The greater the number, the denser it is.

Describe how the density of copper depends on the state it is in.

............................................................................................................................ **(1 mark)**

# Pure substances and mixtures

1 Tick the correct box to show if a substance is pure or a mixture.

|  | Perfume | Pure sugar | Mud | Graphite electrode | Smoke from a fire | Diamond |
|---|---|---|---|---|---|---|
| **Pure** |  |  |  |  |  |  |
| **Mixture** |  |  |  |  |  |  |

> Pure substances contain only one type of substance.

**(2 marks)**

2 Elements and compounds can be represented as models as shown in the diagram below.

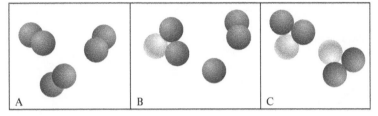

A                    B                    C

(a) State which boxes contain compounds only ................................................. **(1 mark)**

(b) State and explain which box contains a pure substance.

.............................................................................................................................

............................................................................................................................. **(2 marks)**

3 Iron and sulfur heated together in a boiling tube are a mixture, yet when they are heated they form iron sulfide, which is a pure substance. Explain why iron sulfide is pure.

Before heating, iron and sulfur can be separated because they are not joined.

Heating them makes a compound, iron sulfide, that ........................................... **(2 marks)**

4 Chemists were making samples of the drug aspirin in the laboratory. They checked the purity of the drug by measuring the melting point of the samples. They obtained the following data.

| Sample | Melting point (°C) |
|---|---|
| A | 138 |
| B | 138–158 |
| C | 139.5 |

> Pure substances have specific melting points.

(a) Which sample was impure? ........................................................................... **(1 mark)**

(b) Did the impurity have a higher or lower melting point than pure aspirin? ......... **(1 mark)**

(c) The graph sketches the heating curve for the pure aspirin. Add a line to the graph to show how the graph would be different for the impure sample. (Exact temperature values are not required.)

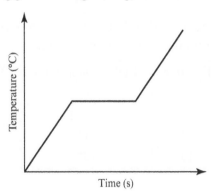

**(1 mark)**

# Distillation

1  What method is most appropriate to separate a mixture of three different liquids that have distinct boiling points? Tick **one** box.

☐  **A**  simple still

☐  **C**  chromatography

☐  **B**  fractional distillation

☐  **D**  distillation          **(1 mark)**

> The question is asking how to separate **three** liquids, not two.

2  There are five main steps to making the alcoholic beverage whisky. One of those steps is fractional distillation. The diagram shows the equipment you would use in a laboratory to do this.

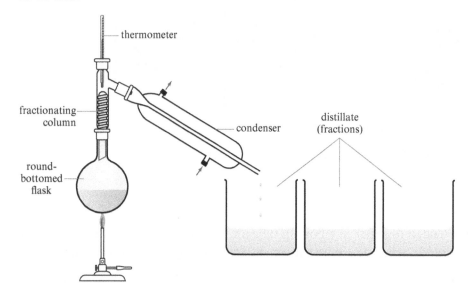

(a)  How could the safety of this experiment be improved? ...................................

.......................................................................................................... **(1 mark)**

(b)  If the alcohol in whisky has a boiling point of 78 °C and water boils at 100 °C,

what substance is collected first in the receiver? .............................................

.......................................................................................................... **(1 mark)**

> The liquid with the lower temperature will boil first.

(c)  Briefly describe how the condenser works.

Hot gas is cooled by condenser ...................................................................

.......................................................................................................... **(3 marks)**

3  Fractional distillation can also be used to separate the fractions in crude oil. The table shows the boiling points of some of the fractions collected in an experiment.

> Guided

| Fraction | Boiling point (°C) |
|----------|--------------------|
| A        | 57                 |
| B        | 85–92              |
| C        | 115                |
| D        | 147                |

Which fractions contain pure substances and why?

.................................................

.................................................

.................................................

.................................................. **(2 marks)**

# Filtration and crystallisation

1  A suspension of flour in water can be separated using the equipment shown. Use the diagram to name:

   (a) the process ................................................

   (b) the filtrate ................................................

   (c) the residue ................................................

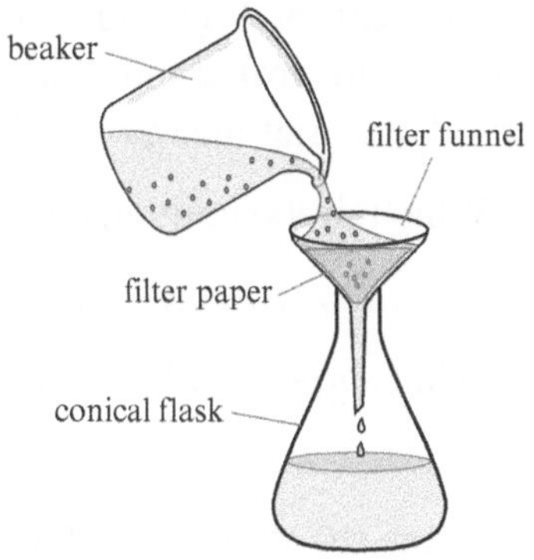

beaker

filter funnel

filter paper

conical flask

**(3 marks)**

2  In an experiment, magnesium sulfate solution was added to sodium carbonate solution.

$$MgSO_4(aq) + Na_2CO_3(aq) \rightarrow MgCO_3(s) + Na_2SO_4(aq)$$

Describe how the magnesium carbonate could be removed from the other product.

Magnesium carbonate is a solid ................................................

................................................

................................................ **(2 marks)**

3  Magnesium sulfate can be made by reacting excess magnesium oxide with sulfuric acid. Magnesium oxide is insoluble in water.

   (a) Why is excess magnesium oxide used?

   ................................................ **(1 mark)**

   (b) The diagram shows how the excess magnesium oxide can be removed. Complete the labels.

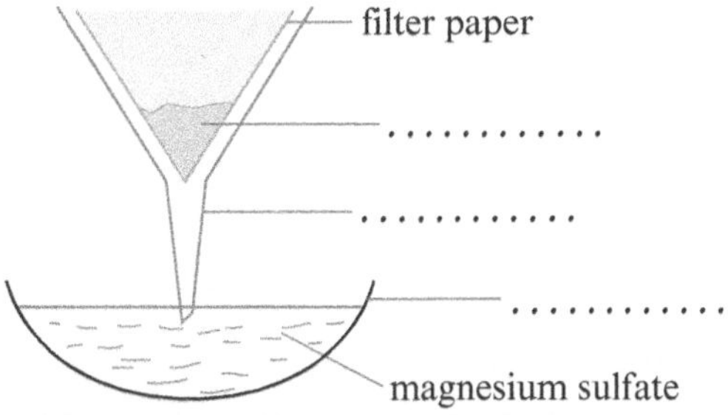

filter paper

. . . . . . . . . . .

. . . . . . . . . . .

. . . . . . . . . . .

magnesium sulfate

**(3 marks)**

   (c) Explain how you could obtain crystals from the solution. ................................

   ................................................

   ................................................ **(3 marks)**

   (d) Complete the word equation for the reaction.

   Magnesium oxide + sulfuric acid → ................... + ................... **(1 mark)**

4  Briefly describe the two physical processes that can be used to separate a mixture of sand, salt and water.

   ................................................

   ................................................ **(2 marks)**

# Paper chromatography

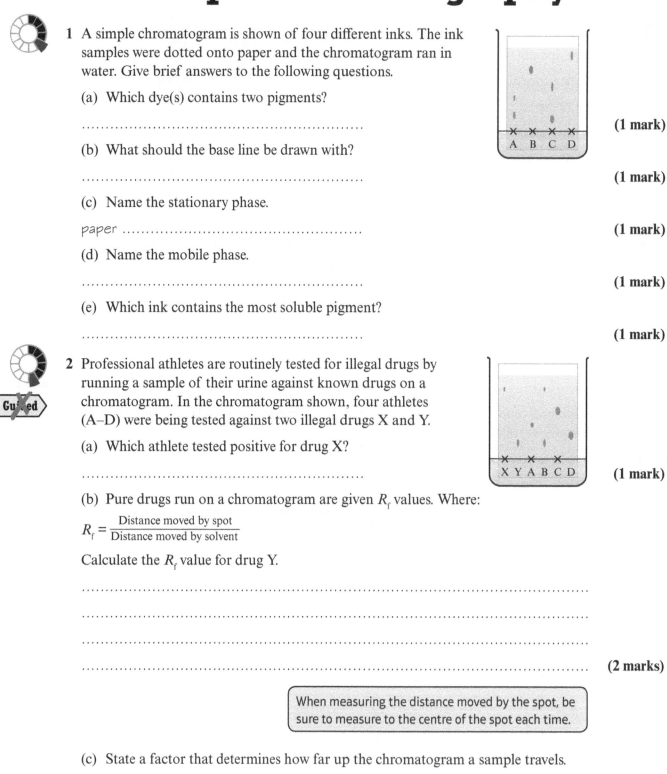

1  A simple chromatogram is shown of four different inks. The ink samples were dotted onto paper and the chromatogram ran in water. Give brief answers to the following questions.

(a)  Which dye(s) contains two pigments?

................................................................ **(1 mark)**

(b)  What should the base line be drawn with?

................................................................ **(1 mark)**

(c)  Name the stationary phase.

paper ................................................ **(1 mark)**

(d)  Name the mobile phase.

................................................................ **(1 mark)**

(e)  Which ink contains the most soluble pigment?

................................................................ **(1 mark)**

2  Professional athletes are routinely tested for illegal drugs by running a sample of their urine against known drugs on a chromatogram. In the chromatogram shown, four athletes (A–D) were being tested against two illegal drugs X and Y.

(a)  Which athlete tested positive for drug X?

................................................................ **(1 mark)**

(b)  Pure drugs run on a chromatogram are given $R_f$ values. Where:

$$R_f = \frac{\text{Distance moved by spot}}{\text{Distance moved by solvent}}$$

Calculate the $R_f$ value for drug Y.

................................................................................................

................................................................................................

................................................................................................

................................................................................................ **(2 marks)**

> When measuring the distance moved by the spot, be sure to measure to the centre of the spot each time.

(c)  State a factor that determines how far up the chromatogram a sample travels.

................................................................................................

................................................................................................ **(1 mark)**

  **Investigating inks**

1  A forensic scientist has been given a sample of ink found at the crime scene and needs to compare this with a bottle of ink found at a suspect's house.

(a)  His first step is to remove a sample of the solvent from the ink. He sets up a simple distillation experiment.

> The solvent will have a low boiling point.

   (i)  Why is it important to sit the collecting test tube in cold water?

   ............................................................................................................................ **(1 mark)**

   (ii)  Why must he heat slowly?

   ............................................................................................................................ **(1 mark)**

   (iii)  Why is it important to record the temperature?

   ............................................................................................................................ **(2 marks)**

(b)  The scientist must then run a chromatogram of the ink and compare it to the ink at the crime scene.

   (i)  What must the scientist consider when choosing a solvent to run the chromatogram in?

   The ink needs to be ......................................................................................... **(1 mark)**

   (ii)  Why must he draw the base line in pencil?

   So it does not .................................................................................................... **(1 mark)**

   (iii)  Why is it important to record the height the solvent reaches?

   So $R_f$ values .................................................................................................... **(1 mark)**

   (iv)  The solvent the scientist uses is a 50 : 50 mix of water : ethanol. Name two safety precautions the scientist should use when using the solvent.

> Ethanol is flammable.

   ............................................................................................................................

   ............................................................................................................................ **(2 marks)**

(c)  The chromatogram for the ink from the crime scene, C, and ink from the suspect's house, S, is shown. Explain if the suspect is guilty or not.

The centre point of each spot has moved up the paper to the same amount for

both inks. Therefore, ...........................................................................................

............................................................................................................................ **(2 marks)**

# Drinking water

1 There are many ways that water can be treated so it is potable. What does 'potable water' mean? ................................................................................................ **(1 mark)**

*Guided*

2 In the UK, 23% of the drinking water comes from rivers. Before the water can be drunk it must be purified. Name two steps in the purification process and for each step give a reason for why it is carried out.

Step 1 ................................................................................................

Reason ................................................................................................

Step 2 ................................................................................................

Reason ................................................................................................

> The word sieving is not detailed enough for this answer.

**(4 marks)**

3 In countries where there are few rivers and lakes they can make drinking water from sea water.

(a) What technique is used to purify water from sea water?

.................................................................................................... **(1 mark)**

(b) Why is it not feasible to purify large amounts of water using distillation?

.................................................................................................... **(1 mark)**

> Consider how much energy is needed to heat the water up.

Desalination of sea water – removal of salt from sea water – can be carried out in the laboratory using the equipment shown.

(c) Briefly describe how sea water is desalinated using this equipment.

> Focus on the chemistry of distillation.

The salt water is heated, and the water boils and evaporates. It then passes to

the condenser where it ...........................................................................

....................................................................................................

.................................................................................................... **(3 marks)**

# Extended response – Separating mixtures

A cloudy white mixture contains three different substances. Some information about each is given in the table.

| Substance | Melting point (°C) | Boiling point (°C) | State at room temperature | Solubility in aqueous solutions |
|---|---|---|---|---|
| A | 0 | 100 | Liquid | Soluble |
| B | −114 | 78 | Liquid | Soluble |
| C | 208 | 1034 | Solid | Insoluble |

Substance A and B mix together completely.

Describe a method to get pure samples of A, B and C from the mixture.

> You will be more successful in extended response questions if you plan your answer before you start writing.
> The command word 'describe' means you need to give an account of what you would do to separate the pure substances. You only need to consider methods that are within your GCSE studies. You are expected to be able to describe the following separation methods at GCSE: simple distillation, fractional distillation, filtration, crystallisation and paper chromatography. You do not need to use them all to answer this question. Use the information in the table to answer the question and at each stage say why you have chosen to use the method you have.

Step 1 – Filtration

I would set up filtration using a conical flask, filter funnel and filter paper. I would pour the solution through the filter paper. Substance C is insoluble and so would remain in the paper. Substances A and B would collect in the conical flask. I could then wash substance C with water and let it dry.

Step 2 – Distillation

I would then distil the mixture of A and B because ...........................................

......................................................................................................................

......................................................................................................................

......................................................................................................................

......................................................................................................................

......................................................................................................................

......................................................................................................................

......................................................................................................................

...................................................................................................... **(6 marks)**

Continue your answer on your own paper. You should aim to write half a side of A4.

# Acids and alkalis

1 Concentrated acids and alkalis will have the following hazard warning on the bottle. What does this symbol mean? Tick **one** box.

☐ **A**  caustic

☐ **B**  corrosive

☐ **C**  oxidising

☐ **D**  flammable

(1 mark)

2 A student takes 10 cm³ of dilute hydrochloric acid and adds a few drops of universal indicator. The student then slowly adds dilute sodium hydroxide and stirs the solution.

(a) What colour does the indicator go when added to the acid?

...................................................................................................................................... (1 mark)

(b) What happens to the colour of the universal indicator as more sodium hydroxide is added?

> The pH will change gradually, not jump from acid to alkali.

......................................................................................................................................

...................................................................................................................................... (2 marks)

3 Complete the table to show the colours of the three indicators shown in acid or alkali conditions.

|  | Acid | Alkali |
|---|---|---|
| **Litmus** |  |  |
| **Methyl orange** |  | Yellow |
| **Phenolphthalein** | Colourless |  |

(4 marks)

4 Hydrochloric acid, HCl, sulfuric acid, $H_2SO_4$, and nitric acid, $HNO_3$, all dissociate when they are added to water.

> What positive ion do all the acids contain?

(a) What ion do they all produce that shows they are acids?

...................................................................................................................................... (1 mark)

(b) Write a balanced equation with state symbols to show the dissociation of nitric acid when it is added to water.

$$HNO_3 \rightarrow \text{...............} + \text{...............}$$ (1 mark)

5 When solid potassium hydroxide, KOH, pellets are added to water they dissolve to form an alkaline solution.

(a) State what ion is responsible for forming an alkaline solution?

...................................................................................................................................... (1 mark)

(b) State what happens to the pH of the solution if the concentration of the KOH solution is increased.

...................................................................................................................................... (1 mark)

# Strong and weak acids

1 A solution has a pH of 5. What would the new pH be if the concentration of hydrogen ions is increased by 100? Tick **one** box.

Guided

☐ **A** 4

☐ **B** 3

☐ **C** 7

☐ **D** 6 **(1 mark)**

2 Hydrochloric acid used for most experiments in schools is dilute hydrochloric acid, but at times concentrated hydrochloric acid is required. Explain in terms of hydrogen ions the difference between dilute and concentrated hydrochloric acid.

Concentrated acids have a greater number of hydrogen ions in ......................

......................................................................................................... **(2 marks)**

3 A student took a 0.1 mol dm$^{-3}$ solution of nitric acid, pH 1 and diluted it using water so it had a concentration of 0.01 mol dm$^{-3}$.

(a) What was the new pH? ................................... **(1 mark)**

> Increasing hydrogen ion concentration by 10 decreases the pH by one.

(b) Explain why the pH changes.

The acid has been diluted by a factor of ...................................................

......................................................................................................... **(1 mark)**

4 A student carried out an experiment reacting three different acids of the same concentration with magnesium metal. The results are in the table below.

| Acid | Observation |
| --- | --- |
| Sulfuric acid, $H_2SO_4$ | Vigorous effervescence |
| Ethanoic acid, $CH_3COOH$ | Slow production of bubbles |
| Hydrochloric acid, HCl | Lots of bubbling |

(a) Name the weak acid. ............................................................... **(1 mark)**

> Consider the difference in dissociation between weak and strong acids.

(b) How is a weak acid different to a strong acid?

.........................................................................................................

......................................................................................................... **(2 marks)**

(c) What gas is responsible for the bubbles in this experiment? ....................... **(1 mark)**

(d) Describe the test and the result you would get to identify the gas named in part (c).

.........................................................................................................

......................................................................................................... **(2 marks)**

# Bases and alkalis

1  Which statement best describes a base? Tick **one** box.

Guided

☐ **A**  All bases form $H^+$ ions.

☐ **B**  A base is a substance that can react with a salt.

☐ **C**  Bases react with acids to make a salt and water only.

☐ **D**  All bases are an alkali.    **(1 mark)**

2  Two solutions of potassium hydroxide are made in a laboratory.

- Solution 1: 10 g of potassium hydroxide in 2 $dm^3$ of solution.
- Solution 2: 50 g of potassium hydroxide in 5 $dm^3$ of solution.

(a)  Which solution has the greater concentration? Show your working.

Solution 1: $\frac{10}{2} = 5$ g dm$^{-3}$   solution 2: $\frac{50}{5} = 10$ g dm$^{-3}$

......................................................................................................................

...................................................................................................................... **(2 marks)**

(b)  What is the general name given to solutions where a base is dissolved?

...................................................................................................................... **(1 mark)**

> Concentration is defined as the amount of solute dissolved in a certain volume of solvent. The units are g dm$^{-3}$.

3  Acid indigestion is caused by the stomach producing too much acid. One component of indigestion tablets is magnesium carbonate, $MgCO_3$.

(a)  Magnesium carbonate, $MgCO_3$, is insoluble in water. When mixed with water, what colour would the pH paper be and why?

.............................................................................................................. **(2 marks)**

(b)  The acid present in the stomach is called hydrochloric acid. Hydrochloric acid, HCl, reacts with magnesium carbonate, $MgCO_3$, to produce magnesium chloride, carbon dioxide and water.

(i)  Complete and balance the equation for this reaction.

......... $HCl(ag) + MgCO_3(s) \rightarrow MgCl_2 + $ ......... (g) $ + H_2O(l)$    **(2 marks)**

(ii)  Describe a test for carbon dioxide. What is the result of this test?

Bubble through limewater, turns ............................................................... **(2 marks)**

4  The table shows the properties of four different solids.

Guided

| | pH in water | Reaction with acid |
|---|---|---|
| **W** | 8 | Salt + water + carbon dioxide |
| **X** | No reaction | Fizzes |
| **Y** | 2 | No reaction |
| **Z** | 10 | Salt + water |

(a)  Which is a metal? ................................................................. **(1 mark)**

(b)  Which is a metal carbonate? ................................................ **(1 mark)**

(c)  Which is a metal hydroxide? ............................................... **(1 mark)**

**Practical
skills**

# Neutralisation

1 The equipment shown is used for neutralisation reactions.

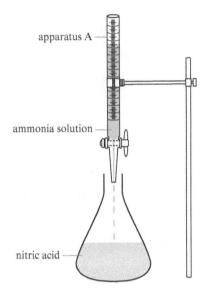

apparatus A

ammonia solution

nitric acid

(a) What is the name of apparatus A? .................................................... **(1 mark)**

(b) Write a word equation for the reaction between the
ammonia solution and nitric acid.

> Only one product is made.

ammonia + nitric acid → .....................................

**(1 mark)**

2 A student decides to react hydrochloric acid, HCl, with potassium hydroxide, KOH.
Each time the student uses the same amount of potassium hydroxide, but he varies the
concentration of the hydrochloric acid added. He records the volume of hydrochloric
acid that needs to be added in the following table.

| Concentration of HCl (g dm$^{-3}$) | Volume HCl required to neutralise (cm$^3$) |
|:---:|:---:|
| 5 | 100 |
| | 80 |
| 20 | 40 |
| 40 | 20 |
| 80 | |

(a) Complete the missing values in the table. **(2 marks)**

(b) Describe the pattern of results seen in the table.

As the concentration of HCl increases, the volume of acid required to neutralise

the KOH ....................................................................................

.................................................................................... **(2 marks)**

(c) The ionic equation that occurs during neutralisation produces water. Complete
the ionic equation.

.............. + .............. → H$_2$O

**(1 mark)**

123

# Salts from insoluble bases

1 A student wants to prepare large crystals of zinc chloride, $ZnCl_2$.

(a) She is given zinc hydroxide powder, $Zn(OH)_2$.

   (i) What acid must she react the zinc hydroxide with to produce zinc chloride?

........................................................    | The acid must contain chloride ions. |    **(1 mark)**

   (ii) Complete the balanced symbol equation for the reaction.

$$Zn(OH)_2 + \text{.....................} \rightarrow ZnCl_2 + \text{...................}$$    **(2 marks)**

(b) She starts the practical and adds the zinc hydroxide a little at a time to the warm acid in the beaker until the zinc hydroxide is in excess.

   (i) Why does the student warm the acid?

................................................................................................................

................................................................................................................    **(2 marks)**

   (ii) What will she observe when the zinc hydroxide is in excess?

................................................................................................................    **(1 mark)**

   (iii) How will the student remove the excess zinc hydroxide? ...........................    **(1 mark)**

(c) Complete the diagram to show how the student then evaporates most of the water and concentrates the zinc chloride.

**(1 mark)**

(d) How will she ensure she obtains large crystals?

................................................................................................................    **(1 mark)**

2 Write the balanced chemical equations with state symbols for the reactions between:

(a) zinc oxide, ZnO, and sulfuric acid, $H_2SO_4$.

$$\text{.........} (s) + H_2SO_4(aq) \rightarrow ZnSO_4(aq) + \text{............} (l)$$    **(2 marks)**

(b) magnesium carbonate, $MgCO_3$, and nitric acid, $HNO_3$.

$$MgCO_3(\text{...}) + \text{.........} HNO_3(aq) \rightarrow Mg(NO_3)_2(aq) + H_2O(l) + \text{.........} (g)$$    **(2 marks)**

# Salts from soluble bases

1  Why can universal indicator not be used in a titration? Tick **one** box.

☐ **A**  It does not have a sharp end point.

☐ **B**  It would react with the acid.

☐ **C**  It would react with the alkali.

☐ **D**  It would form a precipitate.

> Indicators do not take part in the reaction being studied.

**(1 mark)**

2  Name an acid and an alkali that could be used to make these salts.

(a)  Ammonium chloride: Acid .................. Alkali ammonium hydroxide

(b)  Sodium chloride: Acid hydrochloric acid Alkali ......................

**(4 marks)**

3  A student carried out a titration of potassium hydroxide and sulfuric acid to make potassium sulfate salt.

> You need to know what equipment you need to carry out a titration.

(a)  What did she use to put the potassium hydroxide into the flask? ....................  **(1 mark)**

|  | Rough | 1 | 2 | 3 |
|---|---|---|---|---|
| Start point (cm³) | 0.00 | 24.20 | 0.00 | 23.80 |
| End point (cm³) | 24.20 | 47.90 | 23.80 | 41.40 |
| Titre (cm³) | 24.20 | 23.70 | | |

(b)  Fill in the gaps in the results table.  **(2 marks)**

(c)  Why did the student carry out a rough titration?

To get an approximate value for .........................................................  **(1 mark)**

(d)  Which titration is anomalous? ..........................................................  **(1 mark)**

> Rough titrations are not anomalous; look at runs 1–3.

(e)  Calculate the average titre.

..........................................................................................................

..........................................................................................................  **(2 marks)**

> Only use titres that are very close to each other.

(f)  To make the final sample of potassium sulfate the student repeated the experiment using the average titre of sulfuric acid, but did not add any indicator. Why did she do this?

..........................................................................................................  **(1 mark)**

# Making insoluble salts

1 Complete the table by placing a tick to show if a substance is soluble or insoluble in water.

| Substance | Soluble in water | Insoluble in water |
|---|---|---|
| NaCl | | |
| NaNO$_3$ | | |
| AgCl | | |
| KBr | | |
| CaSO$_4$ | | |
| BaCO$_3$ | | |

Do not mark the table except to place ticks in the correct position.

**(6 marks)**

2 Lead iodide is an insoluble salt. Suggest two compounds that could react together to form lead iodide.

(a) Compound 1                          Compound 2

................. nitrate                  potassium iodide          **(2 marks)**

(b) Write a balanced symbol equation for the reaction.

$$Pb(NO_3)_2(aq) + ... KI(aq) \rightarrow PbI_2(s) + ............ (aq)$$          **(2 marks)**

(c) Write an ionic equation for the reaction.

$$Pb^{2+}(aq) + ... I^-(aq) \rightarrow PbI_2(s)$$

Ionic equations show charges and 'spectator' ions are not included.          **(2 marks)**

3 Barium sulfate is an insoluble salt. Some of the instructions for making barium sulfate are shown below.

• Take a solution of barium nitrate and add to a solution of sodium sulfate

• Filter

• Dry the product

(a) The method lacks detail. Add two more details to this method.

The beaker that the solutions were in needs to be washed out with distilled

water and ..................................................................................................

..................................................................................................          **(2 marks)**

(b) Complete the symbol equation for making barium sulfate.

$$Ba(NO_3)_2(aq) + .............. (aq) \rightarrow BaSO_4(s) + .............. (aq)$$          **(2 marks)**

(c) Write the ionic equation for the reaction.

$$Ba^{2+}(......) + ........... (aq) \rightarrow BaSO_4(s)$$          **(2 marks)**

(d) Suggest **two** ways in which the precipitate that is made could be dried.

..................................................................................................

..................................................................................................

..................................................................................................          **(2 marks)**

# Extended response – Making salts

A student wants to make **large** magnesium nitrate crystals. They are supplied with **solid** magnesium hydroxide and a bottle of nitric acid.

Describe a method to produce pure, dry crystals of magnesium nitrate.

> You are expected to be able to describe how to carry out an acid-alkali titration to produce a soluble salt. Longer answers are more successful if you plan your answer. This question can be answered in four sections:
>
> - Make a solution of magnesium hydroxide.
> - Carry out a titration with the magnesium hydroxide solution and nitric acid.
> - Repeat the titration not using any indicator.
> - Evaporate the liquid.

1. Make a solution of magnesium hydroxide by dissolving it in water. Use a similar concentration as the nitric acid.

2. Put the nitric acid into a burette and pipette 25 cm³ of the magnesium hydroxide into a conical flask.

3. Add a suitable indicator to the flask. Titrate the nitric acid and record the value needed to neutralise.

4. Repeat the titration, but do not add indicator.

5. ...........................................................................................................................

6. ...........................................................................................................................

...........................................................................................................................

...........................................................................................................................

...........................................................................................................................

...........................................................................................................................

...........................................................................................................................

...........................................................................................................................

...........................................................................................................................

...........................................................................................................................

...........................................................................................................................

...........................................................................................................................

...........................................................................................................................

...........................................................................................................................

...........................................................................................................................   **(6 marks)**

Continue your answer on your own paper. You should aim to write half a side of A4.

# Electrolysis

1 Aluminium oxide can be electrolysed to produce pure aluminium. Which statement is incorrect? Tick **one** box.

☐ **A** At the cathode aluminium ions gain electrons.

☐ **B** Aluminium ions are reduced at the anode.

☐ **C** At the anode oxygen ions are oxidised.

☐ **D** Oxygen ions lose electrons to become oxygen gas.    **(1 mark)**

> Anode is positive, cathode is negative.

2 A teacher demonstrates the electrolysis of lead bromide $PbBr_2$ using the equipment shown.

(a) Name a suitable material for the electrodes to be made from.

.................................................... **(1 mark)**

(b) Why is the lead bromide solid heated?

....................................................

.................................................... **(2 marks)**

> For electrolysis to occur, ions must be able to move between the electrodes.

Diagram labels: ammeter 0–5A; bulb 12 V, 5 W; 12 V DC power supply; rheostat (optional); two-hole rubber bung; graphite rods; lead bromide; crucible; pipe-clay triangle; tripod

(c) Name the product formed at the anode and explain in terms of charges why it forms.

....................................................................................

.................................................................................... **(2 marks)**

(d) Describe one hazard of this experiment and what safety precautions are taken to minimise risk.

Bromine is toxic ........................................................................

.................................................................................... **(2 marks)**

3 A student electrolyses aqueous copper chloride, $CuCl_2$.

(a) State the **two** ions that copper chloride is made from. ............................... **(1 mark)**

(b) During electrolysis, positive ions move to the cathode and pick up electrons. Write a balanced half equation to show this.

$$Cu^{2+}(aq) + \ldots\ e^- \rightarrow Cu(s)$$    **(2 marks)**

(c) Does oxidation or reduction occur at the cathode?

> Oxidation is loss of electrons, reduction is gain. OIL RIG.

.................................................................................... **(1 mark)**

(d) Deduce the half equation to show the reaction at the anode.

$$\ldots\ + 2e^- \rightarrow \ldots$$    **(2 marks)**

# Electrolysing solutions

1 Aqueous sodium sulfate is electrolysed using the equipment shown.

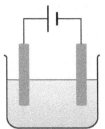

> You must talk about **ions**, not electrons.

    (a) Label the anode, cathode and electrolyte.          **(3 marks)**

    (b) What does the term 'aqueous' mean?

    .................................................          **(1 mark)**

    (c) Why can aqueous sodium sulfate conduct electricity?

    .................................................          **(1 mark)**

2 Electrolysis of aqueous sodium chloride produces three very useful products.

    (a) Name the four ions present in the electrolyte.

    $Na^+, Cl^-,$ ..................................          **(2 marks)**

    (b) Name the gases that form at the electrodes.

    Anode .............................................

    Cathode .......................................          **(2 marks)**

    (c) How could you test for the presence of the gas at the anode?

    .............................................................................          **(1 mark)**

> You need to know the tests for hydrogen, chlorine and oxygen gas.

    (d) How does the electrolyte change as the electrolysis progresses?

    It becomes alkaline as ......................................................

    .............................................................................          **(2 marks)**

    (e) What would you observe if universal indicator was added to the electrolyte at the start of the experiment?

    .............................................................................

    .............................................................................          **(2 marks)**

3 A student electrolyses acidified water for 15 minutes using a Hoffman Voltammeter.

    (a) Name the gases formed at the electrodes.

    Anode ..................................................          **(1 mark)**

    Cathode ..............................................          **(1 mark)**

    (b) Why is there twice as much gas at the cathode than the anode?

    The formula of water is $H_2O$ so .....................................

    .............................................................................          **(2 marks)**

 **Practical skills** # Investigating electrolysis

**1** Aqueous copper sulfate can be electrolysed using inert electrodes.

(a) Name a suitable material for inert electrodes ..................................... **(1 mark)**

(b) What would you observe during the experiment?

Orange substance forming at the cathode and ........................................

...................................................................................................... **(3 marks)**

(c) Copper sulfate solution is blue. Describe and explain why the colour of the electrolyte changes during the experiment.

......................................................................................................

...................................................................................................... **(2 marks)**

> Observe means describe what you would see.

**2** If copper electrodes are used in the electrolysis of copper sulfate they become involved in the reaction. The copper anode will lose mass as copper ions are formed and the cathode will gain mass as copper ions are deposited as copper atoms.

(a) Write balanced half equations for the reactions at the anode and the cathode.

Anode: $Cu(s) \rightarrow Cu^{2+}(aq) + 2e^-$

> Electrons do not need state symbols.

Cathode: ............................................... **(2 marks)**

(b) A student records the mass of the cathode over time. Plot a graph of the data collected.

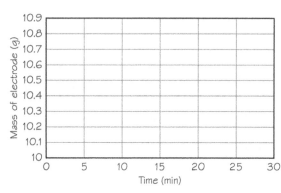

| Time (min) | Mass of electrode (g) |
|------------|----------------------|
| 5 | 10.10 |
| 10 | 10.25 |
| 15 | 10.42 |
| 25 | 10.90 |

**(4 marks)**

(c) Use the graph to describe the relationship between the time the electrolysis cell has been switched on and the mass of copper deposited.

As the time increases, the mass of the electrode ....................................

...................................................................................................... **(2 marks)**

(d) The student missed the reading at 20 minutes. Use the graph to predict the mass of copper that would have been present.

> Draw a trend line on the graph then use it to predict the mass.

......................................................................................................

......................................................................................................

......................................................................................................

...................................................................................................... **(2 marks)**

# Extended response – Electrolysis

Brine is often used to pack fish products into tins. Brine is a concentrated aqueous solution of sodium chloride.

In an experiment brine is electrolysed in an electrolytic cell as shown.

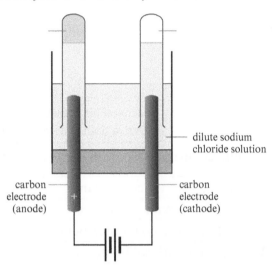

dilute sodium chloride solution

carbon electrode (anode)

carbon electrode (cathode)

Describe, with the use of balanced equations, how the three products, chlorine, hydrogen and sodium hydroxide are formed.

You will be more successful if you plan how you will answer the question.
- State the ions present in brine.
- Describe which ions move to which electrode.
- Determine which ions are discharged and write half equations to show this.
- Then describe what happens to the ions that are left in solution and write an equation to show this.

..........................................

..........................................

..........................................

..........................................

...............................................................................................................

...............................................................................................................

...............................................................................................................

...............................................................................................................

...............................................................................................................

...............................................................................................................

...............................................................................................................

...............................................................................................................

...............................................................................................................

...............................................................................................................

...............................................................................................................

...............................................................................................................

...............................................................................................................   **(6 marks)**

Continue your answer on your own paper. You should aim to write half a side of A4.

# The reactivity series

**1** Different metals have different reactivities. Iron reacts very slowly with water, but will react with steam.

(a) What liquid must be placed in the steam generator? ..................................... **(1 mark)**

(b) What is the gas that is generated?

Hydrogen **(1 mark)**

(c) How can you test for the presence of the gas produced?

......................................................................................................................

...................................................................................................................... **(1 mark)**

> If a metal only reacts with steam then it is less reactive than a metal that will react with cold water.

**2** The table shows how different metals react with steam or water.

| Copper | No reaction with water or steam |
|---|---|
| Potassium | Reacts violently with water |
| Magnesium | Reacts slowly with cold water, but fast with steam |
| Calcium | Reacts rapidly with cold water |
| Zinc | Only reacts if heated very strongly in steam |

Order the metals from least reactive to most reactive.

> < means less than, > means more than.

Least ...... copper < ................................................................ Most **(1 mark)**

**3** Potassium reacts violently with water to produce potassium hydroxide, KOH, and hydrogen, $H_2$.

(a) Write a balanced symbol equation for the reaction.

...... K + ...... $H_2O$ → ...... KOH + ...... $H_2$

(b) Describe a test to show that the solution formed is alkaline.

Add universal indicator; it will turn ........................................................ **(1 mark)**

> The question wants you to say what you would add to the solution.

**4** The reactivity of metals can also be compared by reacting them with acids. Zinc reacts with hydrochloric acid producing bubbles of gas, but platinum does not react.

(a) Write a word equation for the reaction of zinc and hydrochloric acid.

zinc + .......................................................................................................... **(1 mark)**

(b) What can you deduce about the reactivity of platinum compared with zinc?

...................................................................................................................... **(1 mark)**

(c) Magnesium is more reactive than zinc. Describe what you would observe in a reaction between magnesium and hydrochloric acid.

Effervescence and ...................................................................................... **(1 mark)**

> Fizzing or bubbling are acceptable alternatives to effervescence.

# Metal displacement reactions

**1** Which of the following pairs of chemicals would produce a reaction? Tick **one** box.

☐ **A**  Copper + magnesium sulfate solution

☐ **B**  Zinc + iron(II) nitrate solution

☐ **C**  Magnesium + sodium chloride solution

☐ **D**  Tin + aluminium chloride solution

> Use the reactivity series to help you answer the questions on this page.

> A more reactive metal displaces a less reactive metal from its salt.

| potassium | most reactive |
|-----------|---------------|
| sodium | |
| calcium | |
| magnesium | |
| aluminium | |
| zinc | |
| iron | |
| tin | |
| lead | |
| copper | |
| silver | least reactive |

**(1 mark)**

**2** Copper sulfate is a blue solution and magnesium is a shiny grey metal.

(a) What would you observe if magnesium metal was added to copper sulfate?

............................................................................................................. **(2 marks)**

(b) What are the products of the reaction?

.......................................... and .......................................... **(2 marks)**

**3** Complete the following displacement reactions:

(a) calcium + copper oxide → .......................... + copper

(b) $Zn + PbO \rightarrow ZnO +$ ............

(c) $Fe_2O_3(s) + 2Al(s) \rightarrow Al_2O_3(s) +$ ............          **(3 marks)**

**4** A student was investigating the reactivity of an unknown metal, X, they had found in the laboratory. The student reacted the metal with four different metal sulfate solutions.

| Metal sulfate solution | Observation |
|------------------------|-------------|
| Potassium sulfate | No reaction |
| Copper sulfate | Orange/brown coating on X |
| Iron sulfate | Grey coating on X |
| Magnesium sulfate | No reaction |

(a) State and explain which metals are more reactive than X.

Potassium and magnesium because ..............................................................

.............................................................................................................

............................................................................................................. **(3 marks)**

(b) Use the reactivity series table at the top of the page to suggest a metal that X could be.

.............................................................................................................

............................................................................................................. **(1 mark)**

# Explaining metal reactivity

**1** Which of the following processes represents oxidation? Tick **one** box.

☐ **A**  $Cu^{2+} \rightarrow Cu$

☐ **B**  $Na^+ \rightarrow Na$

☐ **C**  $Mg \rightarrow Mg^{2+}$

☐ **D**  $Fe^{3+} \rightarrow Fe^{2+}$

> No electrons have been shown, but work out which equation shows a loss of electrons.

| potassium | most reactive |
|-----------|---------------|
| sodium | |
| calcium | |
| magnesium | |
| aluminium | |
| zinc | |
| iron | |
| tin | |
| lead | |
| copper | |
| silver | least reactive |

**(1 mark)**

**2** Silver is less reactive than copper, but copper is less reactive than zinc. The reaction of silver nitrate with copper is:

$$AgNO_3 + Cu \rightarrow Ag + CuNO_3$$

(a) Write a half equation to show what has happened to the silver ions.

$Ag^+ +$ ............ $\rightarrow$ ............  **(2 marks)**

(b) Have the copper atoms been oxidised or reduced? ..................................... **(1 mark)**

(c) In a reaction with copper and zinc which metal is most likely to form a cation?

..................................................................................................................... **(1 mark)**

**3** Hydrogen is sometimes included in metal reactivity tables so that the reactions of metals with acids, water and steam can be compared. It is placed between lead and copper.

(a) Name two metals that will react with hydrochloric acid.

.....................................................................................................................

..................................................................................................................... **(2 marks)**

(b) Tin is between iron and lead in the reactivity series. Predict if it will react with

sulfuric acid. ........................................................................................... **(1 mark)**

(c) When acids react with metals, hydrogen ions are reduced to hydrogen gas. Complete the half equation.

......... $H^+ +$ ............ $e^- \rightarrow H_2$  **(1 mark)**

(d) Write a word equation for the reaction of calcium and hydrochloric acid.

calcium + ............ $\rightarrow$ ............ + ............  **(2 marks)**

(e) Complete the balanced equation for the reaction.

$Ca(s) +$ ............ $HCl(aq) \rightarrow$ ............(aq) + ............(g)  **(2 marks)**

(f) Write a half equation to show calcium is oxidised.

$Ca + \rightarrow$ ............ + ............  **(2 marks)**

(g) Write the ionic equation for the reaction given that chloride ions are spectator ions.

$Ca + 2H^+ \rightarrow$ ............ + $Ca^{2+} +$ ............  **(2 marks)**

> Ionic equations do not contain electrons.

# Metal ores

1 A metal ore is:

☐ **A**   a compound of the metal made in the laboratory.

☐ **B**   a naturally occurring compound of the metal.

☐ **C**   a sample of the pure metal made in the laboratory.

☐ **D**   a naturally occurring sample of the pure metal.                    **(1 mark)**

2 Some metals, like gold, can be dug straight out of the earth. Explain why these metals are found just as their elements.

They are very unreactive so ........................................................................    **(1 mark)**

3 Extracting metals from their ores has been known for many thousands of years. The first recorded extraction of lead from its ore, galena, was around 6500 BC. One of the steps in the extraction involves the following equation.

$$PbO + C \rightarrow Pb + CO$$

(a)  In terms of oxygen, explain which element has been oxidised and which has been reduced.

Lead has lost oxygen and carbon has gained oxygen ....................................

....................................................................................................    **(2 marks)**

(b)  How else can oxidation and reduction be defined?   | Describe in terms of electrons. |

....................................................................................................

....................................................................................................    **(2 marks)**

In the laboratory, a similar reaction can be observed with the reduction of copper oxide using the equipment shown.

ignition tube

charcoal
copper oxide

Bunsen burner

(c)  What would you observe in the ignition tube after it had been heated?

| Charcoal is a form of carbon and will reduce the copper oxide. |

....................................................................................................

....................................................................................................    **(2 marks)**

(d)  Excess charcoal powder is used in the reaction. Suggest how the excess charcoal could be removed from the copper metal.

Wash with water to suspend the charcoal powder then ....................................

....................................................................................................    **(2 marks)**

# Iron and aluminium

**1** Which of the following metals is most likely to be extracted from its ore by heating with carbon? Tick **one** box.

☐ **A**  aluminium

☐ **B**  magnesium

☐ **C**  potassium

☐ **D**  iron                                                                 **(1 mark)**

**2** Iron is made industrially using hematite ore, $Fe_2O_3$. The process occurs in a blast furnace where the ore is heated together with carbon. One of the reactions that take place is:

$$Fe_2O_3 + 3C \rightarrow 2Fe + 3CO$$

> Carbon must be more reactive than a metal it is trying to displace.

(a)  Using the reactivity series explain why carbon is able to reduce iron(III) oxide.

................................................................................................................. **(1 mark)**

Metals such as potassium and magnesium cannot be extracted from their ores using carbon.

(b)  Name another metal that cannot be extracted from its ore using carbon.

................................................................................................................. **(1 mark)**

(c)  Using the equation above state which reactant has been oxidised and explain why.

Carbon because ........................................................................................ **(2 marks)**

**3** Aluminium is purified using the electrolysis of bauxite ore, $Al_2O_3$. The ore is crushed, cryolite added and the mixture heated to 1000 °C before electrolysis can start.

(a)  Why does the crushed ore mixture need to be heated to 1000 °C?

The ore must be molten ..............................................................................

................................................................................................................. **(2 marks)**

(b)  Why is cryolite added?

To reduce the melting point of ..................................................................

................................................................................................................. **(2 marks)**

(c)  Write the half equations for the reactions that occur at the electrodes.

Cathode: $Al^{3+}(aq) +$ ...........$e^- \rightarrow Al(s)$

Anode: ........... $\rightarrow O_2 + 4e^-$                                          **(2 marks)**

(d)  Carbon dioxide is another gas produced at the anode. Explain how carbon dioxide can be produced.

Oxygen is produced at the anode and this reacts with ...................................

.................................................................................................................

................................................................................................................. **(2 marks)**

(e)  The industrial production of aluminium is expensive despite aluminium being a very common ore. What are the major reasons for the high cost of producing aluminium?

.................................................................................................................

................................................................................................................. **(2 marks)**

# Biological metal extraction

**1** A traditional method of extracting copper from its ore is to heat copper sulfide to produce copper and sulfur dioxide. As the supply of copper sulfide ore diminishes, phytomining is becoming more popular to extract low-grade copper.

(a) Complete the flow chart of the key stages in phytomining. **(1 mark)**

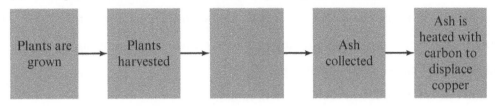

| Plants are grown | → | Plants harvested | → | | → | Ash collected | → | Ash is heated with carbon to displace copper |

(b) Name an environmental consideration when burning the plants.

Carbon dioxide ...........................................................................................

.......................................................................................................... **(2 marks)**

**2** Bioleaching is a technique used to extract copper from low-grade ores using bacteria. The bacteria form a leachate containing copper sulfate and scrap iron is then used to displace the copper.

(a) Define the term ore. .................................................................... **(1 mark)**

(b) The bioleaching process can be made more efficient by controlling the conditions. Name two conditions that could be controlled to maximise the yield of copper.

..........................................................................................................

.......................................................................................................... **(2 marks)**

> Bioleaching uses bacteria, which are biological microorganisms.

(c) Why will iron displace copper from copper sulfate? ................................... **(1 mark)**

(d) Write a word equation for the reaction.

iron + copper sulfate → ......................... + ......................... **(2 marks)**

**3** Bioleaching is a technique that uses biological methods to extract small amounts of metals from land. The key features of the method are summarised in the table.

| | **Main points** |
|---|---|
| Bioleaching | Bacteria grown on low-grade ores<br>Leachate produced that contains toxic chemicals<br>Scrap iron used to displace copper from leachate |

Evaluate if bioleaching would be suitable to extract small amounts of copper from a mountainside next to a drinking water reservoir.

Not suitable because the toxic chemicals in the leachate could .........................

.......................................................................................................... **(2 marks)**

# Recycling metals

1 Most households in the UK now have access to doorstep recycling schemes and many tonnes of metals are recycled this way. Give **one** advantage and **one** disadvantage of recycling metals.

Advantage: Less mining .......................................................................

Disadvantage: the metals need to be collected or taken to recycling centres.   **(2 marks)**

2 A section of text from a leaflet encouraging people to recycle aluminium cans is shown.

- 11 million drinks cans are used each day in the UK.

- Recycling one can uses 95% less energy than making a new one.

- Recycling one tonne of aluminium prevents 9 tonnes of $CO_2$ being produced.

- It takes 60 days for a can from recycling to get back on the shelf.

(a) Name the ore that aluminium is extracted from. ...........................................   **(1 mark)**

(b) Use the information in the text to give two advantages of recycling aluminium cans.

> Only use information from the text.

.........................................................................................................

.........................................................................................................   **(2 marks)**

(c) Calculate how many times in a year an aluminium can could be used and recycled.

$365 \div 60 =$ ...........................................   **(1 mark)**

3 Smartphones contain precious metals including gold, silver, copper and platinum. These metals can be recovered by recycling the phones.

| | Mass of metal in smartphone (g) | Cost of metal per kilogram (£) | Energy saved by recycling (%) |
|---|---|---|---|
| Gold | 0.034 | 32,000 | 75 |
| Silver | 0.37 | 420 | 78 |
| Aluminium | 25 | 2 | 95 |
| Copper | 15 | 5 | 90 |

(a) Give **two** reasons from the information above why recycling mobile phones is a good idea.

.........................................................................................................

.........................................................................................................   **(2 marks)**

(b) How many mobile phones need to be processed to obtain 1 kg of aluminium?

$1000 g \div 25 g =$ ...........................................................   **(2 marks)**

(c) How many mobile phones need to be recycled to obtain £500 worth of copper?

.........................................................................................................

.........................................................................................................

.........................................................................................................   **(3 marks)**

# Life-cycle assessments

1 A life-cycle assessment is a way to assess the environmental impact at every stage of a product's life.

(a) Which factor is **not** considered when carrying out a life-cycle assessment?
Tick **one** box.

☐ **A** energy required to manufacture

☐ **B** disposal of the product

☐ **C** cost of disposal

☐ **D** chemicals required for maintenance      **(1 mark)**

(b) Complete the flow diagram to show the four main stages in a life-cycle assessment.

obtaining raw materials

(ii) .............

(i) .............

using the product

**(2 marks)**

(c) Why are life-cycle assessments often drawn as flowcharts in a circle?

...................................................................................................................

................................................................................................................... **(2 marks)**

2 A supermarket is investigating if they should be offering plastic or paper bags so they carry out a life-cycle assessment. Part of the assessment is shown.

| | Plastic bag | Paper bag |
|---|---|---|
| **Source** | Crude oil | Trees |
| **Greenhouse gas emissions (tonnes)** | 0.08 | 0.04 |
| **Energy used (MJ)** | 1.5 | 1.7 |
| **Solid waste produced (kg)** | 17 | 62 |
| **Fresh water used (l)** | 264 | 4564 |

(a) How much more solid waste is produced making paper bags?

$62 - 17 =$ ................................................................................ **(1 mark)**

(b) Use three pieces of information from the table to justify if paper bags or plastic bags should be used

...................................................................................................................

...................................................................................................................

................................................................................................................... **(3 marks)**

# Extended response – Reactivity of metals

A student found an old text book in the library that described reacting metals with acids to prove their reactivity. The following table was printed.

| | Reaction with acid |
|---|---|
| Zinc | Steady production of bubbles |
| Iron | Slow effervescence |
| Copper | No visible reaction |

The book said that aluminium would not react with acids so its position could not be found.

Describe a different experiment the students could carry out to investigate the reactivity of metals if they were provided with the following chemicals and were allowed to use any basic laboratory equipment.

• Pieces of zinc, iron, copper and aluminium metal
• 0.2 mol dm$^{-3}$ zinc nitrate, iron nitrate, copper nitrate and aluminium nitrate

> Remember to plan your answer first. This allows your answer to be logical and helps you make sure you have remembered to include all the key points.
> In this question you are being asked to describe an experiment that you have probably done in your classroom, only using different chemicals. You are not expected to describe any novel techniques. Stick to what you know.

Plan:

Take a beaker and measure out 20 cm$^3$ of zinc nitrate using a measuring cylinder.

Add a piece of iron to the solution and watch to see if a reaction occurs.

Rather than write out a long list it is okay to make a results table as long as you explain it.

| | Zinc | Iron | Copper | Aluminium |
|---|---|---|---|---|
| Zinc nitrate | x | | | |
| Iron nitrate | | x | | |
| Copper nitrate | | | x | |
| Aluminium nitrate | | | | x |

Describe how reactivity of the meals can be determined from these experiments.

.................................................................................................................................

.................................................................................................................................

.................................................................................................................................

.................................................................................................................................

.................................................................................................................................  **(6 marks)**

> Continue your answer on your own paper. You should aim to write half a side of A4.

# The Haber process

1 Dynamic equilibrium occurs in reversible reactions, but only in a closed system.

(a) What is meant by the term dynamic equilibrium? Tick **one** box.

☐ **A**   Forwards and backwards reactions are occurring at the same time.

☐ **B**   The forward reaction has completed.

☐ **C**   A balance of reactants and products have been made, and the reaction stops.

☐ **D**   The point at which only products are being made.      **(1 mark)**

(b) Why can dynamic equilibrium only occur in a closed system?

................................................................................................................... **(1 mark)**

> Whenever you talk about equilibrium, you have to think about the forward and the backward reactions.

2 Millions of tonnes of ammonia are made each year to make fertilisers, nitric acid and other chemicals. Nitrogen and hydrogen are reacted together along with a catalyst to speed up the reaction. The reaction is carried out at a specific temperature and pressure.

(a) Where do the hydrogen and nitrogen for the reaction come from?

Hydrogen .......................................

Nitrogen .............. air .......................      **(2 marks)**

(b) State the catalyst, temperature and pressure used.

Catalyst iron

Temperature .......................................

Pressure .......................................      **(3 marks)**

3 This graph shows the concentration of hydrogen, nitrogen and ammonia over time.

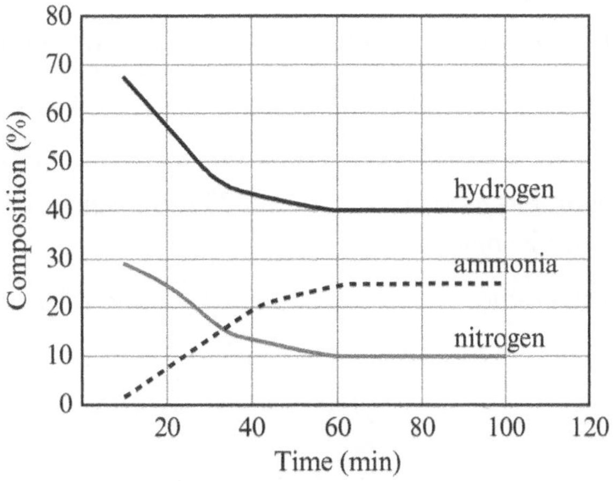

(a) At what time does equilibrium occur? ................................................. **(1 mark)**

(b) The concentration of the hydrogen and nitrogen never drops to zero so what happens to the unreacted reagents?

................................................................................................................... **(1 mark)**

# More about equilibria

1   The graph below shows the percentage yield of ammonia at different temperatures and pressures.

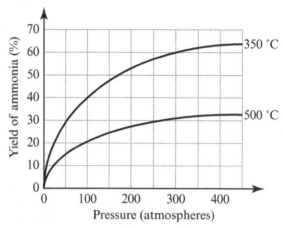

(a)   Draw a line on the graph to show the % yield you would expect at 400 °C.   **(1 mark)**

(b)   Describe the relationship between pressure and yield, and between temperature and yield.

Increasing pressure increases yield. Increasing temperature ..............................

.................................................................................................................   **(2 marks)**

(c)   Temperatures lower than 300 °C often give a yield of 100% of ammonia. Suggest a reason why temperatures of less than 300 °C are not used.

At low temperatures the reaction is not fast enough ......................................

.................................................................................................................   **(2 marks)**

(d)   After reacting the gases with the catalyst, a mixture of unreacted nitrogen, unreacted hydrogen and ammonia is formed. The boiling points of these three gases are ammonia –33 °C, hydrogen –252 °C, nitrogen –196 °C.

Use the information to suggest a method for extracting the ammonia.

The gases are cooled and ammonia turns liquid at ......................................

.................................................................................................................   **(2 marks)**

(e)   The actual conditions used are 450 °C and 200 atmospheres. Explain why this compromise must be made.

Increasing the temperature and pressure increases the rate of the reaction .........

.................................................................................................................

.................................................................................................................

.................................................................................................................   **(2 marks)**

(f)   A fixed amount of iron catalyst is used in the Haber cycle reaction. Why would using more iron catalyst not affect the yield of the reaction?

Catalysts only increase the speed of the reaction ......................................

.................................................................................................................   **(2 marks)**

# The alkali metals

1  The alkali metals have quite different properties to transition metals, such as iron. The table shows the melting point and density of four different metals.

|  | Lithium | Sodium | Potassium | Iron |
|---|---|---|---|---|
| **Melting point (°C)** | 181 | 98 | 64 | 1538 |
| **Density (g cm⁻³)** | 0.54 | 0.97 | 0.89 | 7.90 |

(a)  How does the melting point of alkali metals compare to the melting point of iron?

The melting points of the alkali metals (lithium, sodium and potassium) are lower

...................................................................................................................... **(1 mark)**

(b)  The density of water is $1\,g\,cm^{-3}$. Use the data in the table to predict which metals will sink and which will float in water.

Iron will sink, lithium, sodium and potassium will ............................................

...................................................................................................................... **(1 mark)**

(c)  Use the data in the table to predict the melting point of rubidium.

The melting point will be lower than potassium so between ...............................

...................................................................................................................... **(1 mark)**

2  In a class demonstration a teacher takes a large tray of water and adds a couple of drops of universal indicator solution. She then adds a very small piece of sodium into the water. The sodium forms a ball and rushes around on the surface.

(a)  Write the balanced equation to show the reaction between sodium and water.

.......... + .................... → ......NaOH + ......H₂

(b)  Use the equation above to explain why the indicator changed colour from green to blue.

Sodium hydroxide is produced which is ........................................................... **(2 marks)**

(c)  How would the observations be different if potassium was used?

Describe what you would see.

......................................................................................................................

...................................................................................................................... **(2 marks)**

3  When alkali metals react, they form cations.

(a)  Use a half equation to show how lithium forms a cation.

Li → ............ + .................. **(1 mark)**

(b)  Why does the reactivity of the alkali metals increase down the group?

The atoms gain more shells as you go down the group so it becomes ..............

.................. to lose an .............. and become a ................................. **(1 mark)**

# The halogens

**1** Draw lines to match the description to the halogen.

Chlorine                                    Black solid

Bromine                                    Green gas

Iodine                                     Brown liquid                    **(3 marks)**

**2** The halogens belong to group 7 of the periodic table.

(a) Complete the electron diagram of chlorine and explain why the halogens are in group 7.

......................................................................................

......................................................................................                    **(2 marks)**

(b) The halogens exist as diatomic molecules. Explain what diatomic means.

...................................................................................................................    **(1 mark)**

(c) Show the bonding in $Cl_2$.

> Only show the outer electrons as these are the ones involved in bonding.

**(1 mark)**

Chlorine water can be prepared by bubbling chlorine through water.

(d) Describe a test to show the presence of chlorine.

...................................................................................................................    **(1 mark)**

(e) State a hazard and a safety precaution associated with that hazard for the preparation of chlorine water.

Chlorine is toxic so ...................................................................................    **(2 marks)**

**3** Halogens react readily with metals. The table shows the results of heating the halogen with iron wool.

| Halogen | Result |
|---------|--------|
| Chlorine | Glows bright orange |
| Bromine | Glows dull red |
| Iodine | Iron wool turns black |

(a) Fluorine is above chlorine in the periodic table. Predict what would happen if fluorine was heated with iron wool. Justify your answer.

......................................................................................................................

......................................................................................................................    **(2 marks)**

(b) Explain in terms of atomic structure how the reactivity of the group 7 elements changes as you go down the group.

As you go down the group there are more shells of electrons. This means ...........

......................................................................................................................

......................................................................................................................

......................................................................................................................    **(3 marks)**

# Reactions of halogens

1  A teacher demonstrates the reaction of chlorine with iron wool using the equipment in the diagram. When heated, the iron wool glows brightly.

dry chlorine gas

chlorine gas released into fume-cupboard

iron wool

(a)  What compound forms during the

reaction? ........................................   **(1 mark)**

> The only reactants you have are iron and chlorine, so these will combine together.

(b)  Complete the balanced equation for the reaction.

$2Fe + 3Cl_2 \rightarrow$ ...........................   **(1 mark)**

(c)  Predict the result if fluorine was used instead of chlorine.

More reactive reaction, iron wool ...............................................................

........................................................................................   **(2 marks)**

2  Hydrochloric acid, hydrobromic acid and hydroiodic acid can all be prepared using hydrogen and the relevant halogen gas.

(a)  Write the symbol equation for the reaction between hydrogen gas and iodine.

> Both hydrogen and chlorine are diatomic gases.

$H_2 +$ ............ $\rightarrow$ ....................   **(1 mark)**

(b)  How is the product of part (a) converted into an acid?

........................................................................................   **(1 mark)**

To produce hydroiodic acid a platinum catalyst and 300 °C heat is required, yet hydrofluoric acid will form at –200 °C in the dark.

(c)  Explain how and why the reactivity of the halogens changes as you go down a group.

Reactivity decreases down the group because there are more shells so ............

........................................................................................   **(3 marks)**

3  Chlorine can combine with alkali metals to form ionic compounds or join with non-metals, such as hydrogen, to form simple covalent molecules.

(a)  Use a half equation to show how chlorine atoms can be converted to chlorine ions.

$Cl_2 + 2e^- \rightarrow$ ...........   **(1 mark)**

(b)  In terms of electrons, why does chlorine combine with other elements?

To gain an electron to ...............................................................

........................................................................................   **(2 marks)**

(c)  Write a word equation for the reaction between chlorine gas and potassium metal.

chlorine + ........... $\rightarrow$ ...........   **(2 marks)**

(d)  Write a symbol equation with state symbols to show the reaction between chlorine and sodium metal.

........................................................................................

........................................................................................   **(2 marks)**

# Halogen displacement reactions

1  In the reaction between potassium bromide and chlorine, the potassium ions are described as spectator ions. What is meant by 'spectator ions'? Tick **one** box.

☐  **A**  Ions that do not dissociate.

☐  **B**  Ions that join together to make a solid.

☐  **C**  Ions that appear as both reactants and products.

☐  **D**  Ions that make the solution acidic or alkaline.                    **(1 mark)**

2  Students were asked to find the order of reactivity for three of the halogens. They reacted the chemicals as shown in the table.

|  | Chlorine water | Bromine water | Iodine water |
|---|---|---|---|
| Sodium chloride | X |  |  |
| Sodium bromide |  |  |  |
| Sodium iodide |  |  |  |

(a)  Put an 'X' into boxes where no reaction would be observed.       **(1 mark)**

(b)  Place a tick in the boxes where displacement reactions would occur.    **(1 mark)**

> Displacement reactions only occur when a more reactive halogen can displace a less reactive halogen.

(c)  Why were the students asked to not carry out the reaction between sodium chloride and chlorine water?

Sodium chloride and chlorine both contain ...................................................

.................................................................................................    **(1 mark)**

3  The equation for the reaction of bromine and sodium iodide is written as:

$$Br_2 + 2NaI \rightarrow 2NaBr + I_2$$

(a)  The reaction can be described as a displacement reaction, but how else can it be described?

.................................................................    **(1 mark)**

(b)  In the reaction, one substance is oxidised and one is reduced. Show how this occurs using half equations.

Oxidised .................................................

Reduced .................................................

> Losing electrons = oxidised.
> Gaining electrons = reduced.

**(4 marks)**

4  Astatine is near the bottom of group 7. It is very rare and radioactive so it is not studied very often.

(a)  From what you know of the reactions of the other halogens in the group write a balanced equation for the reaction of sodium astatine with bromine.

$$2NaAt + Br_2 \rightarrow ........ + ........$$    **(2 marks)**

(b)  Predict and explain if astatine will react with sodium iodide, NaI.

No, .......................................................................................................

.................................................................................................    **(2 marks)**

# The noble gases

1  The noble gases belong in group 0 of the periodic table. Why are they in group 0? Tick **one** box.

☐  **A**  There were no other groups to put them in.

☐  **B**  They all have a full outer shell of electrons.

☐  **C**  They have no electrons in their outer shell.

☐  **D**  They do not have electrons.                                                    **(1 mark)**

2  A scientist wanted to investigate the phrase 'go down like a lead balloon'. He took five balloons and filled them with different noble gases.

(a)  Air has a density of $0.0013$ g cm$^{-3}$. Use the data in the table to predict which balloons would sink.

.......................... and ..............................                                **(2 marks)**

| Element | Density (g cm$^{-3}$) |
|---------|----------------------|
| Helium, He | 0.00018 |
| Neon, Ne | 0.0009 |
| Argon, Ar | 0.0018 |
| Krypton, Kr | 0.0038 |

(b)  Children's party balloons are often filled with helium. Use the data in the table and your knowledge of noble gases to explain why this is a suitable gas.

Ensure you answer both parts of the question to get both marks.

........................................................................................................

........................................................................................................  **(2 marks)**

(c)  Xenon is below krypton in the periodic table. Predict two physical properties of xenon.

.................................................... and ....................................................  **(2 marks)**

3  Noble gases will not react even with reactive elements like potassium or chlorine.

(a)  Complete the diagram to show the electron configuration of argon.

**(2 marks)**

(b)  Use the diagram to explain why noble gases are unreactive.

They have a full outer shell of electrons, so ................................................

........................................................................................................  **(2 marks)**

# Extended response – Groups

Alkali metals will react with halogens to form metal halides. For example, sodium will react with chlorine to form sodium chloride.

From the following pairs of alkali metals and halogens explain which pair would be the most reactive?

> lithium and fluorine
> potassium and chlorine
> sodium and bromine

Half equations and a full equation are required as part of the explanation.

> You are always more successful answering long-answer questions if you plan them first.
> In this question you must consider the reactivity of the alkali metal and the reactivity of the halogen and then work out which pair would be the most reactive together.
> You also must remember to use half equations and a full equation as part of your answer.

Plan:

(1) Describe the trend in reactivity of alkali metals.

(2) Describe the trend in reactivity of halogens.

(3) Look at pairs and work out which couple will be most reactive.

(4) Write half equations for the alkali metal and the halogen.

(5) Write a complete equation for the reaction.

................................................................................................................

................................................................................................................

................................................................................................................

................................................................................................................

................................................................................................................

................................................................................................................

................................................................................................................

................................................................................................................

................................................................................................................

................................................................................................................

................................................................................................................

................................................................................................................

................................................................................................................

................................................................................................................

................................................................................................................

................................................................................................................    **(6 marks)**

> Continue your answer on your own paper. You should aim to write half a side of A4.

148

# Rates of reaction

1 Catalysts are used in many reactions to speed up the rate of reaction.

(a) Which statement about a catalyst is incorrect? Tick **one** box.

☐  **A**   Yeast is a catalyst used in the production of alcohol.

☐  **B**   Catalysts lower the activation energy of a reaction.

☐  **C**   Catalysts need to be frequently replaced.

☐  **D**   An enzyme is a biological catalyst.                     **(1 mark)**

(b) Why are metal catalysts often used as powders rather than large lumps?

............................................................................................................

............................................................................................ **(2 marks)**

> Apply your knowledge about the factors that affect
> the rate of a reaction to what happens with a catalyst.

2 Magnesium reacted with hydrochloric acid and produced magnesium chloride
and hydrogen gas. The graph shows the experiment carried out at three different
temperatures.

(a) Rank the experiments from highest temperature to lowest temperature.

Highest temperature ...................................................................... **(1 mark)**

(b) Why do all three graphs end at the same height?

.................................................................................................. **(1 mark)**

> Think about limiting reagents to answer this question.

(c) Explain, in terms of particles colliding, why changing the temperature affects the
rate of reaction.

At higher temperatures, particles have more energy to move around so ...........

............................................................................................................

.................................................................................... **(3 marks)**

(d) Other than temperature, how else could the rate of reaction been increased in
this experiment?

Increase the concentration of the ..................................................

.................................................................................... **(2 marks)**

 **Practical skills** **Investigating rates**

1  A student decided to investigate what happens when calcium carbonate reacts with hydrochloric acid.

$$CaCO_3(s) + 2HCl(aq) \rightarrow CaCl_2(aq) + H_2O(l) + CO_2(g)$$

The student placed 30 g of calcium carbonate into a flask and added 40 cm³ of hydrochloric acid.

(a)  Describe the measurements they could take to investigate the rate of reaction.

.................................................................................................................................

.......................................................................................................... **(2 marks)**

> There is more than one way to measure the rate of reaction for this reaction.

(b)  At the end of the experiment there was still calcium carbonate left in the flask. Explain why.

.................................................................................................................................

.......................................................................................................... **(2 marks)**

> This question does not expect you to calculate anything.

2  A student wanted to find a catalyst that would speed up the decomposition of hydrogen peroxide, $2H_2O_2 \rightarrow 2H_2O + O_2$. He tried using manganese(IV) as a catalyst.

|  | Mass of catalyst at start | Mass of catalyst at end | Time taken to collect 23 cm³ of oxygen (s) |
|---|---|---|---|
| **No catalyst** | 0 | 0 | 300 |
| **Manganese(IV)** | 1.75 | 1.75 | 30 |

(a)  Calculate how much manganese(IV) affected the rate of the reaction.   **(1 mark)**

.............................

.............................

> The rate of reaction is proportional to the time taken to collect 23 cm³ of oxygen, so you can use this value to make the comparison.

(b)  What evidence is there in the table that manganese is a catalyst?

............................................. and .......................................................

.......................................................................................................... **(2 marks)**

3  In a reaction between hydrochloric acid and another reagent a precipitate forms in proportion to the rate of reaction. A student investigated how the concentration of hydrochloric acid affected the reaction by using the equipment shown.

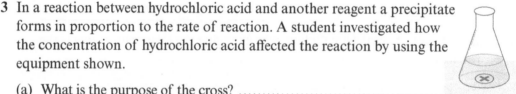

(a)  What is the purpose of the cross? .............................................   **(1 mark)**

(b)  Why must the equipment be washed carefully between each reading?

.......................................................................................................... **(1 mark)**

(c)  Predict, and explain, what will happen to the rate of reaction as the concentration of the acid is decreased.

.................................................................................................................................

.......................................................................................................... **(3 marks)**

# Exam skills – Rates of reaction

A student decided to investigate the reaction between sodium carbonate and sulfuric acid.

$$Na_2CO_3 + H_2SO_4 \rightarrow Na_2SO_4 + H_2O + CO_2$$

The table below gives the volume of gas collected at different times. At the end of the reaction, all the sodium carbonate had reacted.

> When plotting, be careful to place the cross exactly where it needs to be. Use a sharp pencil.

(a) Plot a graph of the volume of $CO_2$ produced against time.

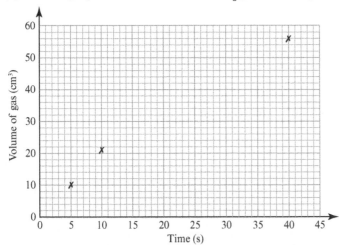

| Time (s) | Volume of gas (cm³) |
|---|---|
| 5 | 10 |
| 10 | 21 |
| 15 | 37 |
| 20 | 47 |
| 25 | 52 |
| 30 | 55 |
| 35 | 56 |
| 40 | 56 |

**(3 marks)**

(b) How does the rate of reaction change over time?

At the start, the rate of reaction is fast up to .................................................

...................................................................................................................

...................................................................................................................

.................................................................................................... **(3 marks)**

> There are three stages to the graph and you need to describe all three to get full marks.

(c) Draw a line on the graph to predict what would happen if more concentrated acid was used.

> The faster the rate of reaction, the steeper the gradient of the graph.

**(2 marks)**

# Heat energy changes

1 Circle the correct word to complete each of the sentences below:

(a) Bond breaking is exothermic/endothermic.

(b) Bond making is exothermic/endothermic.

(c) Endothermic reactions take up/release heat energy.

(d) Exothermic reactions take up/release heat energy.  **(1 mark)**

2 The reaction between sodium hydroxide, NaOH, and hydrochloric acid, HCl, is exothermic.

(a) What is meant by an exothermic reaction?

Energy is transferred from stores of energy in chemical bonds to ....................

........................................................................................................  **(1 mark)**

(b) Explain in terms of energy transfers why the reaction is exothermic.

........................................................................................................

........................................................................................................  **(2 marks)**

> You must talk about bonds being broken and bonds being made.

3 A student wanted to investigate the heat changes when different substances dissolve in water. She used the equipment shown and obtained the following results.

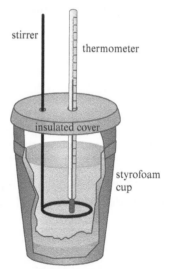

stirrer

thermometer

insulated cover

styrofoam cup

|  | Temperature at start (°C) | Temperature at end (°C) |
|---|---|---|
| **Ammonium nitrate** | 22.0 | 15.2 |
| **Calcium oxide** | 22.5 | 65.4 |

(a) Use the data to state which reaction is endothermic.

........................................................................................................  **(1 mark)**

(b) Why did the student stir the solution? ..........................................  **(1 mark)**

(c) Why was a lid put onto the equipment? ........................................  **(1 mark)**

# Reaction profiles

1  Cool packs are used for athletes to reduce swelling if they injure themselves. The pack contains two reagents, a bag of water and ammonium nitrate. When the inner bag of water is broken the reagents mix and the pack begins to cool.

(a) Complete the energy level diagram to show the process of the water and ammonium nitrate mixing.

> Add labels to show the reagents, products and activation energy.

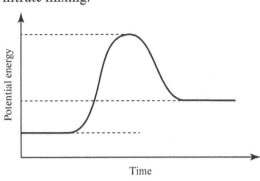

**(1 mark)**

(b) In terms of bonding, why does this reaction take in heat?

...................................................................................................................

...................................................................................................................   **(2 marks)**

2  Self-heating cans are used by mountaineers so they do not have to carry a stove with them. As well as the food, the cans contain a section with two chemicals: aluminium and iron oxide. When the chemicals are mixed an exothermic reaction occurs.

(a) Complete the equation for the reaction between aluminium and iron oxide.

$Fe_2O_3 + \ldots\ldots\ldots Al \rightarrow Al_2O_3 + \ldots\ldots\ldots$   **(1 mark)**

(b) The diagram shows the energy profile of the reaction. Add the following labels: reactants, products, activation energy.

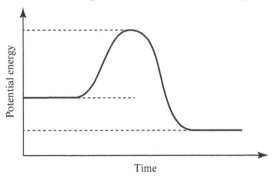

**(3 marks)**

(c) The cans require the heat from a match to start the reaction but then they keep going and give out lots of heat. What is the function of the match?

...................................................................................................................   **(1 mark)**

(d) In terms of bond breaking and bond making describe why this reaction is exothermic.

...................................................................................................................

...................................................................................................................

...................................................................................................................   **(2 marks)**

> Breaking bonds requires energy, making bonds releases energy.

# Calculating energy changes

1 When methane is burned in air it forms carbon dioxide and water.

$$CH_4 + 2O_2 \rightarrow CO_2 + 2H_2O$$

Use the bond energies in the table to answer the following questions.

|  | Bond enthalpy (kJ mol⁻¹) |
|---|---|
| C–H | 413 |
| O=O | 498 |
| C=O | 805 |
| H–O | 464 |

(a) What is the total energy needed to break all of the bonds in the reagents?

> It can help to draw out the molecules to help you work out how many of each type of bond are present.

C–H bonds: 413 × 4 = 1652          O=O bonds: 498 × 2 = 996

Total = 1652 + 996 = ................................................................ **(3 marks)**

(b) How much energy is released when bonds are made forming the products?

C=O bonds: ............................ H–O bonds: ...................................

Total = ...................................... **(3 marks)**

(c) Use your answers to (a) and (b) to calculate the energy change for the reaction.

.............................................................................................................

............................................................................................................. **(2 marks)**

(d) Is the reaction exothermic or endothermic? Explain your answer using the figures you calculated in parts (a)–(c).

........................................ because ...................................... **(2 marks)**

2 Hydrogen and oxygen react to form water. Use the bond energies provided to determine if the reaction is exothermic or endothermic.

$$2H_2 + O_2 \rightarrow 2H_2O$$

|  | Bond enthalpy (kJ mol⁻¹) |
|---|---|
| O=O | 498 |
| H–H | 436 |
| O–H | 464 |

Bonds broken (energy in): .............................................................

Bonds made (energy out): ..............................................................

Energy change = energy in – energy out = .........................................

Reaction is ................................................................................ **(4 marks)**

# Crude oil

1 Crude oil was formed many millions of years ago from microscopic animals and plants living in the ancient seas. Crude oil pumped up from the seabed is a thick black, gloopy liquid. This liquid cannot be described as being pure, why? Tick **one** box.

☐ **A** It will be contaminated with salt water.

☐ **B** It will contain fossils of the marine animals.

☐ **C** It contains a mixture of hydrocarbons.

☐ **D** It has not been cleaned.

> A pure substance contains only a single substance with nothing else mixed with it.

**(1 mark)**

2 Most compounds in crude oil contain only two elements. The diagram shows an example of two compounds found in crude oil.

Cyclopentane and heptane.

(a) Name the **two** elements found in both the compounds.

Carbon and .............................. **(2 marks)**

(b) What name is given to compounds that **only** contain the elements listed in part (a)?

................................................. **(1 mark)**

3 The table contains information about four different hydrocarbons found in crude oil.

|  | Formula | Boiling point (°C) |
|---|---|---|
| **Methane** | $CH_4$ | −162 |
| **Ethane** | $C_2H_4$ | −89 |
| **Octane** | $C_8H_{18}$ | 125 |
| **Cyclooctane** | $C_8H_{16}$ | 149 |

(a) Which compound has the smallest molecules? .......................................... **(1 mark)**

(b) From the information above, which compounds are most likely liquid at 100 °C?

.................................................................................................... **(1 mark)**

(c) Which compounds contain the same number of carbon atoms?

.............................. and .................................................. **(1 mark)**

> Look at the formula of the compounds to help you answer these questions – do not be put off by unfamiliar names.

4 It is estimated that worldwide 95 million barrels of oil are used every day. Crude oil can be processed to make fuels, such as petrol and diesel, turned into plastics and used as a feedstock for chemical reactions. Despite its high use, crude oil is described as being a finite resource.

(a) Define the term 'finite resource'.

.................................................................................................... **(2 marks)**

(b) Why can crude oil be used as a feedstock?

....................................................................................................

.................................................................................................... **(2 marks)**

# Fractional distillation

**1** Fractional distillation is used to separate out fractions in crude oil.

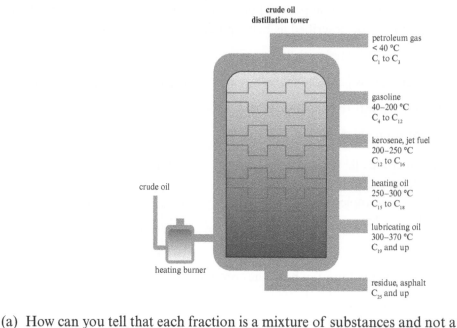

crude oil
distillation tower

petroleum gas
< 40 °C
$C_1$ to $C_3$

gasoline
40–200 °C
$C_4$ to $C_{12}$

kerosene, jet fuel
200–250 °C
$C_{12}$ to $C_{16}$

heating oil
250–300 °C
$C_{15}$ to $C_{18}$

lubricating oil
300–370 °C
$C_{19}$ and up

crude oil

heating burner

residue, asphalt
$C_{25}$ and up

(a) How can you tell that each fraction is a mixture of substances and not a pure substance?

........................................................................................................................ **(1 mark)**

(b) Evaporating and condensing both occur during fractional distillation. Where do these two changes occur?

........................................................................................................................ **(2 marks)**

(c) How is the size of the molecules linked to the boiling points?

The larger the molecule ...............................................................................

........................................................................................................................ **(2 marks)**

**2** The fractions that come from the fractionating column have different physical properties. Three different fractions are shown in the table.

Guided

| | Boiling point (°C) | Viscosity | Ease of ignition |
|---|---|---|---|
| **A** | 174 | medium | medium |
| **B** | −42 | low | high |
| **C** | 343 | high | low |

(a) What is meant by the term viscosity?

........................................................................................................................ **(1 mark)**

(b) Methane, $CH_4$, is a gas at room temperature, extremely flammable and highly volatile. Use this information to rank the compounds in the table in terms of size.

biggest .................... > .................... > .................... smallest    **(2 marks)**

**3** The fractions from the fractionating column have different uses related to their physical properties.

Guided

Give **one** use for each of the following fractions:

Bitumen ............................................................ **(1 mark)**

Fuel oil ............................................................ **(1 mark)**

Kerosene ............................................................ **(1 mark)**

# Alkanes

1 A teacher wanted to demonstrate the formation of products from combusting hydrocarbons. She set up the equipment as shown.

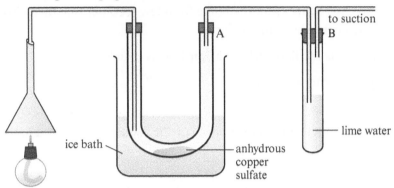

(a) The anhydrous copper sulfate tests for the presence of water. Why is the U-tube containing it placed in an ice bath?

..................................................................................................................... **(1 mark)**

(b) How will the teacher prove that carbon dioxide, $CO_2$, is present?

..................................................................................................................... **(1 mark)**

(c) The teacher then repeats the experiment using a spirit burner containing the hydrocarbon pentane, $C_5H_{12}$. Write a balanced equation to show the complete combustion of pentane.

$C_5H_{12}$ + .........$O_2$ → ............................... + ..................... **(2 marks)**

2 Methane, ethane and propane are the first three members of the alkane homologous group.

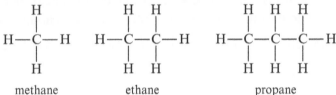

methane               ethane               propane

(a) From the diagram how are the compounds similar?

..................................................................................................................... **(3 marks)**

(b) Butane is the next member of the group. Predict its molecular formula.

..................................................................................................................... **(1 mark)**

(c) What is the general formula for an alkane? ............................................... **(1 mark)**

3 This graph shows how the number of carbons in an alkane affects boiling point.

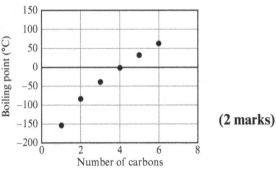

(a) State the relationship between the number of carbon atoms and the boiling point.

....................................................

.................................................... **(2 marks)**

(b) Predict the boiling point for an alkane with

seven carbons. .................................... **(1 mark)**

# Incomplete combustion

**1** A teacher wants to demonstrate complete and incomplete combustion using a Bunsen burner and a glass beaker. She turns the Bunsen burner on and opens the air hole. She then puts the glass beaker into the flame for a few seconds. She then closes the air hole and places the beaker back in the flame.

(a) What colour is the flame when the air hole is open? ................................... **(1 mark)**

(b) Incomplete combustion occurs when the collar is closed. Why?

..............................................................................................................................
**(1 mark)**

(c) Explain why soot forms on the bottom of the beaker when placed in the yellow flame.

..............................................................................................................................

..............................................................................................................................
**(2 marks)**

> The soot is a product formed during the combustion process, not an impurity.

**2** When fuels such as propane burn in a limited supply of oxygen, carbon monoxide and carbon particles form.

**Guided**

(a) Complete the word equation to show the incomplete combustion of propane.

propane + oxygen → ............. + ............... + ...............
**(1 mark)**

(b) Why is carbon monoxide described as toxic?

..............................................................................................................................
**(1 mark)**

(c) Name a problem associated with carbon particles?

..............................................................................................................................
**(1 mark)**

**3** A gas fire in an old house has not been serviced recently. The owner notices that it is burning with a yellow flame and soot has built up on the heating elements.

Explain what evidence there is to show incomplete combustion is occurring?

..............................................................................................................................

..............................................................................................................................
**(2 marks)**

> There are always two main observations to look out for in a 2 mark question.

**4** Butane can be used as a fuel for cigarette lighters. Under normal conditions butane will undergo complete combustion, but when oxygen is limited, incomplete combustion occurs. Write balanced equations for:

Complete combustion:

$$2C_4H_{10} + ......O_2 \rightarrow ............CO_2 + ............H_2O$$

> Balance the carbon first, then the hydrogen, and the oxygen last.

Incomplete combustion where twice as much carbon dioxide forms as carbon monoxide or carbon:

$$C_4H_{10} + ......O_2 \rightarrow ...\ CO + ...\ C + ...\ 2CO_2 + ...\ H_2O$$
**(2 marks)**

# Acid rain

1 Most of the acid rain that falls comes from man-made emissions, such as burning fuels. It is created when sulfur dioxide, $SO_2$, reacts with water in rain clouds.

(a) Describe what atoms are present in $SO_2$.

One sulfur and ........................................................................... **(2 marks)**

(b) Fuels are hydrocarbons yet can produce $SO_2$ when burned. Where does the $SO_2$ come from?

Sulfur impurities in the ........................................................... **(1 mark)**

(c) Sulfurous acid, $H_2SO_3$, is produced when $SO_2$ reacts with water. This is then oxidised to sulfuric acid.

(i) Write the symbol equation for the formation of sulfurous acid.

$H_2O(l) +$ ............$(g) \rightarrow$ ....................... $(aq)$ **(1 mark)**

(ii) Write an equation show how sulfurous acid is oxidised to sulfuric acid.

...............$(aq) + O_2(g) \rightarrow$ ....................... $(aq)$ **(1 mark)**

> Work out the reactants and products first and then balance the equation.

2 Large amounts of sulfur dioxide are produced naturally by volcanic eruptions, but man-made sulfur dioxide emissions are being blamed for the increased volumes of acid rain that is falling.

**Guided**

(a) State **two** ways that acid rain damages the environment.

1. ...............................................................................

2. ........................................................................... **(2 marks)**

(b) State **two** ways that acid rain can damage buildings.

1. ...............................................................................

2. ........................................................................... **(2 marks)**

3 Oxides of nitrogen, $NO_x$, are also responsible for forming acid rain.

(a) What acid is formed when $NO_x$ gases react with water in clouds?

........................................................................... **(1 mark)**

(b) $NO_x$ gases are produced when two gases are heated under high pressure in car engines. Name the two gases.

Nitrogen and ........................................................... **(2 marks)**

(c) What can be done to prevent $NO_x$ emissions from cars?

Fit a ........................................................................... **(1 mark)**

# Choosing fuels

**1** Decide if the statements apply to renewable or non-renewable energy sources.

| Statement | Renewable | Non-renewable |
|---|---|---|
| (a) These are the energy resources which cannot be exhausted | | |
| (b) Solar energy, wind energy, tidal energy, etc. are the examples | | |
| (c) It is present in limited quantity and will be used up one day | | |
| (d) Resources are quickly replenished by natural processes | | |
| (e) Life of resources is finite | | |

**(5 marks)**

**2** Hydrogen can be burned in a rocket or combined in a fuel cell to produce electricity.

(a) State **two** ways that hydrogen can be produced.

From fossil fuels and ................................................................................. **(2 marks)**

(b) Write the balanced equation to show the combustion of hydrogen in a rocket.

$$......H_2 + ......O_2 \rightarrow ...H_2O$$

**(2 marks)**

(c) Why is hydrogen described as a clean fuel?

................................................................................................................. **(1 mark)**

(d) Hydrogen is a gas, but it is best stored as a liquid. Name two ways that hydrogen gas can be turned into a liquid.

Compress gas, ......................................................................................

.................................................................................................................

**(2 marks)**

**3** Some of the advantages and disadvantages of hydrogen fuel cells are listed below. Use the information to evaluate if hydrogen fuel cells could replace petrol and diesel.

- Hydrogen and oxygen react to produce water, which isn't a pollutant so doesn't affect climate change.
- The only by-products are water and heat.
- It is a clean reaction.
- Hydrogen is difficult to store safely.
- Hydrogen is very explosive.
- Hydrogen is a gas so takes up a lot more space to store than liquid fuels like petrol.

.................................................................................................................

.................................................................................................................

.................................................................................................................

.................................................................................................................

.................................................................................................................

.................................................................................................................

**(3 marks)**

# Cracking

**1** Which of the statements about the cracking of alkanes is correct? Tick **one** box.

☐ **A** It produces better quality alkanes.

☐ **B** It converts long chain alkanes into shorter alkanes and alkenes.

☐ **C** Hydrogen is removed from long alkanes to make shorter alkanes.

☐ **D** Short-chain alkanes are turned into long-chained alkanes. **(1 mark)**

**2** Cracking alkanes industrially is an expensive and lengthy process.

(a) Use the data in the chart to answer the following questions.

  (i) How much greater is the demand for petrol than the supply?

  Supply is 25 million, demand is 40 million ........................................ **(2 marks)**

  (ii) Which fractions have a greater supply than demand?

  Paraffin, ..................................... and ........................................ **(1 mark)**

(b) Why are fractions such as petrol and diesel in high demand?

Used to fuel vehicles ................................................................................

............................................................................................................ **(2 marks)**

**3** During cracking one reaction that may be seen is shown below.

hexane              ⟶         butane   +   ethene

(a) How can you tell that the two products belong to two different homologous series?

............................................................................................................ **(1 mark)**

(b) Write a symbol equation for this reaction:

$$C_6H_{14} \rightarrow \text{..................} + \text{..................}$$ **(2 marks)**

**4** What do you understand by the term cracking?

.................................................. ┌─────────────────────────────────┐
.................................................. │ Make sure you say what has been reacted and │
.................................................. │ what has been produced during the reaction. │
.................................................. └─────────────────────────────────┘

............................................................................................................ **(2 marks)**

# Extended response – Fuels

The term acid rain was first used in 1872 by Scottish chemist Robert Smith after he observed rain that had a lower than expected pH in Manchester, England. Acid rain has a pH of less than 5.2.

Acid rain can occur naturally, but since the Industrial Revolution the effects of acid rain have increased significantly.

- Describe how acid rain is formed.
- Why are the effects of acid rain more common now than 150 years ago?
- Give two consequences of acid rain.

> It is always better to plan your answer so your ideas are put down in a logical and clear way. This question has three parts to it and each must be included in your answer.

..................................................................................................................
..................................................................................................................
..................................................................................................................
..................................................................................................................
..................................................................................................................
..................................................................................................................
..................................................................................................................
..................................................................................................................
..................................................................................................................
..................................................................................................................
..................................................................................................................
..................................................................................................................
..................................................................................................................
..................................................................................................................
..................................................................................................................
..................................................................................................................
..................................................................................................................
..................................................................................................................
..................................................................................................................
..................................................................................................................
..................................................................................................................
..................................................................................................................
.................................................................................................. **(6 marks)**

> You should aim to write half a side of A4.

# The early atmosphere

**1** Most scientists believe that the early atmosphere was initially created by which activity? Tick **one** box.

☐ **A** volcanoes erupting

☐ **B** asteroid impacts

☐ **C** land masses colliding

☐ **D** solar winds

**(1 mark)**

**2** The early atmosphere was very different to our current atmosphere. The table shows the main gases thought to be present in the early atmosphere.

|  | Percentage in early atmosphere |
|---|---|
| **Carbon dioxide** | 86 |
| **Oxygen** | Trace |
| **Water vapour** | 12 |
| **Nitrogen and other gases** | Trace |

(a) The water vapour in the air is believed to have formed the oceans.

  (i) What occurred to the Earth to allow this process to happen?

  .................................................................................................................. **(1 mark)**

  (ii) Describe how the water vapour could turn into an ocean.

  The gaseous water cooled and ...........................................................

  .................................................................................................................. **(2 marks)**

(b) Describe and explain how the formation of the oceans affected the concentration of carbon dioxide in the atmosphere.

The concentration of carbon dioxide decreased because ................................

.................................................................................................................. **(2 marks)**

(c) The early atmosphere contained trace amounts of oxygen yet now around one fifth of the atmosphere is oxygen.

  (i) Name **two** pieces of evidence that suggest the early atmosphere contained little or no oxygen?

  Ancient rocks contain pyrite that could not have formed in the presence of oxygen

  .................................................................................................................. **(2 marks)**

  (ii) Describe the test for oxygen.

  ..................................................................................................................

  .................................................................................................................. **(1 mark)**

This is a test you must know for your exam.

  (iii) The atmosphere now contains around 21% oxygen. Explain what caused the increase.

  Photosynthesis of .........................................................................

  .................................................................................................................. **(2 marks)**

# Greenhouse effect

**1** The greenhouse effect is essential for life on Earth as without it the temperature would be too cold for organisms to exist.

(a) Name the **three** main greenhouse gases.

carbon dioxide, .......................... and .................................................. **(3 marks)**

(b) Briefly describe how radiation from the Sun warms the planet.

The Earth absorbs solar radiation and emits infrared radiation. Greenhouse gases

.................................................................................................................................. **(3 marks)**

**2** Climate change may be occurring due to increased levels of greenhouse gases.

Name **two** activities that could be responsible for increasing the concentrations of greenhouse gases in the atmosphere.

...............................................................

...............................................................

> The question does not want you to describe natural processes.

**(2 marks)**

**3** The graph shows global temperatures and carbon dioxide levels over the last 450 000 years.

Guided

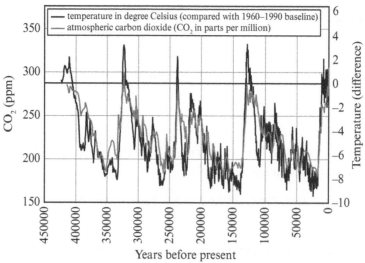

(a) State if there is a correlation between the global temperature and carbon dioxide levels.

..................................................................................................................................

.................................................................................................................................. **(2 marks)**

(b) Does the data give enough evidence for a causal link? Explain your answer briefly.

.................................................................................................................................. **(2 marks)**

(c) What may be limitations of the data?

.................................................................................................................................. **(1 mark)**

(d) Name **one** consequence of increased global warming.

.................................................................................................................................. **(1 mark)**

# Extended response – Atmospheric science

Climate change scientists are predicting a global temperature rise of two to eight degrees over the next thousand years.

Describe three negative effects of a rise in global temperatures and suggest three ways that would limit the impact of this rise.

> It is always best to plan your answer so it is in a logical order and contains all the points needed to gain maximum marks.
> The question states that it wants three examples of negative impacts of global warming, so make sure you give three different points. You also need to give three ways of limiting this impact. You are not being asked to give your opinion or evaluate these effects or impacts.

Plan

| Negative effects | Impacts |
|---|---|
| 1 Sea level rises – flooding | 1 Use renewable energy |
| 2 | 2 |
| 3 | 3 |

..........................................................................................................................................

..........................................................................................................................................

..........................................................................................................................................

..........................................................................................................................................

..........................................................................................................................................

..........................................................................................................................................

..........................................................................................................................................

..........................................................................................................................................

..........................................................................................................................................

..........................................................................................................................................

..........................................................................................................................................

..........................................................................................................................................

..........................................................................................................................................

..........................................................................................................................................

..........................................................................................................................................

..........................................................................................................................................

..........................................................................................................................................

..........................................................................................................................................    **(6 marks)**

Continue your answer on your own paper. You should aim to write half a side of A4.

# Key concepts

**1** State the number of significant figures for each of the following numbers.

|  | **Number of significant figures** |
|---|---|
| 1.00034 | 6 |
| 2200 |  |
| 0.0002503 |  |

> Significant figures are not zero numbers, unless they are between other numbers. Count the numbers from the first non-zero number to the last.

**(1 mark)**

**2** In an experiment a student records the time taken in a table. Convert each time into seconds.

| **Time taken** | **Time (sec)** |
|---|---|
| 1 min and 33 sec | 93 |
| 1 hour 4 min and 56 sec |  |

> Simply multiply the number of minutes by 60 and add on the number of seconds.

**(2 marks)**

**3** The power output of two different power stations is shown below.

| **Type of power station** | **Power output** |
|---|---|
| Hydroelectric | 2.1 GW |
| Nuclear | 1860 MW |

> Learn the prefixes:
> kilo × 1000
> mega × 1 000 000
> giga × 1 000 000 000

State the power in watts for each power station. Write your answer in standard form.

..................... **(3 marks)**

**4** A car travels at 60 km/h. Calculate the speed in m/s. Write your answer to two significant figures.

60 km = 60 000 m

There are 3600 s in an hour

> First convert km to m and hours to seconds. Speed = distance ÷ time

Speed = .................. ÷ .................. =

Speed = ........................... m/s to 2 sf    **(3 marks)**

**5** An atom has a diameter of 10 nm. Calculate how many atoms could fit in a line 6 μm long (the approximate diameter of the nucleus of a cell).

10 nm = 10 × $10^{-9}$ m

6 μm = 6 × $10^{-6}$ m

> Find out how many times 10 nm divides into 6 μm.

Therefore, number = .................. m ÷ .................. m

= 600 times    **(3 marks)**

# Scalars and vectors

1  Sort these quantities into scalar or vector.

|  | Scalar | Vector |
|---|---|---|
| **Friction** |  | ✓ |
| **Kinetic energy** | ✓ |  |
| **Displacement** |  | ✓ |
| **Acceleration** |  |  |
| **Temperature** |  |  |
| **Mass** |  |  |
| **Air resistance** |  |  |
| **Potential energy** |  |  |

> Is the direction it acts important? If yes, it's a vector.

> All forces are vectors.

> All types of energy are scalars.

**(8 marks)**

2  Explain the difference between distance and displacement.

Distance has size only.

> One of them is a vector quantity.

Displacement has both ................... and ...................    **(2 marks)**

3  A formula one driver completes one lap in 74 seconds. The lap is 3.3 km.

(a) Calculate the speed of the driver. Give your answer to 2 significant figures.

speed = ?, distance = 3.3 km = 3300 m, t = 74 s ...................................

speed = distance ÷ time ...............................................    **(2 marks)**

(b) State the displacement of driver as they complete one lap

Since the driver is back at the start the displacement is ...............................    **(1 mark)**

(c) State the average velocity of the driver

.....................................................................................    **(1 mark)**

> Velocity = displacement ÷ time

4  A train travels on a straight track with a velocity of 40 km/h. State the velocity if it travels **back** along the same track at twice the speed.

Twice the speed = 2 × 40 =

> How do you show the direction has changed?

Velocity = ...............................................    **(2 marks)**

5  A car has the same acceleration and deceleration. If the acceleration is 5 m/s², state the deceleration.

> Guided

.....................................................................................    **(1 mark)**

6  A toy car races round a circular track at a constant speed. State and explain whether the velocity is constant.

> Is velocity a scalar or a vector? Write a definition as part of your answer and link to question.

Velocity is not constant.

Velocity has both size and direction (velocity is a ...................).

Since the direction is changing, the ........................ is changing.    **(3 marks)**

167

# Speed, distance and time

**1** State which of the following are units of speed.

☐ **A** m/s

☐ **B** m/s$^2$

☐ **C** km

☐ **D** km/h

> The '/' symbol in the units means divided by. If you ever forget a formula, the units can help you remember it.

(1 mark)

**2** The distance/time graph shows a walker's journey.

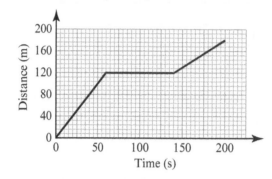

(a) Describe the motion of the walker between 60 s and 140 s.

............................................................................................................ (1 mark)

**Maths skills**

(b) Calculate the speed between 140 s and 200 s.

Speed = change in distance ÷ time taken

Speed = (180 – 120) ÷ (200 – 140) = ................................................. m/s  **(2 marks)**

(c) Calculate the average speed of the walker's journey.

............................ **(2 marks)**

**3** A light year is the distance light travels in a year. The speed of light is $3 \times 10^8$ m/s. Calculate the distance light travels in one year to two significant figures. (One year = 365 days.)

............................ **(3 marks)**

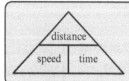

> Rearrange the equation for speed to make the distance travelled the subject of the equation. (You can use an equation triangle if you find this difficult.)

# Equations of motion

1  In the equations of motion, letters are used to represent each of the quantities. State the quantity each of these letters represents.

$v$ = ................................................

$u$ = ................................................

$x$ = ................................................                    **(1 mark)**

2  A car starts from rest at traffic lights and accelerates to 15 m/s in 3 seconds. Calculate the car's acceleration.

$u = 0$, $v = 15$ m/s, $t = 3$ s, $a = ?$

$a = \frac{v-u}{t}$                    ............................. **(3 marks)**

> Write down all the quantities you know and the ones you want to work out. This will help you decide which equation to use.

3  In an emergency stop a car leaves tyre marks on the road 70 m long. Calculate the car's initial velocity assuming the car has a deceleration of 6.5 m/s². State your answer to two significant figures.

$a = -6.5$ m/s², $u = ?$, $v = 0$ m/s, $x = 70$ m

$v^2 - u^2 = 2 \times a \times x$                    ................................. **(3 marks)**

> - Since it is a deceleration: $a = -6.5$ m/s².
> - Since it is $v^2 - u^2$, both sides of the equation are negative which means you can make them both positive. This is important because you want $v$ and not $v^2$.

4  A plane needs to achieve a velocity of 234 km/h to take off.

(a) Show that the take-off velocity is 65 m/s.

...........................

(b) Calculate the average acceleration of the plane if it takes 42 seconds to achieve take-off velocity.

...........................

(c) Calculate the minimum length the runway can be for take off to two significant figures.

...........................  **(7 marks)**

> To make $x$ the subject of the equation, divide both sides of the equation by $2a$.

# Velocity/time graphs

**1** In a theme park ride, the cars accelerate from 0 to 34 m/s in 2 seconds. It then takes 8 seconds for them to stop.

(a) Calculate the acceleration for the first 2 seconds.

$u = 0$, $v = 34$ m/s, $t = 2$ s, $a = ?$

$a = \frac{v - u}{t}$

............................ **(2 marks)**

(b) Sketch a velocity/time graph of the ride on the axes below assuming acceleration constant.

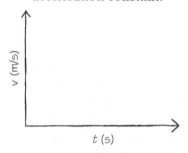

> The numbers on the axes are not needed on a sketch graph, but they may help you to draw the correct shape.

**(3 marks)**

**2** This velocity/time graph shows how the velocity of an athlete changes as they run along a straight track.

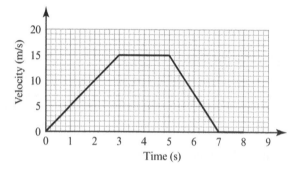

(a) Calculate the acceleration of the athlete in the first 3 seconds.

............................ **(2 marks)**

(b) Calculate the distance travelled by the runner in the first 5 seconds.

............................ **(3 marks)**

> The area under the graph is made of two shapes: a triangle and a rectangle. Calculate the area of each and add them together.

(c) Calculate the acceleration between 5 and 7 seconds.

............................ **(3 marks)**

# Determining speed

1 Complete the table showing typical speeds for different activities.

| Activity | Speed in m/s |
|---|---|
| Running | 3 |
| Swimming | |
| Light breeze | |
| Commuter train | 55 |

> Learn typical speeds for a range of activities, such as walking, driving and train rides, then you can estimate others from those.

**(2 marks)**

2 Describe the measurements you would need to take to calculate the speed of a car between lampposts on a road.

You could use a stopwatch to measure the ......................................................

..............................................................................................

..............................................................................................  **(2 marks)**

3 While watching a horse race a student estimates the horse can reach its top speed in less than 5 seconds. A horse can run at about 30 mph. Estimate the acceleration of a racehorse and compare this with acceleration of free fall.

..............................................................................................

..............................................................................................

..............................................................................................  **(3 marks)**

> • The speed in m/s is approximately half the speed in mph.
> • In a compare question you have to say if the acceleration is the same, less or greater than the acceleration of free fall.

4 Describe and explain how you could use light gates to calculate the speed of a falling ball. You should include any additional equipment you need. Suggest a source of uncertainty in this experiment.

..............................................................................................

..............................................................................................

..............................................................................................

..............................................................................................  **(4 marks)**

5 The diagram shows a speed camera. The camera takes two photos a few milliseconds apart if a car is speeding. Explain how the police can use the two photos and the markings in the road to calculate the speed of the car.

......................................................

......................................................

..............................................................................................

..............................................................................................  **(3 marks)**

> To calculate the speed the police need to know the time and the distance. How can they get that information from the photos?

171

# Newton's first law

1   Force diagrams show the size and direction of forces acting on objects.

(a) Draw and label a force diagram for a book resting on a table.   **(3 marks)**

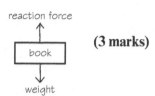
reaction force
book
weight

(b) Draw and label a force diagram for a skydiver falling at a constant speed through the air.

Skydiver

> • The length of the arrow represents the magnitude of the force.
> • The direction of the arrow represents the direction of the force.

**(3 marks)**

2   The diagram shows an object initially at rest. Two forces A and B are then applied to the object. The table shows the sizes of these forces in each experiment.

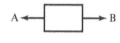
A ←☐→ B

Complete the table below. The first line has been done for you.

| Force A (N) | Force B (N) | Resultant force (N) | Direction of resultant force | Description of movement |
|---|---|---|---|---|
| 50 | 100 | 50 | To the right | Accelerating to the right |
| 75 | 5 | 70 | To the left | |
| 100 | 100 | | | |

**(2 marks)**

3   The graph below shows the velocity/time graph for a car. The car experiences a thrust force from the engine and a drag force from friction and air resistance. Describe and explain the motion of the car:

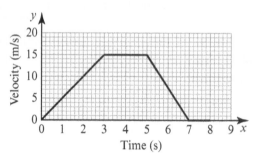

(a) in the first three seconds.

The car is accelerating at a constant rate. This means the thrust must be greater

than the drag   **(2 marks)**

(b) between 3 and 5 seconds.

The car is .........................................................................................

.................................................................................................   **(2 marks)**

(c) between 5 and 7 seconds.

.................................................................................................

.................................................................................................   **(2 marks)**

> In a 'describe and explain' question you must describe the motion first then explain, using your knowledge of forces.

# Newton's second law

**1** Identify the situations where the forces acting are unbalanced.

☐ A car driving at 30 mph along a straight road.

☐ A plane landing on a runway.

☐ A bike accelerating from the lights.

☐ A swimmer swimming at their top speed.

> If the forces acting on an object are unbalanced then it will accelerate or change direction.

**(2 marks)**

**2** Calculate the resultant force that causes a 5 kg mass to accelerate by 2 m/s².

$F = ?, m = 5\,kg, a = 2\,m/s^2$

$F = ma$

$F =$ ............................................................................................... **(2 marks)**

**3** A space shuttle has a mass of 2000 tonnes and the resultant force at launch is 10 million newtons. Calculate the initial acceleration of the space shuttle.

$F = 10 \times 10^6\,N, m = 2\,000\,000\,kg, a = ?$

.............................. **(3 marks)**

> 1 tonne = 1000 kg
> $F = ma$
> Divide both sides of the equation by $m$ to change the subject of the formula (or use the equation triangle).
>

**4** A force of 10 N accelerates a remote control car. The friction acting on the car is 6 N and the car has a mass of 500 g. Calculate the acceleration of the car.

$m = 500\,g = 0.5\,kg, a = ?,$ Resultant force $= ?$

.............................. **(3 marks)**

> In $F = ma$, the $F$ is the resultant force. Start by calculating the resultant force.

**5** A car accelerates along a road at a constant rate of 1.5 m/s². The resultant force acting on the car is 1.7 kN. Calculate the mass of the car. Give your answer to three significant figures.

.........................................................................................................................

.........................................................................................................................

.............................. **(3 marks)**

> • Identify the quantities you have been given.
> • Make sure they are in SI units.
> • Use the triangle to rearrange the equation.

# Weight and mass

**1** State the definition for the quantities below. State whether the quantity is a vector or a scalar.

(a) Mass

Mass is a measure of the amount of matter contained in a 3D space

Mass is a scalar quantity

**(1 mark)**

(b) Weight

............................................................................................................................

............................................................................................................................ **(1 mark)**

**2** Complete this table.

Maths skills

| Mass of object | Gravitational field strength (N/kg) | Weight (N) |
|---|---|---|
| 5 kg | 26 | 5 × 26 = |
| 10 kg | 1.6 | |
| 100 g | 3.6 | |

**(3 marks)**

In the equation $W = mg$, the mass must be in kg. (There are 1000 g in 1 kg.)

**3** A student writes the following in their book: "This rock weighs 10 kg on Earth, but it would weigh less on the moon because the gravitational field strength is less."

Guided

Identify and correct the physics mistake given in this description.

............................................................................................................................

............................................................................................................................ **(2 marks)**

**4** On Earth an astronaut weighs 1200 N. On planet X their weight is 420 N.

(a) Show that the mass of the astronaut is 120 kg. $g = 10$ N/kg on Earth.

Maths skills

$W = 1200$ N, $m = ?$, $g = 10$ N/kg

$W = m \times g$. Divide both sides of the equation by $g$

............................ **(2 marks)**

(b) Calculate the gravitational field strength on planet X.

............................ **(2 marks)**

- $W = mg$
- Divide both sides of the equation by $m$.

# Force and acceleration

A student investigates how changing the mass of the trolley affects its acceleration down a slope. The diagram below shows how they set up their apparatus.

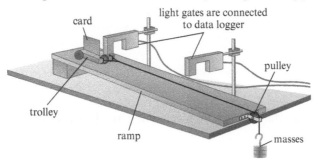

(a) State the independent variable in this investigation.

............................................................................................................................ **(1 mark)**

(b) State one control variable in this investigation.

............................................................................................................................ **(1 mark)**

(c) Explain why one end of the ramp is propped up.

............................................................................................................................

............................................................................................................................ **(2 marks)**

> The falling mass needs to be the only unbalanced force acting on the trolley. What other force could be acting on the trolley as it rolls?

(d) The falling mass provides the force on the trolley in the investigation. Calculate the force pulling on the trolley if the falling mass is 200 g.

$w = ?, g = 10 \,N/kg, m = 200g =$

.............................. **(2 marks)**

Below is part of the table the student recorded their results in. The timing card on the trolley is 10 cm long.

| Mass of trolley (kg) | Time through light gate A (s) | Velocity at A (cm/s) | Time through light gate B (s) | Velocity at B (cm/s) | Time between light gates (s) | Acceleration (cm/s²) |
|---|---|---|---|---|---|---|
| 1.0 | 0.488 | 20.5 | 0.120 | 83.3 | 2.5 | |

(e) Complete the table by calculating the acceleration of the trolley. Give your answer to two significant figures.

$a = \frac{v-u}{t}, v = 83.3, u = 20.5, t = 2.5s$    .............................. **(3 marks)**

(f) Explain how the investigation could be adapted to investigate how changing the accelerating force affects acceleration of the trolley.

............................................................................................................................

............................................................................................................................

............................................................................................................................ **(3 marks)**

# Circular motion

1 State the force providing the centripetal force on the Earth as it orbits the Sun.
Tick **one** box.

☐ **A** tension

☐ **B** friction

☐ **C** gravitational

☐ **D** electrostatic

**(1 mark)**

2 State the force providing the centripetal force when an electron orbits a nucleus.
Tick **one** box.

☐ **A** tension

☐ **B** friction

☐ **C** gravitational

☐ **D** electrostatic

**(1 mark)**

3 The diagram shows a rollercoaster doing a loop. State which arrow on the diagram shows the direction of the centripetal force. Tick **one** box.

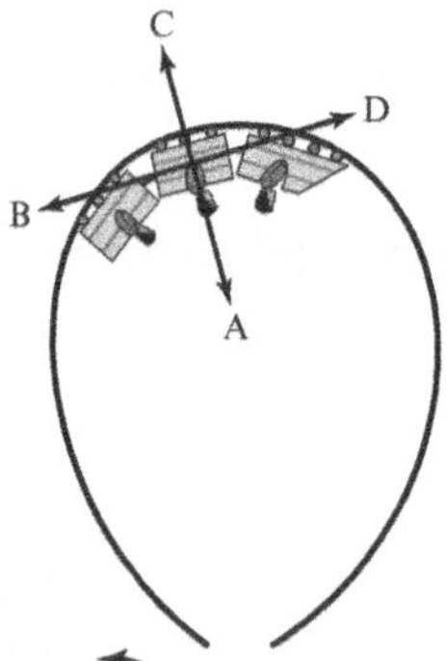

☐ **A**

☐ **B**

☐ **C**

☐ **D**

**(1 mark)**

4 An apple is tied to a piece of string by its stalk and spun in a circle. The string breaks. Draw an arrow to show the direction the apple will move the moment the string breaks. Explain your decision using Newton's first law.

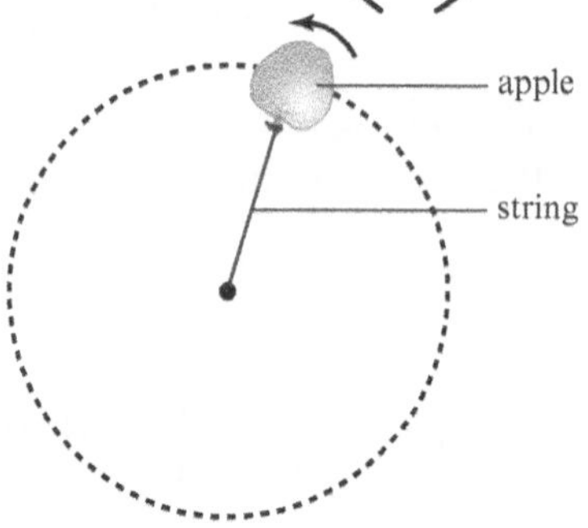

When the string breaks there is no resultant force

keeping the apple moving in a circle.....................

..................................................................

..................................................................  **(3 marks)**

> Don't just quote Newton's first law, as that won't get you the marks. Remember to apply it to the question.

5 Explain why there must be a resultant force acting on a car as it turns a corner at a constant speed.

Velocity is a vector quantity, since direction is changing, ...............................

..................................................................

..................................................................

..................................................................  **(4 marks)**

> • Velocity is a vector quantity.
> • Look back at Newton's first law to explain whether the forces are balanced or unbalanced.

# Momentum and force

 **1** A car has a mass of 1200 kg and is moving at 12 m/s. Calculate the momentum of the car. State the units.

$m = 1200$ kg, $v = 12$ m/s, momentum = ?

momentum = mass × velocity

.............................. **(2 marks)**

> The units for momentum are the units of mass (kg) multiplied by the units for velocity (m/s).

 **2** Crash mats in the school gym are designed to reduce the impact force when people land on them. Why is this? Tick **one** box.

☐ **A** They reduce the time taken to stop.

☐ **B** They reduce the change in momentum.

☐ **C** They increase the time taken to stop.

☐ **D** They increase the change in momentum.

> Remember:
> $\text{force} = \dfrac{\text{change in momentum}}{\text{time}}$

**(1 mark)**

 **3** A horse (mass = 500 kg) and a person (mass = 100 kg) both have the same momentum. Explain whether they both have the same velocity.

The horse has five times the mass of the person ..........................................

............................................................................................ **(3 marks)**

> Remember to link back to the equation for momentum in your answer.

 **4** During a kick, a football accelerates from 0 to 30 m/s and has a mass of 450 g. The football is in contact with the boot for 0.05 s. Calculate the force on the ball from the footballer's kick.

$u = 0$ m/s, $v = 30$ m/s, $m = 450g = 0.45$ kg, $t = 0.05$ s

$\text{force} = \dfrac{mv - mu}{t}$

.............................. **(2 marks)**

 **5** Crumple zones on a car are designed to crumple when the car is in an accident. Explain how the crumple zone reduces the impact force on the car.

............................................................................................

............................................................................................

............................................................................................ **(3 marks)**

> • The question is worth three marks so try to make three points in your answer.
> • It will help to refer back to the equation when planning your answer:
> $\text{force} = \dfrac{\text{change in momentum}}{\text{time}}$

# Newton's third law

**1** State which of the following are examples of Newton's third law.

☐ **A** The gravitational pull of the Earth on a book and the gravitational pull of the book on the Earth.

☐ **B** Your weight and the reaction force of the floor on you.

☐ **C** The thrust of a car engine and the drag force acting on the car.

☐ **D** Pushing down on a table and the table pushing back.

**(2 marks)**

**2** Define Newton's third law.

...................................................................................................................................

...................................................................................................................................  **(2 marks)**

**3** To jump up in the air a kangaroo has to first push down on the ground with its powerful back legs. Explain, using Newton's third law, how the kangaroo is able to jump up.

The kangaroo pushes down and the Earth pushes back with an equal and ...............

...................................................................................................................................  **(2 marks)**

> • The Earth has a much greater inertial mass than the kangaroo.
> • For the same force, which has the greater acceleration, the kangaroo or the Earth?

**4** A car travelling at 15 m/s with a mass of 1500 kg bumps into a stationary car of mass 1000 kg. The cars are stuck together after the collision and keep moving forward.

**Maths skills**

(a) Calculate the total momentum before the collision.

Momentum before: Car 1: $u_1$ = 15 m/s, $m_1$ = 1500 kg, Car 2 $u_2$ = 0 m/s, $m_2$ = 1000 kg

Total momentum before = momentum of car 1 + momentum of car 2

.............................  **(2 marks)**

(b) Calculate the initial velocity of the two cars stuck together after the collision.

Conservation of momentum .................................................................................

...................................................................................................................................  **(3 marks)**

> • As the two cars are now stuck together you can consider them as one object with a mass of 2500 kg.
> • To change the subject of the equation simply divide both sides by mass.

**5** An astronaut is stationary and floating in a weightless environment. They throw an apple to a second astronaut. Describe and compare the motion of the astronaut and the apple after the apple is thrown.

...................................................................................................................................

...................................................................................................................................

...................................................................................................................................  **(3 marks)**

> What was the momentum of the astronaut and the apple before the apple was thrown? How can momentum be conserved?

# Human reaction time

1 Human reaction time is the time between a stimulus occurring and a response.

(a) State **one** factor that increases human reaction time.

Tiredness increases human reaction time.                                    **(1 mark)**

(b) State **one** factor that decreases human reaction time.

...................................................................................................................... **(1 mark)**

**Maths skills**

2 A student wishes to compare the reaction times of their teacher with a student in the class.

(a) Describe a simple experiment they could perform using a ruler to measure the reaction times.

Hold a ruler just above the test subject's hand ...............................................

...................................................................................................................... **(2 marks)**

(b) Explain why you need two people to complete this test.

......................................................................................................................

...................................................................................................................... **(1 mark)**

The student took five results. The table below shows their results.

| | Distance ruler dropped (cm) | | | | | |
| | Trial | Trial | Trial | Trial | Trial | Average |
|---|---|---|---|---|---|---|
| **Student** | 16.4 | 14.8 | 15.5 | 15.3 | 14.8 | 15 |
| **Teacher** | 25.2 | 18.4 | 16.3 | 12.7 | 9.9 | |

(c) Calculate the average distance dropped for the teacher. Give your answer to two significant figures.



.............................. **(2 marks)**

(d) The student finds a formula to calculate the reaction time from the distance the ruler dropped. Calculate the student's reaction time. Give your answer to two significant figures.

$$\text{time}^2 \text{ (s)} = \frac{\text{distance}}{500}$$



.............................. **(2 marks)**

> Don't forget to square root your answer to find the reaction time.

(e) The teacher has a reaction time of 0.18 s. Calculate how far the teacher would travel in their car driving at 13 m/s between seeing an obstacle in the road and applying the brakes. Give your answer to two significant figures.

Distance = ?, speed = 13 m/s, time = 0.18 s

Distance = speed × time

.............................. **(3 marks)**

> Before a driver applies the brakes they have to react. To calculate the distance the car moves, use the reacton time and the speed of the car.

# Stopping distances

**1** Which of these is the correct definition for thinking distance? Tick **one** box.

☐ **A** Distance a car takes to stop

☐ **B** Distance travelled while the driver reacts

☐ **C** Time taken to react

☐ **D** Time between seeing and reacting to obstacle **(1 mark)**

**2** Which of the following increases braking distance? Tick **one** box.

☐ **A** The driver being tired

☐ **B** The driver being distracted

☐ **C** Car carrying more passengers

☐ **D** Driving at a slower speed **(1 mark)**

**3** Define the stopping distance of a car.

Stopping distance = thinking distance + ..................................................... **(2 marks)**

**4** A car moves at a constant speed. Explain how and why the stopping distance changes if the driver is tired.

The thinking distance will ..................................................................................

.................................................................................................................. **(2 marks)**

**5** A car driver sees a cat on the road. The driver makes an emergency stop. The graph shows the velocity of the car from the moment the driver sees the cat to the moment the car stops.

(a) State the driver's reaction time.

.......................................................... 

(b) Calculate the stopping distance of the car. **(1 mark)**

.......................................................... **(3 marks)**

> How can you calculate distance from a velocity/time graph? – See page 170.

(c) Suggest a value for the stopping distance if the car was travelling at twice the velocity when the driver saw the cat. Explain your answer.

..................................................................................................................

..................................................................................................................

..................................................................................................................

.................................................................................................................. **(4 marks)**

> Consider how a faster velocity will change both the thinking distance and the braking distance.

# Extended response – Motion and forces

**Practical skills**

Describe how a student should carry out an investigation to see how changing the mass of a trolley affects its acceleration.

> Your answer should include:
> - a labelled apparatus diagram
> - the measurements needed and the equipment used to make those measurements
> - the independent, dependent and control variables
> - a clear method
> - how to calculate acceleration.

........................................................................................................

........................................................................................................

........................................................................................................

........................................................................................................

........................................................................................................

........................................................................................................

........................................................................................................

........................................................................................................

........................................................................................................

........................................................................................................

........................................................................................................

........................................................................................................

........................................................................................................

........................................................................................................

........................................................................................................

........................................................................................................

........................................................................................................

........................................................................................................

........................................................................................................

........................................................................................................

........................................................................................................

........................................................................................................

........................................................................................................

**(6 marks)**

# Energy stores and transfers

**1** Explain what is meant by conservation of energy.

Energy cannot be created or destroyed it can only be transferred from ...........

................................................................................................................... **(2 marks)**

**2** The diagram below shows a Sankey diagram for an energy-efficient light bulb.

(a) Complete the diagram by adding the value for the energy transferred by light.

25 J supplied each second

energy transferred by light every second ...................... J

6 J   energy transferred by heat every second

**(1 mark)**

(b) Older style light bulbs were more wasteful of energy. Suggest how the values for the Sankey diagram might be different for an older style lamp.

The energy transferred by light would be lower and the energy transferred by

heating would be...........................................................................................

................................................................................................................... **(2 marks)**

> Dissipated energy is transferred to the thermal store of the surroundings.
> A less efficient device will often increase the thermal store more.

**3** Sketch a Sankey diagram to show the energy transfers for an electric kettle bringing water to the boil. The input energy is 800 J and the energy transferred to the thermal store of the water is 720 J. Label the inputs and output and fill in the values.

**(3 marks)**

**4** Analyse the changes in the way energy is stored in a car driving on a road when the driver applies the brakes and comes to a standstill.

The fuel is a store of ..................... which is transferred to ................... As the

car brakes the ................. store decreases. This ................. is transferred to

the ...........................................

**(3 marks)**

**5** Analyse the changes in the way energy is stored when a car accelerates at a constant rate.

...................................................................................................................

...................................................................................................................

................................................................................................................... **(2 marks)**

# Efficient heat transfer

**1** A firm sells insulation for new houses. They have two insulation materials for sale at the same cost. The thermal conductivity of the two materials is shown below.

|  | Thermal conductivity (W/m K) |
|---|---|
| Insulation A | 0.037 |
| Insulation B | 0.032 |

(a) State which material, A or B, is the better insulator and explain why.

Insulation B because it has ...................................................................

......................................................................................................... **(2 marks)**

(b) Suggest a second factor the buyer should consider when deciding between the two insulating materials.

.........................................................................................................

......................................................................................................... **(1 mark)**

> The rate of thermal energy transfer depends on the temperature difference across the material, what the material is made from and one other thing.

**2** Older houses were built with a cavity between the inner and outer walls. It is possible to fill this cavity with a foam which sets after it has been injected into the walls. Explain why a householder would want to have the cavity filled with insulation.

Foam contains many small air pockets ...................................................

......................................................................................................... **(2 marks)**

**3** A wind turbine transfers 800 J electrically for every 2000 J of kinetic energy.

(a) Determine how much energy is wasted by the wind turbine as heat and sound.

......................................................................................................... **(1 mark)**

(b) Calculate the percentage efficiency of the wind turbine.

Efficiency = ?, useful energy transferred = 800 J, total energy in = 2000 J

Efficiency = (useful energy transferred ÷ total energy in) × 100% .....................

Efficiency = ............................................................................................ **(2 marks)**

**4** A motor has an efficiency of 30%. The motor is used to lift a weight from the floor. The useful energy transferred by the motor is 900 J.

Calculate the total electrical energy transferred to the motor.

Efficiency (%) = (useful energy transferred ÷ total energy in) × 100% ..............

.........................................................................................................

.........................................................................................................

......................................................................................................... **(2 marks)**

> • Efficiency is a ratio and is often expressed as a percentage.
> • It can also be expressed as a decimal, for example, 50% efficient is an efficiency of 0.5.

# Energy resources

1  The main energy resources include both renewable and non-renewable.

(a)  State the definition of a renewable resource and give an example.

Renewable energy resources will not run out. An example is ............................. **(2 marks)**

(b)  State the definition of a non-renewable resource and give an example.

................................................................................................................

................................................................................................................ **(2 marks)**

2  Biofuels are often described as carbon neutral. Explain what this statement means and explain whether or not the statement is accurate.

When biofuels are burned they release the same amount of carbon dioxide they

................................................................................................................ **(2 marks)**

3  In remote areas, speed signs are sometimes powered by solar panels. The panel charges a battery so the sign works continuously.

**Maths skills**

(a)  The solar panel is 40 cm long and 30 cm wide. Calculate the area of the solar panel.

.............................. **(1 mark)**

YOUR SPEED

26

(b)  Each second, 0.14 J of energy from the Sun reaches 1 cm² of the panel. Calculate the total amount of energy reaching the whole screen in 1 second.

.............................. **(2 marks)**

> If the area of the panel were 1 cm² the panel would receive 0.14 J.
> If the area were 2 cm² the panel would receive 2 × 0.14 J = 0.28 J.

(c)  The efficiency of the solar panel is 0.15. Calculate the energy transferred to electricity each second by the solar panel.

.............................. **(2 marks)**

> The energy received by the panel from the Sun is the total energy supplied to the solar panel.

(d)  A company selling these signs suggests that a wind turbine can be installed as a back up. Explain why you might need an alternative energy resource.

................................................................................................................

................................................................................................................ **(1 mark)**

# Patterns of energy use

1 Describe the causes for the increase in the world's energy use over the last 100 years.

Increased population growth .................................................................................

.......................................................................................................................

....................................................................................................................... **(3 marks)**

> There are three marks so try to make three points in your answer – you could use bullet points.

2 Explain why many governments are investing in renewable energy resources.

Burning fossil fuels releases carbon dioxide, which is ....................................

....................................................................................................................... **(2 marks)**

3 There are many teams currently working on the challenges faced by starting a colony on Mars.

(a) Describe what the energy requirements would be for a Mars colony.

The colonists would need .................................... to power their equipment

and for transport. **(2 marks)**

> In a question like this you could also give examples, e.g., energy is required to maintain the atmosphere in the living spaces, or to maintain conditions for growing food.

(b) When deciding on energy resources to take to Mars suggest what the colonists would have to consider.

Renewable resources as deliveries from Earth would take too long, but any source

would need back-up as it will not be possible to survive without ........................

....................................................................................................................... **(2 marks)**

> • 'Suggest' questions expect you to apply your knowledge to come up with some ideas, e.g., mass and size of materials needed to build the resource.
> • Can you think of any more considerations?

4 The UK has a larger population, but uses less energy than it did in the 1970s. Suggest how this is possible.

Guided

.......................................................................................................................

....................................................................................................................... **(2 marks)**

5 Describe and explain how patterns in the world's energy use are likely to change over the next 100 years.

.......................................................................................................................

.......................................................................................................................

....................................................................................................................... **(3 marks)**

> Start by considering whether the demand will increase and if it does how the sources will change.

# Potential and kinetic energy

**1** A box of mass 20 kg is lifted onto a shelf 1.5 m high. Calculate the increase in the gravitational potential store of the box. ($g$ = 10 N/kg)

$m$ = 20 kg, $h$ = 1.5 m, $g$ = 10 N/kg, GPE = ?

GPE = $m \times g \times h$

.............................. **(1 mark)**

> Write out the information given as this may help you to remember the equation.

**2** A horse of mass 450 kg runs at 8 m/s. Calculate the kinetic energy of the horse. Give your answer in standard form and to two significant figures.

$m$ = 450 kg, $v$ = 8 m/s, kinetic energy = ?

kinetic energy = $\frac{1}{2} \times m \times v^2$

.............................. **(2 marks)**

**3** A ball of mass 800 g increases its gravitational potential energy store by 24 J as it is thrown up into the air. Calculate the maximum height the ball was thrown to.

$m$ = 800 g = 0.8 kg, $h$ = ?, $g$ = 10 N/kg, GPE = 24 J

GPE = $m \times g \times h$

GPE ÷ ($m \times g$) = $h$

.............................. **(2 marks)**

> If you think you may have rearranged an equation incorrectly simply try your value for $h$ in the equation GPE = $mgh$ and check you get 24 J for GPE.

**4** A 1000 kg car has 84 500 J of kinetic energy. Calculate the speed of the car.

$m$ = 1000 kg, $v$ = ?, KE = 84 500 J

kinetic energy = $\frac{1}{2} \times m \times v^2$

.............................. **(2 marks)**

> • Divide both sides of the equation by $m$.
> • Multiply both sides of the equation by 2.
> • Don't forget that you need to square root this answer to get $v$.

**5** A rollercoaster starts from a height of 62 m.

(a) Show that the increase in gravitational potential energy of a 60 kg rider at the top of the rollercoaster is 37 200 J.

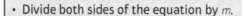

......................................................................................................

...................................................................................................... **(2 marks)**

(b) Assuming all energy from the rider's gravitational potential store is transferred to their kinetic energy store, calculate their speed at the bottom of the rollercoaster. Give your answer to two significant figures.

> If energy is conserved, KE = GPE

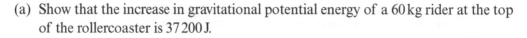

.............................. **(3 marks)**

# Extended response – Conservation of energy

A farmer in a remote part of the country is able to get a grant towards a renewable energy resource. Because of the position of their farm they have decided the choice is between a generator running on biogas or a wind turbine. Assess the two renewable resources and decide which would be the best choice for the farmer.

> • In 'assess' questions, you have to consider all the factors and make a judgement about which would be the best choice.
>
> • It might help to think about each resource in turn and then to make a judgement. There will not be a right choice, you simply have to support your choice.

You need to consider:

- Advantages of biogas
- Advantages of wind turbine
- Disadvantages of biogas
- Disadvantages of wind turbine

Then give a final conclusion.

.............................................................................................................................................

.............................................................................................................................................

.............................................................................................................................................

.............................................................................................................................................

.............................................................................................................................................

.............................................................................................................................................

.............................................................................................................................................

.............................................................................................................................................

.............................................................................................................................................

.............................................................................................................................................

.............................................................................................................................................

.............................................................................................................................................

.............................................................................................................................................

.............................................................................................................................................

.............................................................................................................................................

.............................................................................................................................................

.............................................................................................................................................

.............................................................................................................................................

.............................................................................................................................................

..................................................................................................................   **(6 marks)**

# Waves

**1** State the definition of a wave.

Waves transfer energy without ..................................................................

.................................................................................................. **(2 marks)**

**2** The diagram below shows a water wave.

(a) What is the amplitude of the wave?
Tick **one** box.

☐ **A**  10.0 cm     ☐ **C**  5.0 cm

☐ **B**  2.1 cm     ☐ **D**  1.1 cm

**(1 mark)**

> The amplitude is the maximum distance of the wave above its rest position.

(b) What is the wavelength of the wave?
Tick **one** box.

☐ **A**  10.0 cm     ☐ **C**  5.0 cm

☐ **B**  2.1 cm     ☐ **D**  1.1 cm

**(1 mark)**

> The wavelength is the distance between a point on the wave to the same position on the next wave.

(c) Water waves are transverse waves. Give one other example of a transverse wave.

.................................................................................................. **(1 mark)**

(d) Give an example of a longitudinal wave and describe how the particles move in a longitudinal wave.

..................................................................................................

.................................................................................................. **(2 marks)**

**3** Describe evidence that shows that with water it is the wave that moves and not the water.

If you drop a ball onto a pond the ball ...................................................

.................................................................................................. **(2 marks)**

**4** The diagram shows a wave.

(a) Each horizontal square represents 0.2 s.
Determine the time period of the wave.

.................................................................... **(2 marks)**

> The time period is the time taken for the wave to pass a point.

(b) Calculate the frequency of the wave and state the units.

> Frequency = 1 ÷ time period.

.......................................... **(2 marks)**

# Wave equations

**1** In the deep ocean a tidal wave can travel one kilometre in 4.2 s. Calculate the speed of the tidal wave and state the units.

$x = 1\,km = 1000\,m,\ t = 4.2\ s,\ v = ?$

$v = x \div t$

............................. **(2 marks)**

**2** A seismic wave has a frequency of 2 Hz and a wavelength of 2 km. Calculate the speed of the seismic wave through the Earth's crust.

$f = 2\ Hz,\ \lambda = 2\,km = 2000\,m,\ v = ?$

$v = f\lambda$

............................. **(2 marks)**

**3** At a fireworks display a student hears the bang of a firework 1.2 s after seeing the firework explode. Calculate the distance the student is from the display if the speed of sound in air is 330 m/s.

$t = 1.2\ s,\ v = 330\ m/s,\ x = ?$

$v = x \div t$

............................. **(2 marks)**

> To make distance (x) the subject of the equation, multiply both sides of the equation by time.

**4** Violet light has a wavelength of $4.0 \times 10^{-7}$ m and red light has a wavelength $7.0 \times 10^{-7}$ m. The speed of light is $3.0 \times 10^8$ m/s.

(a) Calculate the frequency of violet light. Give your answer to two significant figures.

$\lambda = 4.0 \times 10^{-7}\ m,\ v = 3.0 \times 10^8\ m/s,\ f = ?$

$v = f\lambda$ (divide both sides of the equation by $\lambda$)

$v \div \lambda = f$

............................. **(2 marks)**

(b) Calculate the frequency of red light. Give your answer to two significant figures.

............................. **(2 marks)**

**5** A surfer watches the waves coming onto the beach. They count five waves in 10 seconds. The waves have a velocity of 2 m/s. Calculate the wavelength of the wave.

$v = 2\ m/s,\ f = ?,\ \lambda = ?$

............................. **(3 marks)**

> • Frequency is the number of waves per second and is equal to 1 ÷ time period.
> • If there are five waves in 10 seconds what is the time period of one wave?

# Measuring wave velocity

**1** The diagram shows waves as they pass between two ladders. It takes 6 seconds for a wave to pass between the two ladders. Calculate the speed of the waves. Give your answer to two significant figures.

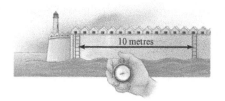

Time = 6s, distance = 10, speed = ?

Speed = distance ÷ time

Speed = ............................... **(2 marks)**

**2** A student stands 80 m in front of a cliff face and claps their hands. They can hear an echo and start to clap so that they clap at the same time as the echoes.

(a) The student claps eight times in 4 seconds. Calculate the time between claps.

Time between claps = time ÷ number of claps = 4 ÷ 8 = 0.5s  **(1 mark)**

(b) Explain why it is better to time several claps rather than the time between two claps.

The time between claps is very short ...............................................

................................................................................ **(1 mark)**

(c) Calculate the speed of sound in air.

Speed = ?, distance = time = 0.5s

speed = distance ÷ time

............................... **(2 marks)**

> The sound has travelled from the student to the cliff and back again to make an echo so the distance needs to be doubled.

**3** A student uses two microphones and an oscilloscope to measure the speed of sound in air. The microphones have been positioned so they are one wavelength apart. The frequency of the sound is 550 Hz. Calculate the speed of sound in air.

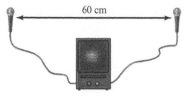

wavelength = 60 cm = 0.6 m, frequency = 550 Hz, speed = ?

speed = frequency × wavelength

............................... **(2 marks)**

**4** In an experiment to measure the speed of sound in a solid a sound pulse is sent down a plastic block. An oscilloscope records the time it takes to travel 0.5 m.

⟩Guided⟩

(a) The time taken from the oscilloscope is 0.29 ms. Calculate the speed of sound in the plastic block. Give your answer to two significant figures.

............................................................................... **(2 marks)**

(b) The speed of sound in steel is 5790 m/s. Explain why it would be difficult to measure the speed of sound in steel using this method. Calculate values to support your answer.

................................................................................

................................................................................

................................................................................ **(2 marks)**

# Waves and boundaries

**1** Classrooms are often noisy because of the many reflections of sound off the walls and floor of the room.

(a) State the name given to a sound reflection.

.......................................................................................................... **(1 mark)**

(b) A teacher suggests that introducing carpeting and cork wall displays to the classroom will reduce the noise level. Explain how this works.

The smooth classroom walls are good reflectors of sound waves ...................

..........................................................................................................

.......................................................................................................... **(2 marks)**

**2** Explain why the hands can be seen through the plastic bag when using an infrared camera.

Visible light is absorbed by the plastic but

infrared is ..................................................

..................................................

..................................................

.................................................. **(2 marks)**

**3** Complete the diagram below to show what happens to light as it enters and leaves glass. Explain your diagram.

The light slows down as ........................

..................................................

..................................................

..................................................

..........................................................................................................

.......................................................................................................... **(5 marks)**

**4** Explain why a bird that dives for fish might need to take refraction into account.

..........................................................................................................

.......................................................................................................... **(2 marks)**

> To see the fish, light has to have been reflected from the fish and come out of the water and into the bird's eye.

**5** Ultrasound is used to view unborn babies. A jelly is put on the body where the ultrasound transmitter will be placed. The jelly has a similar density to the body. Suggest why the jelly is needed.

..........................................................................................................

..........................................................................................................

.......................................................................................................... **(2 marks)**

> Waves are reflected at boundaries between materials. If the speeds in the two materials are very different there will be more reflection.

# Waves in fluids

**Practical skills**

**1** The diagram shows a ripple tank used to measure the speed of waves in water.

(a) Describe how the ripple tank is used to produce parallel waves of a suitable wavelength.

A motor is attached to a straight-edged dipper.

The motor ............ making the dipper ...............

The current through the motor is changed until the

.................................................................................... **(3 marks)**

(b) A student took a photo of the waves in the ripple tank. The photo is shown to the right. Use the photo to determine the approximate wavelength of the waves in the ripple tank. Tick **one** box.

☐ **A** 2 cm          ☐ **C** 4 cm

☐ **B** 3 cm          ☐ **D** 8 cm     **(1 mark)**

> • Find a start point where a wave lines up with the grid, for example, 10 cm.
> • Count the number of waves to the next clear point where a wave lies next to the grid.
> • Divide the distance by the number of wavelengths counted.

**Waves in a ripple tank**

(c) Describe how to determine the frequency of the waves.

....................................................................................

.................................................................................... **(2 marks)**

(d) The student determines the frequency to be 11 Hz. Calculate the speed of the waves in the ripple tank.

speed = ?, frequency = 11 Hz, wavelength = ................................................

speed = frequency × wavelength .................................................... **(2 marks)**

**2** To measure the speed of sound in a solid a suspended metal rod 40 cm long is hit with a hammer. The wavelength of the wave is equal to twice the length of the metal rod.

(a) Sound waves are longitudinal waves. Describe longitudinal waves.

....................................................................................

.................................................................................... **(1 mark)**

(b) The student records a peak frequency of 7.5 kHz using an app on their smart phone. Calculate the speed of sound in the rod.

.................................... **(3 marks)**

> • You have been given a way to calculate the wavelength of the wave and told the frequency.
> • Simply use the wave equation to calculate the speed of the sound wave.

# Extended response – Waves

Ripple tanks can be used to model the behaviour of all types of waves. Justify the use of ripple tanks to model both transverse and longitudinal waves.

> - 'Justify' questions are asking for evidence to support an idea – here, the idea that ripple tanks can be used to model all waves.
> - Start by considering what a wave is and describing the two types of waves.
> - Then explain what properties of a wave the ripple tank can show, for example, amplitude, wavelength, refraction, reflection.

Waves transfer energy without transferring matter. There are two types of waves

longitudinal and ........................................... In longitudinal waves the vibrations

of the particles are parallel to the direction of the wave, an example is ..................

............................................................................................................................

............................................................................................................................

............................................................................................................................

............................................................................................................................

............................................................................................................................

............................................................................................................................

............................................................................................................................

............................................................................................................................

............................................................................................................................

............................................................................................................................

............................................................................................................................

............................................................................................................................

............................................................................................................................

............................................................................................................................

............................................................................................................................

............................................................................................................................

............................................................................................................................

............................................................................................................................

............................................................................................................................

Conclusion: The ripple tank demonstrates wave behaviour such ...........................

............................................................................................................................

............................................................................................................................

............................................................................................................................

and allows you to understand terms such ........................................... of a wave.   **(6 marks)**

# Electromagnetic spectrum

1  The electromagnetic waves that make up the electromagnetic spectrum are all transverse waves.

(a) State **one** other property all the electromagnetic waves have in common.

..................................................................................................... **(1 mark)**

(b) The table below shows the electromagnetic spectrum in order of decreasing wavelength. Complete the table by filling in the gaps.

| Radio | | | Visible | | X-rays | |
|-------|--|--|---------|--|--------|--|

**(4 marks)**

> Use a mnemonic to help you remember the electromagnetic spectrum in order, e.g., **R**aging **M**artians **i**nvaded **V**enus **u**sing **X**-ray **g**uns.

(c) As you move from left to right on the table another property increases. State this property.

..................................................................................................... **(1 mark)**

> • speed = frequency × wavelength
> • If the speed is the same for all members of the electromagnetic spectrum, as the wavelength decreases the frequency must increase.

2  An infrared source has a wavelength of 1 mm and a frequency of 300 GHz. Calculate the speed of the wave, showing all your working.

**Maths skills**

$v = ?, \lambda = 1\,mm = 0.001\,m, f = 300\,GHz = 300 \times 10^9\,Hz$

$v = f\lambda$

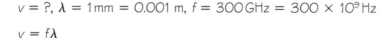 ............................... **(2 marks)**

3  Calculate the frequency of a microwave used in an oven if the wavelength is 12 cm. Speed of electromagnetic waves is $3 \times 10^8$ m/s. Write your answer in standard form.

**Maths skills**

$v = 3 \times 10^8\,m/s, \lambda = 12\,cm = 0.12\,m, f = ?$

$v = f\lambda$

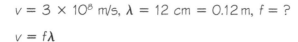 ............................... **(3 marks)**

> • Make $f$ the subject of the equation.
> • Divide both sides of the equation by $\lambda$.

4  A popular radio station has a frequency of 99.7 MHz. Calculate the wavelength of the signal given that the speed of an electromagnetic waves is $3 \times 10^8$ m/s.

**Maths skills**

............................... **(3 marks)**

> • M stands for Mega = $1 \times 10^6$.
> • To make $\lambda$ the subject of the equation divide both sides by $f$.

# Investigating refraction

A student is investigating refraction as light enters glass.

(a) Draw the normal and label the angle of incidence and angle of refraction on the diagram.

> The student is investigating refraction as light enters the glass. Draw the normal where the light enters the glass.

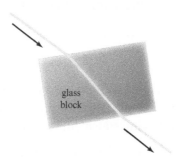

glass block

**(3 marks)**

(b) Describe how the student achieved a thin beam of light.

Use a single slit to obtain a single ray of light and place the slit near the end of

the ray box.                                                                **(1 mark)**

(c) Describe how to record the ray of light so that the angles can be measured.

Start by drawing crosses on the light ray and then ......................................

.................................................................................................... **(1 mark)**

(d) The student achieved the following results. Plot the results on the graph paper below and draw a line of best fit.

| Angle of incidence (°) | Angle of refraction (°) |
|:---:|:---:|
| 30 | 19 |
| 40 | 25 |
| 50 | 59 |
| 60 | 35 |
| 70 | 39 |
| 80 | 41 |

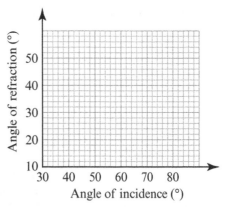

**(4 marks)**

> • Take care plotting the points – they will be checked.
> • Lines of best fit can be straight or curved – decide which you think best suits this data.

(e) Identify the anomalous result.

.................................................................................................... **(1 mark)**

(f) Describe the pattern of the result.

....................................................................................................

.................................................................................................... **(2 marks)**

# Wave behaviour

**1** State the name of the electromagnetic wave used to communicate with satellites.

.................................................................................................................................... **(1 mark)**

⟩Guided⟩

**2** When white light enters a glass prism it separates into the different colours or wavelengths. Red is refracted the least and violet the most. Decide which of the following statements is true. Tick **one** box.

☐ **A**   All the wavelengths are slowed down by the same amount as they enter the prism.

☐ **B**   The red wavelengths slow down the most as they enter the glass.

☐ **C**   The violet wavelengths slow down the most as they enter the glass.

☐ **D**   The wavelengths travel at $3 \times 10^8$ m/s in the glass.

> Remember refraction. Why does the light change direction? What would make the change in direction greater?

**3** A student states that all electromagnetic waves are the same. Discuss the extent to which you agree or disagree with this statement.

All electromagnetic waves travel at the same speed in a vacuum and can be reflected, refracted, transmitted or absorbed as they pass through materials. However, they

have a range of wavelengths ...................................................................................

....................................................................................................................................

....................................................................................................................................

.................................................................................................................................... **(4 marks)**

> Start by considering the similarities and differences and then decide whether you agree with the statement.

**4** Explain why the range for communication using radio waves is much greater than the range for microwave communication. It may help you to draw a diagram to explain your answer.

Microwaves can pass through the ionosphere. Since the Earth is curved, the waves can only be received by an aerial line of sight of the transmitter. This makes the

distances quite short. Radio waves are ...................................................................

....................................................................................................................................

.................................................................................................................... **(4 marks)**

# Dangers and uses

**1** The members of the electromagnetic spectrum have varying effects on living cells.

(a) Name the electromagnetic wave that does not cause any harm to living cells.

.................................................................................................................... **(1 mark)**

(b) State the names of **two** electromagnetic waves that cause mutations in living cells.

X-rays and ......................................................................................................

.................................................................................................................... **(2 marks)**

(c) Describe how the danger of an electromagnetic wave changes with frequency.

As the frequency increases the ..........................................................................

.................................................................................................................... **(1 mark)**

**2** Describe how gamma radiation can be used in medicine.

Gamma can be used to sterilise medical equipment and ........................................

.................................................................................................................... **(2 marks)**

**3** (a) X-rays are used to detect broken bones in a patient's body. Explain how an X-ray image works.

X-rays are transmitted through soft tissue, but are ..............................................

.................................................................................................................... **(2 marks)**

> The black areas on an X-ray image show where the film has been exposed to X-rays. White areas have not been exposed.

(b) The X-ray technician always leaves the room when the machine is on. Explain why they have to leave when you have your X-ray.

The technician does many X-rays every day and so is ..........................................

.................................................................................................................... **(2 marks)**

> • Consider how many times a day the technician uses the X-ray machine. Does that increase risk?
> • Think of it as similar to being caught in a mist – the longer you are in it the wetter you get.

**4** Microwave ovens and mobile phones both use microwaves. Microwave ovens need shielding. Use the information below to discuss whether mobile phones should have shielding.

|  | Frequency (GHz) | Power (W) |
|---|---|---|
| **Mobile phone** | 1.9 | 3 |
| **Microwave oven** | 2.5 | 900 |

.....................................

.....................................

.....................................

.....................................

> Points to consider:
> • Power is the rate of transfer of energy. The higher the power the faster energy is transferred.
> • How does harm to living cells relate to frequency?

....................................................................................................................

.................................................................................................................... **(3 marks)**

197

# Changes and radiation

**1** Describe what is meant by energy level in atoms.

Electrons can only have certain discrete energy levels. Protons and neutrons only

.................................................................................................................... **(2 marks)**

**2** The diagram shows the energy levels in an atom.

(a) Which answer represents the largest absorption
of radiation by an electron? Tick **one** box.

☐ **A** Jumping up from $n = 1$ to $n = 3$

☐ **B** Jumping down from $n = 3$ to $n = 1$

☐ **C** Jumping down from $n = 6$ to $n = 1$

☐ **D** Jumping up from $n = 1$ to $n = 6$

**(1 mark)**

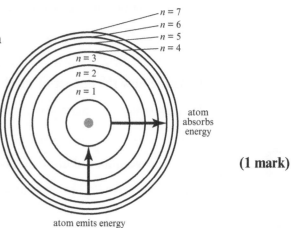

- To go up an electron must absorb energy.
- When an electron drops down it emits energy.

(b) Which answer represents the emission of the largest amount of radiation? Tick **one** box.

☐ **A** Jumping up from $n = 1$ to $n = 3$

☐ **B** Jumping down from $n = 3$ to $n = 1$

☐ **C** Jumping down from $n = 6$ to $n = 1$

☐ **D** Jumping up from $n = 1$ to $n = 6$

**(1 mark)**

(c) Which answer represents the emission of radiation with the highest frequency?
Tick **one** box.

☐ **A** Jumping up from $n = 1$ to $n = 3$

☐ **B** Jumping down from $n = 3$ to $n = 1$

☐ **C** Jumping down from $n = 6$ to $n = 1$

☐ **D** Jumping up from $n = 1$ to $n = 6$

Remember, the electromagnetic
waves with the highest frequency
have the highest energy.

**(1 mark)**

(d) Which answer represents the absorption of radiation with the longest wavelength?
Tick **one** box.

☐ **A** Jumping up from $n = 1$ to $n = 3$

☐ **B** Jumping down from $n = 3$ to $n = 1$

☐ **C** Jumping down from $n = 6$ to $n = 1$

☐ **D** Jumping up from $n = 1$ to $n = 6$

Remember the longest wavelength electromagnetic waves
have the lowest energy.

**(1 mark)**

**3** Some markings on banknotes are only visible under ultraviolet light. Explain, in terms
of energy levels, why we can see the markings under ultraviolet light when the eye can
only detect visible light.

The electrons in the ink used in the banknotes absorb the UV radiation. The electrons

then jump up to higher energy levels ........................................................................

..................................................................................................................................

.................................................................................................................. **(4 marks)**

- Visible light has less energy than UV light.
- Link this idea to the different energy levels in the atom.

# Extended response – Light and the electromagnetic spectrum

Comment on the use of gamma radiation in medicine despite the risks of cancer.

> A 'Comment' question requires you to summarise the information and present a conclusion.
> • Explain how gamma radiation is used.
> • Explain the risks of the use and how the risk is minimised.
> • Conclude if the risk is worth it.

..............................................................................................................

..............................................................................................................

..............................................................................................................

..............................................................................................................

..............................................................................................................

..............................................................................................................

..............................................................................................................

..............................................................................................................

..............................................................................................................

..............................................................................................................

..............................................................................................................

..............................................................................................................

..............................................................................................................

..............................................................................................................

..............................................................................................................

..............................................................................................................

..............................................................................................................

..............................................................................................................

..............................................................................................................

..............................................................................................................

..............................................................................................................

..............................................................................................................

..............................................................................................................

..............................................................................................................

..............................................................................................................

..............................................................................................................

..............................................................................................................

..............................................................................................................

**(6 marks)**

# Structure of the atom

**1** Complete the diagram by adding the correct labels to show the structure of the atom.

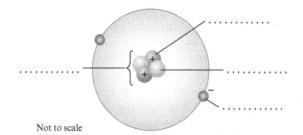

Not to scale

Remember:
• **p**rotons are **p**ositive
• **n**eutrons are **n**eutral

**(4 marks)**

**2** Complete the table below to show the relative mass and charge of the subatomic particles. The first row has been completed for you.

| Subatomic particle | Relative mass | Charge |
|---|---|---|
| Proton | 1 | +1 |
| Neutron |  | O |
| Electron | O/negligible |  |

**(4 marks)**

**3** An atom has a diameter of $10^{-10}$ m and the nucleus has a diameter of $10^{-15}$ m.

**Maths skills**

(a) Calculate how many times larger an atom is than a nucleus.

$1 \times 10^{-10} \div 1 \times 10^{-15} =$ ................................................................................. **(1 mark)**

On your calculator is a button labelled '×10ˣ'. This allows you to simply type in numbers in standard form. Type the number 1, then press the button then type in −10.

(b) A student is making a model and wishes to make it to scale. The nucleus has a diameter of 5 cm. Calculate the diameter of the atom if their model is to be made to scale.

............................ **(2 marks)**

The atom must be as many times larger as your answer to part (a).

(c) Suggest why atoms are never drawn to scale.

.......................................................................................................................... **(1 mark)**

**4** Scientists have made a motor $3.2 \times 10^{-9}$ m long. If the atoms were arranged side by side, calculate the minimum number of atoms long the motor could be.

............................ **(2 marks)**

You are expected to recall the diameter of an atom.

# Atoms and isotopes

1　The periodic table contains a list of elements. Each element is displayed with its mass and atomic number.

(a) State the meaning of the mass number of an element.

The mass number is the total number of .............. and .............. in the nucleus　**(1 mark)**

(b) State the meaning of the atomic number of an element.

The atomic number is .................................................................................

.................................................................................　**(1 mark)**

(c) Explain how you calculate the number of neutrons in a nucleus using the mass number and the atomic number.

.................................................................................

.................................................................................　**(1 mark)**

> The mass number is always the bigger number. To find the number of neutrons take the atomic number from the mass number.

2　These are the stable isotopes of magnesium.

$$^{24}_{12}\text{Mg} \quad ^{25}_{12}\text{Mg} \quad ^{26}_{12}\text{Mg}$$

(a) State the number of protons in a magnesium nucleus.

12 protons　**(1 mark)**

(b) Determine the number of neutrons in magnesium-26.

.................................................................................　**(2 marks)**

(c) Explain what an isotope is.

An isotope of an element has .................................................................

.................................................................................　**(1 mark)**

3　The element uranium (U) has 92 protons and 143 neutrons. Draw the symbol for uranium with the correct mass and atomic numbers.

**Guided**

**(3 marks)**

4　Chlorine appears on the periodic table as $^{35.5}_{17}\text{Cl}$. Suggest why the mass number is 35.5.

The mass number is an average, and for most atoms is approximately a whole number.

For chlorine, however ...............................................................　**(2 marks)**

# Atoms, electrons and ions

**1** Atoms contain three subatomic particles.

(a) State the name and charge of each subatomic particle found inside an atom.

In the nucleus you find protons, which are positive, and ...................................

.........................................................................................................................

......................................................................................................................... **(3 marks)**

(b) Explain why atoms are always neutral.

> This is a really important fact to know for both physics and chemistry. Make sure you learn it.

Protons have a charge of +1 and

electrons have a charge of ................................................................................ **(2 marks)**

**2** In an atom, electrons exist in distinct energy levels. When electrons move between levels they can emit or absorb radiation. Draw a diagram and explain what happens if an electron absorbs an electromagnetic wave.

>Gu ed

.........................................................................................................................

......................................................................................................................... **(2 marks)**

**3** A magnesium atom loses two electrons when it forms a magnesium ion. State the overall charge of the magnesium ion.

......................................................................................................................... **(2 marks)**

> Atoms are normally neutral. If they lose electrons they will have more protons than electrons. What will that do to the overall charge?

**4** (a) Explain how electrons can leave an atom.

The electrons can absorb enough energy to escape the pull of the nucleus or

......................................................................................................................... **(2 marks)**

(b) Suggest why gamma radiation is called ionising radiation and can damage living cells.

Gamma radiation has enough energy to help electrons to escape the pull of the

nucleus. This causes the atoms to become ................................................

.........................................................................................................................

......................................................................................................................... **(3 marks)**

> Molecules are made from atoms. What might happen to a molecule if its atoms are ionised?

# Ionising radiation

1 Describe the difference between beta-plus ($\beta+$) and beta-minus ($\beta-$) radiation.

Beta-minus radiation is a fast-moving electron and has a negative charge of –1.

Beta-plus is a ...............................................................................................

..............................................................................................................

..............................................................................................................   **(4 marks)**

2 Explain the difference between the key words radioactive and radiation.

A nucleus can be described as radioactive. It means it is unstable and will undergo

radioactive decay. Radiation is ...........................................................................

..............................................................................................................   **(2 marks)**

> You have met electromagnetic waves; they are all forms of radiation. They all transfer energy from one place to another. Why is a radioactive nucleus unstable? Because it wants to get 'rid' of some energy.

3 Explain why only some types of radiation are affected by magnetic fields.

Gamma and neutron radiation are not affected by magnetic fields. This is because

..............................................................................................................   **(1 mark)**

4 Describe an experiment you could perform to determine whether a radioactive source emitted alpha, beta or gamma radiation.

..............................................................................................................

..............................................................................................................

..............................................................................................................

..............................................................................................................   **(3 marks)**

> Remember alpha, beta and gamma have different properties. Which property could you easily compare to decide which type it is?

5 Suggest why alpha radiation only travels a few centimetres in air.

Alpha is a helium nucleus and has a charge of +2. ...........................................

..............................................................................................................

..............................................................................................................

..............................................................................................................   **(4 marks)**

> Ionising radiation has kinetic energy when it leaves the nucleus. When it ionises an atom it must lose energy. Why would alpha radiation lose its energy more quickly?

# Background radiation

**Maths skills**

1  The pie chart shows the sources of background radiation.

(a)  Name **one** natural source of background radiation.

..............................................................................

..............................................................................

**(1 mark)**

ground and
buildings
14.0%

medical
14.0%

nuclear
power
0.3%

radon gas
50.0%

cosmic rays
(from space)
10.0%

food and
drink
11.5%

other
0.2%

(b)  Determine the percentage of radiation that comes from man-made sources.

..............................................................................

..............................................................................

**(2 marks)**

> On this pie chart only two man-made sources have been identified.

(c)  Homes have much better insulation to reduce transfer of energy to the outside. This improved insulation has made radon gas in the home more of a problem. Suggest why this is.

Homes have less draughts due to double-glazing. This stops air from escaping.

This means ...................................................................... **(2 marks)**

The average radiation dose per year in the UK is 2.7 mSv.

(d)  Explain why this is only an average.

..............................................................................

..............................................................................

**(2 marks)**

> Think of all the sources of background radiation, will they be the same all over the UK?

(e)  Calculate the dose due to food and drink, in mSv.

.......................................   **(2 marks)**

> Food and drink represent 11.5% of the radiation. The 2.7 mSv represent 100%. You have to calculate 11.5% of 2.7 mSv.

2  For every hour of a long haul flight the radiation dose increases by 0.004 mSv. Explain whether this should be of concern to passengers and crew of an airplane.

Passengers are at less risk than the crew as they will be in the air for a lot less time.

However, you would have to fly ......................................................................

..............................................................................   **(3 marks)**

> The average dose is 2.7 mSv. Consider how much flying you would have to do to double your dose? Is this a problem? Are there other factors that affect your radiation dose?

# Measuring radioactivity

**1** State **two** methods of detecting radiation.

Photographic film and ........................................................................................

..............................................................................................................................

.............................................................................................................. **(2 marks)**

**2** Medical tracers often contain a gamma source. The syringes used to administer them have lead linings and are carried in lead containers. Explain why.

..............................................................................................................................

.............................................................................................................. **(2 marks)**

> The tracer is going to be injected into the patient. Who else might the lead linings protect and why are they at more risk?

**Maths skills**

**3** A student investigates a radioactive source. They want to see how much radiation it emits. They achieve the following data.

| | Count for 30 seconds | | | |
| --- | --- | --- | --- | --- |
| | **1** | **2** | **3** | **Mean count** |
| **Background count** | 10 | 8 | 12 | (10 + 8 + 12) ÷ 3 = |
| **Radioactive source (distance 10 cm)** | 90 | 78 | 85 | |

(a) Explain why the source is unlikely to be an alpha emitter.

Alpha can only travel a few centimetres in air so .................................................

.............................................................................................................. **(2 marks)**

(b) Explain why the student repeated their results.

Radiation is random and so repeating results improves the ...........................

.............................................................................................................. **(2 marks)**

(c) Calculate the mean background count and mean count for the radioactive source.



............................. **(2 marks)**

(d) The corrected count is the count from the source minus the background count. Calculate the corrected count for the radioactive source.

Corrected count = mean count – mean background count ............................

corrected count = ................................................................. **(1 mark)**

**4** Explain why a film badge has to have an open window.

The film badge has to detect all types of radiation. Gamma and beta can both

penetrate the plastic window, but ............................................................... **(2 marks)**

# Models of the atom

1 Explain why the discovery of the electron led to the 'plum pudding' model of the atom.

Atoms are neutral. An electron has a negative charge and is much smaller than an atom.

The new model ...............................................................................

................................................................................................... **(3 marks)**

2 The diagram shows the gold atoms and the alpha particles that were fired into them.

(a) The alpha particles were fired at the gold foil in a vacuum. Explain why the apparatus needed to be in a vacuum.

tiny positive alpha particles

......................................................................

......................................................................

......................................................

| How far does alpha travel in air? | **(1 mark)** |

(b) Complete the paths of the alpha particles as they pass through the gold nucleus.  **(3 marks)**

> • The alpha has to be near the nucleus to be deflected.
> • To be deflected back it has to hit the nucleus directly.

(c) Explain how the results of the investigation led to the Rutherford model of the atom.

...................................................................................................

...................................................................................................

...................................................................................................

................................................................................................... **(3 marks)**

> Start by describing the observations and linking them to the new model.

3 Describe how Bohr amended the Rutherford model of the atom.

Bohr showed that the electrons ..........................................................

................................................................................................... **(1 mark)**

4 In a neon tube the electricity excites the electrons in the neon atoms. The gas then glows and emits electromagnetic radiation.

(a) Explain why the gas emits electromagnetic radiation

Electrons can jump up to higher energy levels. When electrons jump down they......

................................................................................................... **(2 marks)**

(b) Explain whether if you analysed the emitted radiation you would see all the wavelengths of electromagnetic radiation, like you do in a rainbow.

...................................................................................................

...................................................................................................

................................................................................................... **(3 marks)**

> A rainbow contains visible light of all energy levels, so all wavelengths.

# Beta decay

1  Describe the difference between beta-minus and beta-plus decay.

In beta-minus, a neutron decays into a proton and an electron. The mass number

remains the same, but the atomic number increases by 1. In beta-plus .................

..................................................................................................

.................................................................................................. **(4 marks)**

2  Isotopes of protactinium (Pa) and fluorine (F) both undergo beta-plus decay.
   Complete the symbol equations below.

> **Guided**

(a)  $^{230}_{91}\text{Pa} \rightarrow {}^{0}_{+1}\beta + \boxed{\phantom{x}}\text{Th}$

(b)  $^{18}_{9}\text{F} \rightarrow {}^{0}_{+1}\beta + \boxed{\phantom{x}}\text{O}$  **(4 marks)**

3  Caesium-137 and radium-228 both undergo beta-minus decay. Complete the symbol
   equations below.

> **Guided**

(a)  $^{137}_{55}\text{Cs} \rightarrow {}^{0}_{-1}\beta + \boxed{\phantom{x}}\text{Ba}$

(b)  $^{228}_{88}\text{Ra} \rightarrow {}^{0}_{-1}\beta + \boxed{\phantom{x}}\text{Ac}$  **(4 marks)**

4  A fundamental particle is one that cannot be broken down into a smaller particle.
   Explain what happens in both beta-plus and beta-minus decay, and suggest whether
   you think protons and neutrons are fundamental particles.

In beta-plus decay a proton decays into a neutron and in beta-minus a neutron

decays into a proton. This suggests that ....................................................

..................................................................................................

..................................................................................................

.................................................................................................. **(4 marks)**

> You are not expected to have been taught the answers to 'suggest' questions. Use your
> scientific knowledge and understanding to help you think what the answer might be.

5  Study the elements that undergo beta decay and suggest why they might decay this way.

..................................................................................................

..................................................................................................

..................................................................................................

.................................................................................................. **(2 marks)**

> Is there a similarity? How does their mass number compare with their atomic number?

# Radioactive decay

**1** State the **two** quantities that are conserved in any nuclear decay.

Mass and ..........................................................................................................

.......................................................................................................... **(2 marks)**

**2** Nuclear decay either leads to the formation of a different isotope or a new element.

   (a) Describe whether alpha, beta, gamma or neutron decay leads to new isotopes or new elements or the nucleus is unchanged.

In alpha and beta decay a new element is formed. In ........................................

.......................................................................................................... **(3 marks)**

> An isotope of an element has the same atomic number, but a different mass number. How would each of these decays change the mass and atomic numbers?

   (b) Explain how a new element can be formed by nuclear decay.

Different elements have different atomic numbers. An alpha particle .....................

..........................................................................................................

.......................................................................................................... **(2 marks)**

**3** A barium nucleus, $^{137}_{56}$Ba undergoes gamma decay. Describe the remaining nucleus after this decay.

Gamma radiation is ..............................................................................

.......................................................................................................... **(2 marks)**

**4** Uranium-238 and actinium-221 both undergo alpha decay. Complete the symbol equations for these decays shown below.

   (a) $^{238}_{92}\text{U} \rightarrow \dfrac{\boxed{4}}{\boxed{\phantom{0}}}\alpha + \dfrac{\boxed{\phantom{0}}}{\boxed{\phantom{0}}}\text{Th}$       **(3 marks)**

   (b) $^{221}_{89}\text{Ac} \rightarrow \dfrac{\boxed{\phantom{0}}}{\boxed{\phantom{0}}}\alpha + \dfrac{\boxed{\phantom{0}}}{\boxed{87}}\text{Fr}$       **(4 marks)**

**5** Suggest how the mass number and atomic number would change if a nucleus underwent alpha decay followed by beta-plus decay.

..........................................................................................................

..........................................................................................................

..........................................................................................................

..........................................................................................................

..........................................................................................................

..........................................................................................................

..........................................................................................................

.......................................................................................................... **(3 marks)**

> • Break the question into steps.
> • First, how would the mass number and atomic number change for alpha decay?
> • Then consider the changes for beta-plus decay.

# Half-life

1 The half-life of a radioactive source is often measured by monitoring the activity of the source over a period of time.

(a) Define half-life.

Half-life is the time taken for half ..............................................................

.................................................................................................................. **(1 mark)**

(b) Define activity.

Activity is the number of .....................................................................

.................................................................................................................. **(1 mark)**

2 A radioactive source has a count rate of 1400 counts per second. The source has a half-life of two hours.

(a) Determine the counts per second after two hours.

In one half-life the activity will halve. After 2 hours activity will be 1400 ÷ 2 =

.................................................................................................................. **(1 mark)**

(b) Determine how long it would take for the counts per second to be 175.

.................................................................................................................. **(2 marks)**

> • After each half-life the activity will halve.
> • Represent the half-life time with an →.
> • 1400 → 700 → 350 → 175.
> • Count the arrows, that is the number of half lives.

3 A radioactive sample has an activity of 160 Bq. After nine hours the activity is 20 Bq. Calculate the half-life of the radioactive sample.

............................... **(2 marks)**

> Calculate the number of times the activity has halved. This will give you the number of half-lives that occurred in 9 hours.

4 The graph shows how the activity of a radioactive sample changes with time.

(a) Use the graph to determine the half-life of the radioactive sample.

.................................................................... **(2 marks)**

> Draw lines on the graph to show how you calculated the half-life. If you then read an axis wrongly you should still get a mark for knowing how to get the information from the graph.

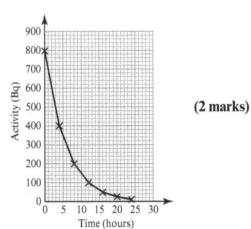

(b) Sketch and label a line on the graph to show how activity changes with time for a source with the same initial activity, but a longer half-life.

> With a longer half-life will the sample decay faster or slower?

**(2 marks)**

209

# Dangers of radiation

1  Describe how ionising radiation can affect living cells.

Ionising radiation can remove electrons from atoms to form ions. These ions can

cause .............................................................................................................

.................................................................................................................. **(2 marks)**

2  School radioactive sources are brought to the lesson when needed and removed immediately after they are finished with.

> There are three main ways to protect people working with radioactive sources. Each of these questions is about each of these methods.

(a)  Explain why the sources are only in the room when they are being used.

..................................................................................................................

.................................................................................................................. **(1 mark)**

(b)  Teachers use long tweezers or tongs to handle the sources. Explain why they do not handle the sources directly.

..................................................................................................................

.................................................................................................................. **(1 mark)**

(c)  Explain why the radioactive sources are often stored in lead-lined cases.

..................................................................................................................

.................................................................................................................. **(1 mark)**

3  In a treatment called gamma knife surgery, tumours in the brain can be killed using gamma rays. The diagram to the right shows the procedure.

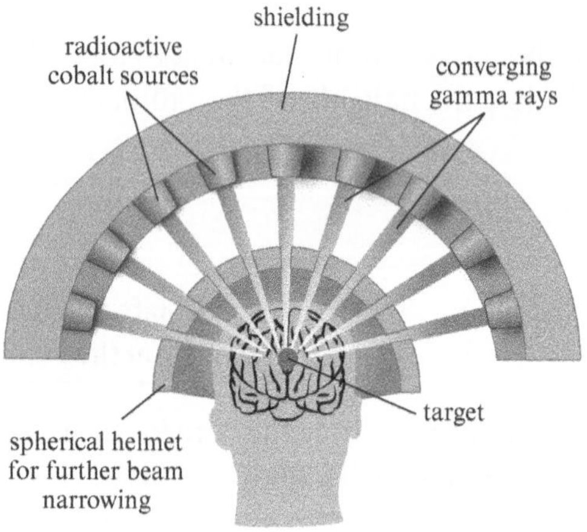

Explain how the procedure attacks the tumour and minimises the risk to the rest of the brain.

Gamma rays are fine beams. ...............

.................................................................

.................................................................

radioactive
cobalt sources

shielding

converging
gamma rays

spherical helmet
for further beam
narrowing

target

..................................................................................................................

..................................................................................................................

.................................................................................................................. **(4 marks)**

> The gamma radiation causes ionisations and kills cells. This means the brain is exposed to ionising radiation. Look carefully at the diagram and see which part of the brain is receiving the most radiation.

# Contamination and irradiation

1  Decide which of these is an example of contamination. Tick **one** box.

   ☐   **A**   an X-ray

   ☐   **B**   sterilising surgical instruments

   ☐   **C**   a plant absorbing radioactive strontium from the soil

   ☐   **D**   exposure to cosmic rays

> Contamination occurs when there is direct contact of the radioactive material with the living organism.

2  In a nuclear accident radioactive materials might escape into the environment. Explain how workers could become both irradiated and contaminated by such an accident.

..................................................................................................................

..................................................................................................................

.................................................................................................................. **(2 marks)**

3  Sometimes a radioactive material is placed in the body for period of time to help kill a cancerous tumour. It is called a radioactive seed. Explain how this is an example of contamination and irradiation.

Since the radioactive material is inside the body and in direct contact with it this is an

example of contamination. As the seed is .......................................................

.................................................................................................................. **(2 marks)**

4  Some fresh fruit is exposed to radiation to prolong its shelf life. The food is sold with a symbol to show it has been irradiated.

(a) Explain why irradiating food prolongs the shelf life.

The radiation kills the microorganisms and insects that might be on the food.

It is these microorganisms that cause ....................................................... **(2 marks)**

(b) Some people believe eating irradiated food exposes them to radiation. Explain why this is not the case.

..................................................................................................................

.................................................................................................................. **(2 marks)**

> Is there radioactive material in the food?

5  Explain why a modern LCD television does not irradiate you.

..................................................................................................................

.................................................................................................................. **(2 marks)**

> Light is a form of radiation. Is it a harmful form of radiation?

# Extended response – Radioactivity

Compare the dangers of alpha, beta and gamma radiations both inside and outside of the human body.

> The following answer has started well by explaining how ionising radiation can cause mutations and explaining the extent to which an alpha source is a danger.

Ionising radiation can knock electrons out of atoms and turn the atoms into ions. This can cause mutations in the cell DNA. Alpha is the most ionising as it is large and has a 2+ charge. However, alpha particles cannot pass through skin and so unless an alpha source is eaten or breathed in it cannot harm people.

> Since the question asks you to compare all three you now need to talk about the dangers of beta and gamma, and decide which is most dangerous inside and which is most dangerous outside the body.

....................................................................................................

....................................................................................................

....................................................................................................

....................................................................................................

....................................................................................................

....................................................................................................

....................................................................................................

....................................................................................................

....................................................................................................

....................................................................................................

....................................................................................................

....................................................................................................

....................................................................................................

....................................................................................................

....................................................................................................

....................................................................................................

....................................................................................................

....................................................................................................

....................................................................................................

....................................................................................................

....................................................................................................

....................................................................................................

.................................................................................................... **(6 marks)**

# Work, energy and power

**1** Calculate the work done pushing a box 3 m if the pushing force is 20 N.

$E = ?, F = 20\,N, d = 3\,m$ .................................................................

$E = F \times d =$ ..................................................................................... **(1 mark)**

**Maths skills**

**2** Calculate the power of a hairdryer that transfers 750 000 J in 5 minutes.

$P = ?, E = 750000\,J, t = 5\,min = 5 \times 60\,s =$ .................................

$P = E \div t =$ ...................................................................................... **(2 marks)**

**Maths skills**

**3** A supermarket employee is lifting cans of beans onto a shelf 60 cm high. Each can of beans has a mass of 415 g. The employee lifts 16 cans altogether.

> • Remember $W = mg$. This is a formula you have to learn.
> • The mass has to be in kg.

**Maths skills**

(a) Calculate the weight of one can of beans ($g = 10\,N/kg$).

$W = ?, g = 10\,N/kg, m = 415\,g =$ .................................................

................................................................................................. **(2 marks)**

(b) Calculate the work done lifting all the cans onto the shelf.

$E = ?, d =$ ................. $F =$ ...................................................

................................................................................................. **(3 marks)**

> • The distance must be in metres.
> • The force is the total weight lifted – 16 × your answer to part (a).

(c) A supervisor says the employee should work harder and lift the cans faster. Explain whether lifting the cans faster does increase the work done.

The work done is the same if the job is done faster. ........................................

.........................................................................................................

......................................................................................................... **(3 marks)**

> Work done in physics has a very specific meaning. Start by defining work done and explain what has increased if the employee works faster.

**4** A crane lifts a 30 000 N yacht a height of 3 m. The power rating of the crane is 2800 W. Calculate the time taken to lift the yacht out of the water. Give your answer to two significant figures.

**Maths skills**

$P = 2800\,W, E = ?, F = 30000\,N, d = 3\,m$

.......................... **(4 marks)**

> • Calculate the work done lifting the yacht.
> • You will then have to rearrange the equation for power to make $t$ the subject.
> • $P = E \div t$
> • Multiply both sides by $t$.
> • Divide both sides by $P$.

# Extended response – Energy and forces

In an effort to stay fit a teacher is trying to decide whether it is better to walk up the stairs or jump up and down on the spot 10 times. Describe the measurements and calculations you would make to compare the two activities. You should include calculations of the work done and power in each case.

> The following answer has begun by talking about work done while jumping up and down. They did not actually explain how to calculate work done.

To calculate work done when jumping up and down you would need to know the weight of the teacher and the height of the jump. Simply multiply the work done for one jump by 10 to get the total work done. To calculate the power you would need to record the time it took to jump up and down 10 times. Divide the work done by time to calculate the power.

> • Finish the answer by explaining the measurements needed to calculate the work done and power when climbing up the stairs.
> • How will you know which activity is best?

..........................................................................................................................

..........................................................................................................................

..........................................................................................................................

..........................................................................................................................

..........................................................................................................................

..........................................................................................................................

..........................................................................................................................

..........................................................................................................................

..........................................................................................................................

..........................................................................................................................

..........................................................................................................................

..........................................................................................................................

..........................................................................................................................

..........................................................................................................................

..........................................................................................................................

..........................................................................................................................

..........................................................................................................................

..........................................................................................................................

..........................................................................................................................

..........................................................................................................................

**(6 marks)**

# Interacting forces

**1** Which list contains only contact forces. Tick **one** box.

☐  **A**  friction, magnetism and drag

☐  **B**  gravity, magnetism and electrostatic

☐  **C**  tension, upthrust and friction

☐  **D**  upthrust, gravity and friction                                                    **(1 mark)**

**2** Force is a vector quantity. Explain what a vector quantity is.

Vector quantities have both .......................................................................

..........................................................................................................  **(2 marks)**

**3** A diver jumps off a diving board. For each of the stages below identify an action-reaction pair of forces.

(a)  As the diver stands on the board preparing to dive,

the diver pushes ............... on the board and the board ............... on the diver   **(2 marks)**

(b)  As the diver falls through the air,

the gravitational force of the Earth on the diver pulls the diver down and the.........

...............................................................

...............................................................

(c)  As the diver hits the water,

| The forces will always be:
| • the same type of force
| • the same size
| • acting in opposite directions
| • acting on different bodies. |

**(2 marks)**

...............................................................

...............................................................

..........................................................................................................  **(2 marks)**

**4** Forces can be represented by arrows. Draw a diagram to show the forces acting between two magnets that are:

(a)  attracting each other.

**(1 mark)**

(b)  repelling each other.

**(1 mark)**

**5** Compare and contrast the force due to a gravitational field with the force due to an electrostatic field.

Gravitational forces act on all objects with mass .......................................

..........................................................................................................

..........................................................................................................

..........................................................................................................  **(3 marks)**

| • In a 'compare and contrast' question, think
|   about the similarities and differences.
| • Make sure you talk about both types of force. |

# Free-body force diagrams

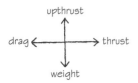

**1** Draw a free-body diagram for a submarine:

(a) moving at a constant speed, at a constant depth.

upthrust

drag ←———↕———→ thrust

weight

> • The drag and thrust are the same length because the submarine is moving at a constant speed.
> • The upthrust and weight are the same length to show the submarine is at a constant depth.

**(4 marks)**

(b) accelerating upwards as it moves forwards at a constant speed.

> • How can your diagram show the submarine is moving at a constant speed?
> • How can it show the submarine is accelerating upwards?

**(3 marks)**

**2** Draw a 45 N force acting at 30° to the horizontal and resolve it into its horizontal and vertical components.

> • Use a protractor to draw a 4.5 cm line at an angle of 30°.
> • Carefully draw on the horizontal and vertical components.
> • Measure the length of the components.
> • Don't forget to turn the answer back into newtons (×10).

**(3 marks)**

**3** A tennis ball is hit by a racket.

(a) Draw a free-body diagram for the ball as it flies through the air. The ball is moving from left to right.

> • Once the ball has left the racket there is no forward force acting on it.
> • There should only be two forces acting on your tennis ball.

**(2 marks)**

(b) The ball is moving at a constant speed. Explain, using ideas of resultant forces, whether the ball is accelerating.

........................................................................................................

........................................................................................................

........................................................................................................   **(3 marks)**

> • You can see from your diagram that there is a resultant force acting on the ball.
> • Think about how velocity is different from speed.

# Resultant forces

**1** Draw a diagram to show how two forces of 5 N can have a resultant force of:

(a) 10 N to the left.

**(1 mark)**

(b) 0 N.

**(1 mark)**

**2** A balloon on a piece of string has a force of 2 N downwards and a force of 3 N forwards.

 Maths skills

(a) Draw a free-body diagram of the balloon.

> • A free-body diagram shows the forces acting on an object.
> • The object can be represented by a simple dot
> • The length and direction of the arrows show the size and direction of the forces.

**(3 marks)**

(b) Draw a scale diagram and calculate the magnitude of the resultant force acting on the balloon. Scale 1 cm = 1 N.

> • In a vector diagram the arrows are joined nose to tail.
> • The resultant arrow shows the force that could do the same job as all the other forces in one move.

**(4 marks)**

**3** The diagram shows the forces acting on an aeroplane.

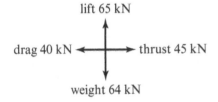

lift 65 kN

drag 40 kN ← → thrust 45 kN

weight 64 kN

Maths skills

(a) Determine the resultant force in the vertical direction.

65 000 – 64 000 = 1000 N upwards

**(2 marks)**

(b) Determine the resultant force in the horizontal direction.

..............................................................................................................................

**(2 marks)**

(c) In the space below, draw a scale drawing and calculate the magnitude of the resultant force acting on the aeroplane. Scale 1 cm = 1000 N.

> • Draw an arrow to represent the resultant force in the vertical direction.
> • Draw an arrow to represent the resultant force in the horizontal direction.
> • The resultant force of these two will be the resultant force acting on the aeroplane.

**(4 marks)**

# Extended response – Forces and their effects

**Maths skills**

An article about dogs pulling on the lead states that the more you pull the dog back the harder it will pull forwards. Study the diagrams below and suggest whether the owner should use a long lead or a short lead for a dog that pulls.

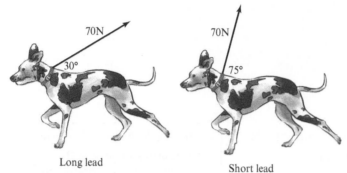

Long lead

Short lead

> Start by finding the horizontal component of the force in each case.

..................................................................................................................................

..................................................................................................................................

..................................................................................................................................

..................................................................................................................................

..................................................................................................................................

..................................................................................................................................

..................................................................................................................................

..................................................................................................................................

..................................................................................................................................

..................................................................................................................................

..................................................................................................................................

..................................................................................................................................

..................................................................................................................................

..................................................................................................................................

..................................................................................................................................

..................................................................................................................................

..................................................................................................................................

..................................................................................................................................

.................................................................................................................. **(6 marks)**

# Circuit symbols

1  Draw the circuit symbol for a cell. Identify the positive and negative terminals.

> The positive terminal is always represented by the longer line.

**(2 marks)**

2  Two circuit symbols are shown in the diagram. Identify the components and compare them.

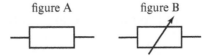

figure A                    figure B

Figure A shows a fixed resistor and figure B is a ...........................................

.............................................................................................................

.............................................................................................................  **(3 marks)**

3  A student sets up the circuit shown to measure the current through and the potential difference across an LED. The circuit does not work.

Give **three** modifications the student should make so that the circuit works correctly.

1. The LED only allows current to flow in one direction. Reverse the LED or swap the batteries

   round .....................................................

2. ...........................................................................................

   ...........................................................................................

3. ...........................................................................................

   ...........................................................................................  **(3 marks)**

4  A student builds a circuit containing a battery, two filament lamps and two switches. The circuit has been designed so that each lamp has its own switch, like the lights in a house. Draw a circuit diagram of the student's circuit.

> • A circuit must be complete for a current to flow.
> • Each switch needs to be placed so that it breaks the loop in the circuit to the lamp.

**(2 marks)**

# Series and parallel circuits

1  A series circuit contains one loop. A parallel circuit contains more than one loop.

(a)  Describe how current changes in a series circuit.

The current is the .................. throughout a series circuit          **(1 mark)**

(b)  Describe how potential difference changes in a series circuit.

.................................................................................................... **(1 mark)**

(c)  Describe how current changes in a parallel circuit.

.................................................................................................... **(1 mark)**

(d)  Describe how potential difference changes in a parallel circuit.

Components in parallel with each other have the same potential difference          **(1 mark)**

2  Complete the missing ammeter and voltmeter readings for the series circuit shown.

$A_1$ = 1.5 A ................................................................................................

$A_2$ = ...........................................................................................................

$V_1$ = 12 V – 4 V = .................................................................          **(3 marks)**

3  Complete the missing ammeter and voltmeter readings for the parallel circuit shown.

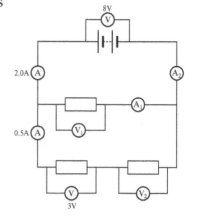

$A_1$ = 2.0 A – 0.5 A = ...................................

$A_2$ = ...............................................................

$V_1$ = 8 V...........................................................

$V_2$ = ...............................................................          **(4 marks)**

> This circuit has components in parallel and series. There are two loops in the circuit. Follow a loop and apply your circuit rules carefully.

4  Explain why a circuit will not work if a student places a voltmeter in series with a component instead of in parallel with it.

Voltmeters have a very large resistance. ...........................................

....................................................................................................

.................................................................................................... **(2 marks)**

> The potential difference is shared between components in series.

# Current and charge

1 The diagram shows a simple circuit.

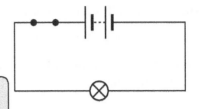

(a) Add a label and arrow to show the direction of
conventional current.    **(1 mark)**

> • Conventional current shows the direction a positive
>   charge would go.
> • A positive charge would be repelled by the positive
>   terminal and attracted by the negative terminal.
> • Which terminal is positive?

(b) Add a label and arrow to show the direction the electrons move.    **(1 mark)**

(c) Explain why the electrons move in this direction.

Electrons are negatively charged so they are attracted to the .........................

.................................................................................................................... **(2 marks)**

2 Calculate how much charge flows when a current of 3 A flows for:

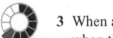

(a) 30 seconds.

$Q = ?, I = 3A, t = 30s$ .............................................................

$Q = It = 3 \times 30 =$ .................................................... **(1 mark)**

(b) 10 minutes.

$Q = ?, I = 3A, t = 10\,min = 10 \times 60s$ ...........................................

$Q = It =$ .................................................................... **(1 mark)**

> The time has to be in seconds.

3 When a car starts 120 C flow in 0.8 s. Calculate the current drawn from the car battery
when the car starts.

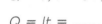

$Q = 120C, I = ?, t = 0.8s$

$Q = It$

........................ **(2 marks)**

> To make $I$ the subject of the equation simply divide both sides by $t$.

4 A current of 360 mA to a lamp transfers $6.5 \times 10^3$ C. Calculate how long the light
was left on for, in hours.

$Q = 6.5 \times 10^3 C, I = 360mA = 0.36A, t = ?$

$Q = It$

........................ **(3 marks)**

> To make $t$ the subject of the equation simply divide both sides by $I$.

# Energy and charge

**1** State the definition of potential difference.

Potential difference is the energy transferred per ........................................... **(1 mark)**

**2** Complete the table and fill in the missing values. Give all your answers to three significant figures.

| Energy transferred (J) | Potential difference (V) | Charge (C) |
|---|---|---|
| $E = 230 \times 1800 =$ | 230 | 1800 |
| 540 000 | 230 | $Q = E \div V =$ |
| 10 800 | $V = E \div Q =$ | 450 |

**(6 marks)**

> Use the triangle to help you rearrange the equations.

**3** Calculate the energy transferred to a lamp when a current of 2.0 A flows for 2 minutes. The potential difference across the lamp is 12 V.

$E = ?, I = 2.0 \text{ A}, t = 2 \text{ min} = 2 \times 60 = 120 \text{ s}, V = 12 \text{ V}$

........................... **(3 marks)**

> Use $Q = It$ to calculate the charge and $E = QV$ to calculate the energy transferred.

**4** In an electron gun, an electron is accelerated by a potential difference of 1.5 kV. The charge on an electron is $1.6 \times 10^{-19}$ C.

(a) Calculate the energy transferred to the electron by the electron gun.

$E = ?, V = 1.5 \text{ kV} = 1500 \text{ V}, Q = 1.6 \times 10^{-19} \text{ C}$ .................................................

$E = QV =$ ........................................................................................ **(2 marks)**

> It doesn't matter if you are not sure what an electron gun is, simply write out the information given in the question and find an equation that will solve the problem.

(b) Calculate the speed of the electron as it leaves the electron gun given that the electron mass is $9.1 \times 10^{-31}$ kg. Give your answer to two significant figures.

Assume all electrical energy transferred = kinetic energy of the electron
kinetic energy $= \frac{1}{2} mv^2$

........................... **(3 marks)**

> • Kinetic energy = your answer to part (a).
> • To make $v$ the subject:
>   • Multiply both sides of the equation by 2
>   • Divide both sides of the equation by $m$.
> • Don't forget to square root the answer to find $v$.

# Ohm's law

**1** Ohm's law states that the current is directly proportional to the potential difference across a component.

(a) State the equation relating to Ohm's law.

potential difference = ...................................................................... **(1 mark)**

(b) Explain how you could tell from a graph of potential difference versus current that a component obeys Ohm's law.

The graph would be a straight line through the ........................................... **(1 mark)**

> What does a graph showing a directly proportional relationship look like?

**2** A current of 5 A flows through a 10 Ω resistor. Calculate the potential difference across the resistor.

$I$ = 5 A, $R$ = 10 Ω, $V$ = ?

$V = IR$

........................ **(2 marks)**

**Maths skills**

**3** The potential difference across a lamp is 14 V and a current of 2 A flows through it. Calculate the resistance of the lamp.

$I$ = 2 A, $R$ = ?, $V$ = 14 V

$V = IR$

........................ **(2 marks)**

> To make $R$ the subject of the equation, divide both sides by $I$.

**Maths skills**

**4** A simple circuit contains two lamps A and B in series. The current flowing through the circuit is 0.5 A.

(a) Lamp A has a resistance of 4 Ω. Calculate the potential difference across lamp A.

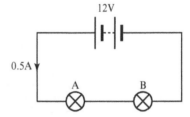

........................ **(2 marks)**

> Write down the quantities you are given in the question.

(b) Calculate the resistance of lamp B.

........................ **(3 marks)**

> • Remember, the potential difference is shared between lamps in series.
> • You know the potential difference across B and the current.

# Resistors

1 Variable resistors can be used to change the resistance in a circuit.

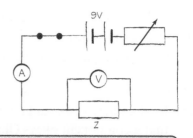

(a) Draw a circuit diagram to show how a variable resistor can be used to change the resistance in a circuit and how the resistance of a second resistor could be measured.

**(3 marks)**

> This diagram would be awarded full marks. It includes the correct symbol for the variable resistor, and the voltmeter and ammeter have been connected correctly.

(b) Explain how you can use your circuit to calculate resistance.

Resistance can be calculated by dividing the .............................................

.................................................................................................... **(2 marks)**

(c) Explain how changing the resistance of the variable resistor changes the current in the circuit.

.................................................................................................... **(1 mark)**

2 A simple series circuit is made consisting of two resistors in series.

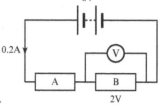

(a) Calculate the total resistance in the circuit.

$V = 8$ V, $I = 0.2$ A, $R = ?$

........................ **(2 marks)**

(b) There is a potential difference of 2 V across resistor B. Calculate the resistance of resistor B.

$V = 2$ V, $I = 0.2$ A, $R = ?$

........................ **(2 marks)**

(c) State the resistance of resistor A.

.................................................................................................... **(1 mark)**

> In a series circuit the total resistance equals the sum of each resistor.

3 A 40 Ω and a 20 Ω resistor are connected in parallel with a 10 V power supply.

(a) Calculate the current through the 40 Ω resistor.

$V = 10$ V, $I = ?$, $R = 40$ Ω

$I = V \div R = 10 \div 40 = 0.25$ A      **(2 marks)**

(b) Calculate the current through the 20 Ω resistor.

$V = 10$ V, $I = ?$, $R = 20$ Ω

........................ **(2 marks)**

(c) State the total current drawn from the power supply.

Current is conserved so total current = 0.25 A + ........................ **(1 mark)**

(d) Calculate the total resistance of this parallel circuit.

$V = 10$ V, $I = $     $R = ?$

........................ **(2 marks)**

> Remember: the total resistance in a parallel circuit is always less than the smallest resistor.

# I–V graphs

1 Match the components with their symbols and the correct characteristic I–V graph.

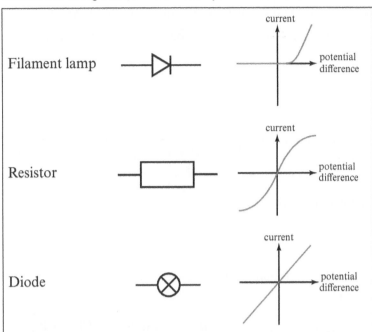

Filament lamp

Resistor

Diode

> It is important that you learn all the circuit symbols and can recognise the characteristic I–V graphs for a filament lamp, resistor and diode.

**(3 marks)**

2 The characteristic I–V graphs for different components show how the resistance varies with increasing potential difference.

(a) Explain how resistance changes with potential difference for a filament lamp.

As the potential difference increases the filament gets hotter. ..........................

.................................................................................................... **(2 marks)**

(b) Explain how resistance changes with potential difference for a diode.

In the reverse direction the diode has a very high resistance. In the forward

direction ...................................................................................................

.................................................................................................... **(3 marks)**

(c) Explain how resistance changes with potential difference for a fixed resistor.

....................................................................................................

.................................................................................................... **(2 marks)**

3 A student is given a mystery component in a box and asked to identify the component by measuring how resistance changes with potential difference. Draw a diagram to show the circuit the student should build and explain how they can use their data to identify the component.

....................................................................................................

.................................................................................................... **(4 marks)**

# Electrical circuits

**Practical skills**

A student is investigating identical filament lamps in series and in parallel. The student begins by building a circuit to determine the resistance of one filament lamp.

(a) Draw a circuit diagram to show how to determine the resistance of one of the filament lamps.

**(2 marks)**

(b) Calculate the resistance of the filament lamp used in the investigation if the student recorded the following data.

> Write down the values given in the questions and rearrange the equation carefully.

Potential difference = 6.0 V, current = 0.30 A

$V = IR$ ...........................................................................................................

$R =$ .................................................................................................... **(2 marks)**

The student builds circuits A and B to investigate filament lamps in series and parallel.

The student records their results in the table below.

| Meter readings | Circuit A | Circuit B |
|---|---|---|
| $A_1$ | 0.15 A | 0.60 A |
| $A_2$ | 0.15 A | |
| $A_3$ | | 0.30 A |
| $V_1$ | 3.0 V | |
| $V_2$ | 3.0 V | 6.0 V |

circuit A          circuit B

(c) The student didn't write all of their results down. Complete the results table by filling in the missing values.

> Remember your rules for series and parallel circuits.

**(4 marks)**

(d) Describe how current through each lamp varies as you add more identical lamps of identical resistance in series and parallel circuits.

In a series circuit the current decreases if you add more lamps (= increased

resistance); in a parallel circuit the current...................................................

........................................................................................................... **(2 marks)**

(e) The student adds a third filament lamp of the same resistance to circuits A and B. The third lamp is added in series in circuit A and in a third parallel loop in circuit B. They keep the potential difference of the supply at 6 V. Predict the values of the current through and the potential difference across each lamp in each circuit and explain how the total current changes in each circuit.

> Look at the patterns from the student's results and use those to predict what happens if you add a third lamp.

In the extended series circuit, the pd divides in three, so the pd across each bulb

will be 2.0 V. The current through each bulb will be ........................................

...........................................................................................................

........................................................................................................... **(5 marks)**

# The LDR and the thermistor

1  A student investigates how the resistance of a thermistor varies with temperature. Their results are shown in the table below.

| Temperature (°C) | Resistance (Ω) |
|---|---|
| 20 | 12 200 |
| 30 | 7800 |
| 40 | 5000 |
| 50 | 3900 |
| 60 | 3000 |

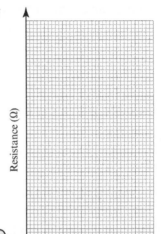

**Resistance (Ω)** (vertical axis)

**Temperature (°C)** (horizontal axis)

**Practical skills**

(a)  Plot the data on the graph paper provided.

> • Plot points carefully – they will be checked in an exam.
> • Remember to draw a smooth line of best fit. A line of best fit can be straight or curved.

**(3 marks)**

(b)  The student used a water bath to conduct this experiment. Explain why the student used a water bath.

.................................................................................................................

................................................................................................................. **(2 marks)**

> It is hard to monitor the temperature of the thermistor directly. Heating slowly allows the thermistor and water to reach thermal equilibrium. Why is that important?

(c)  State a method which would allow the student to improve the range of the data.

Ice can be used ...........................................................................................

................................................................................................................. **(2 marks)**

(d)  Describe how the resistance of a thermistor varies with temperature.

As the temperature increases ........................................................................

................................................................................................................. **(1 mark)**

(e)  Explain how you could use your thermistor as a thermometer. State the temperature range you would use it for.

Use the resistance/temperature graph to find out the temperature based on the

resistance. The thermistor's resistance changes the most between ....................

................................................................................................................. **(3 marks)**

2  Describe how you would investigate how the resistance of an LDR changes with light intensity.

.................................................................................................................

.................................................................................................................

................................................................................................................. **(3 marks)**

> • Describe how you would change the light intensity and how you would measure the resistance.
> • Explain what you would do with the results.

# Current heating effect

**1** An electric current has a heating effect.

(a) Describe, with an example, when this effect is an advantage.

In a kettle the heating effect of the current is useful for .................................

............................................................................................................... **(2 marks)**

(b) Describe, with an example, when this effect is a disadvantage.

In a light bulb .......................................................................................

............................................................................................................... **(2 marks)**

> Think back to efficiency of appliances. A light bulb is designed to transfer energy by light.

**2** The diagram shows the model of a resistor as a lattice of ions.

(a) Use the model to explain resistance inside the resistor.

As the electrons flow through the vibrating ions they collide with the

ions. The more .............................

.............................................

............................................. **(3 marks)**

potential difference (voltage)

> Remember the electrical current does work against the electrical resistance.

(b) Explain why the resistor becomes hot as the current flows through.

Kinetic energy of the electrons is transferred to .............................................

...............................................................................................................

............................................................................................................... **(3 marks)**

(c) Describe three ways the heating effect in metal wires could be reduced.

1 Using a low resistance wire ...................................................................

2 .........................................................................................................

3 ......................................................................................................... **(3 marks)**

> Any change which reduces the number of collisions of the electrons with the lattice will reduce the heating effect.

**3** A common cause of house fires is overloaded extension leads. Explain why this can cause a fire and whether the type of appliance plugged in affects the risk.

...............................................................................................................

...............................................................................................................

............................................................................................................... **(3 marks)**

> • Appliances plugged into a socket are connected in parallel – what effect does this have on the current drawn through the socket?
> • An appliance such as an iron will draw a much larger current than a radio.

# Energy and power

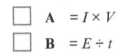

1  Which equation is used to calculate energy transferred? Tick **one** box.

☐  **A**  $= I \times V$

☐  **B**  $= E \div t$

☐  **C**  $= I \times t \times V$

☐  **D**  $= I^2 \times R$          **(1 mark)**

2  The potential difference across a hairdryer is 230 V and the current drawn is 5 A.

(a)  Calculate the power of the hairdryer.

$P = ?, V = 230 \text{ V}, I = 5 \text{ A}$

$P = I \times V$          .......................  **(2 marks)**

(b)  Calculate the resistance of the hairdryer.

$P = ?, V = 230 \text{ V}, I = 5 \text{ A}, R =$

$P = I^2 \times R$

.......................  **(3 marks)**

> • Use the power you calculated in part (a).
> • Divide both sides of the equation by $I^2$.

3  A 1.8 kW kettle is on for 4 minutes. Calculate the energy transferred by the kettle.

$P = \text{.............................}, t = \text{...........................} E = ?$

.......................  **(3 marks)**

> Remember power must be in watts and time must be in seconds.

4  A 6 V motor lifts a 0.2 kg mass onto the desk in 5 seconds. The current in the motor circuit is 0.1 A.

(a)  Calculate the energy transferred to the motor.

$E = ?, V = 6 \text{ V}, I = 0.1 \text{ A}, t = 5 \text{ s}$

$E = ItV =$          .......................  **(2 marks)**

(b)  The height of the desk is 0.8 m. Calculate the increase in the gravitational potential store of the mass.

$m = 0.2 \text{ kg}, g = 10, h = 0.8 \text{ m}$

$GPE = mgh =$          .......................  **(2 marks)**

> Gravitational potential $= mgh$ ($g = 10$)

(c)  Calculate the efficiency of the motor.

.......................  **(2 marks)**

> • Efficiency = useful energy transferred ÷ total energy input.
> • Remember efficiency cannot be greater than 100 %.

# a.c. and d.c. circuits

1 Which statement, A to D, has appliances in order of increasing energy transferred per second? Tick **one** box.

☐ **A** kettle, microwave, shaver

☐ **B** shaver, microwave, electric oven

☐ **C** microwave, kettle, shaver

☐ **D** electric oven, kettle, shaver

> Appliances designed to heat often have really high power ratings. The higher the power rating the more energy transferred per second.

**(1 mark)**

2 A student records the potential difference across a 1.5 V cell every minute for 3 minutes.

(a) Sketch a graph to show how the potential difference across the cell changes with time.

**(3 marks)**

(b) The 1.5 V cell is connected to a lamp. Describe how the electrons move in the circuit. State the name for this type of current.

The electrons move in one direction only. This is a ........................................

**(2 marks)**

(c) The student places a second 1.5 V cell in series with the first, connecting positive terminal to negative terminal. Describe how the potential difference versus time graph will change when the second cell is added.

.................................................................................................

.................................................................................................

**(2 marks)**

3 The UK domestic supply is a.c., at a frequency of 50 Hz and a voltage of about 230 V. Explain what this statement means. Your answer should include a sketch graph of potential difference versus time for the domestic supply.

a.c. stands for alternating current. This means ...........................................

.................................................................................................

.................................................................................................

**(4 marks)**

4 A laptop charger is labelled 19.5 V d.c. To charge the laptop the charger must be plugged into the mains.

(a) Describe how the charger changes the mains electricity.

Mains electricity is 230 V a.c. This means the charger must ...........................

.................................................................................................

.................................................................................................

**(2 marks)**

(b) Suggest a component that could be used to change a.c. voltage to d.c. voltage.

.................................................................................................

.................................................................................................

**(2 marks)**

> Think of a component that only allows the current to flow in one direction.

# Mains electricity and the plug

**1** The live, neutral and earth wires are all at different potential differences.

(a) Determine the potential difference between the live and neutral wires.

The live is at 230 V and the neutral is at 0 V. This means the potential difference

between them is ..................................................................................................

.......................................................................................................................... **(2 marks)**

(b) Determine the potential difference between the earth and neutral wires.

..........................................................................................................................

.......................................................................................................................... **(2 marks)**

**2** This plug has been assembled incorrectly. Identify the three faults with the plug.

> Guided

- • ..................................................................

- • ..................................................................

- • .................................................................. **(3 marks)**

green and yellow stripes
blue
brown

**3** Earthing, fuses and circuit breakers are safety features which help prevent electrocution.

(a) Explain how an earth wire and a fuse prevent electrocution when a live wire comes loose.

If a live wire comes loose and touches the metal casing the whole appliance is live.

The earth wire is connected to the ...............................................................

..........................................................................................................................

.......................................................................................................................... **(4 marks)**

(b) Suggest why a plastic hairdryer does not need a fuse.

..........................................................................................................................

.......................................................................................................................... **(2 marks)**

> The danger is if the metal case becomes live and you touch it. You then provide a route to earth and are electrocuted. Can a plastic case do this?

(c) Explain how circuit breakers prevent electrocution.

If the current is too high ...............................................................................

.......................................................................................................................... **(2 marks)**

**4** Explain why switches and fuses have to be connected to the live wire and not the neutral.

..........................................................................................................................

..........................................................................................................................

.......................................................................................................................... **(2 marks)**

> Think of the potential difference of the live and neutral wires with respect to the earth wire.

# Extended response – Electricity and circuits

An electrical safety website suggests a simple guide to picking the right fuse for an appliance. The guide suggests any appliance rated below 700 W should use a 3 A fuse and anything above 700 W should be fitted with a 13 A fuse.

Explain why fuses are important and why not all appliances should be fitted with a 13 A fuse. Your answer should include why 700 W was chosen as a cut-off value.

These items are all plugged into the mains. What will the potential of the mains be? Calculate the current for a 700 W appliance.

Fuses prevent fires, electrocutions and protect equipment.

If a live wire touches the metal casing a large current flows to earth and the fuse melts and breaks the circuit.

To calculate the max current in an appliance: ............................................................................

............................................................................

............................................................................

............................................................................

............................................................................

If the appliance is less than 700 W the maximum working current will be less so a 3 A fuse will ............................................................................

............................................................................

If you used a 3 A fuse in an appliance rated 750 W ............................................................................

............................................................................

............................................................................

............................................................................

If you used a 13 A fuse for all appliances ............................................................................

............................................................................

............................................................................

............................................................................

............................................................................

............................................................................

............................................................................

............................................................................

............................................................................

............................................................................

**(6 marks)**

# Magnets and magnetic fields

**1** Identify the magnetic material from these metals. Tick **one** box.

☐ **A** copper                    ☐ **C** cobalt

☐ **B** aluminium               ☐ **D** zinc                    **(1 mark)**

**2** State which of these uses only a temporary magnet. Tick **one** box.

☐ **A** door bell                ☐ **C** loudspeaker

☐ **B** motor                    ☐ **D** fridge magnet          **(1 mark)**

**3** The diagrams below show a bar magnet (Figure 1) and two attracting magnets (Figure 2).

Figure 2

Figure 1

N          S

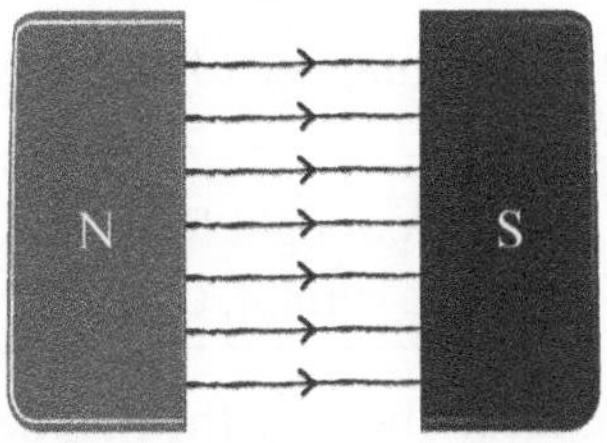

(a) Draw the magnetic field lines on Figure 1 and Figure 2.          **(3 marks)**

> • Magnetic field lines always point from north to south.
> • The closer the field lines the stronger the field.

(b) Add labels to your diagrams to show a uniform field, a weak magnetic field and a stronger magnetic field.          **(3 marks)**

(c) Describe how you could use a plotting compass to show a magnetic field.

Place the plotting compass at the pole of the magnet. .....................................

.................................................................................................................

.................................................................................................................          **(3 marks)**

> • It may help to use a labelled diagram when you try to explain this.
> • You could explain one step at a time.

**4** The figure shows a magnet holding four paper clips. Explain why the paper clips behave like this and why the magnet cannot hold more than four.

The paper clips are made of steel which is a magnetic material.

A magnet ...............................................................................

.........................................................................................          **(4 marks)**

**5** Explain how a compass works and how this is evidence of the Earth's magnetic field.

.................................................................................................................

.................................................................................................................

.................................................................................................................          **(3 marks)**

> A compass always points north. How does it 'know' which way is north?

# Current and magnetism

1 Which one of these changes would **not** change the strength of the magnetic field around a current-carrying wire? Tick **one** box.

☐ **A** increasing the current

☐ **B** changing the direction of the current

> • The magnetic field strength is proportional to the current.
> • The magnetic field strength is inversely proportional to the distance.

☐ **C** decreasing the current

☐ **D** adding a second wire carrying current next to the first wire     **(1 mark)**

2 The diagram shows a current-carrying wire. The arrow shows the direction of the current.

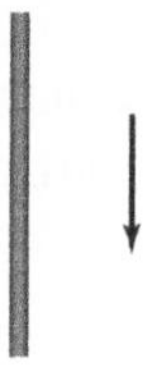

(a) Draw magnetic field lines around the wire.

> Use your right hand. The thumb points in the same direction as the current, the fingers show the direction of the field.

**(2 marks)**

(b) Describe how the magnetic field pattern would change if the current was doubled.

The magnetic field would be stronger so the magnetic field lines would be .........

..................................................................................................................

.................................................................................................................. **(2 marks)**

3 A solenoid has the same field pattern as a bar magnet. Explain how the field lines around the individual coils add together to make this pattern. Include a diagram to help explain your answer.

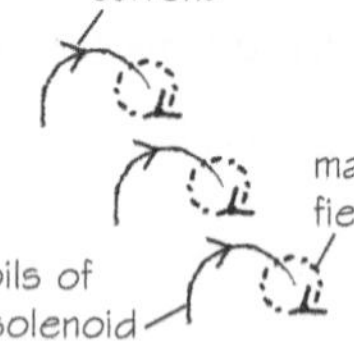

The current on one side of the solenoid coils is all flowing in the same direction. This means each coil has the same

magnetic field. These fields ...........................................................................

..................................................................................................................

.................................................................................................................. **(3 marks)**

> Imagine just one side of the coil. You would have a series of wires next to each other each with a circular field in the same direction.

4 The current flowing through a wire is halved and the distance from the wire is doubled. What will the magnetic field strength be? Tick **one** box.

☐ **A** halved          ☐ **C** the same

☐ **B** doubled          ☐ **D** quartered          **(1 mark)**

> • Will the field be the same? Will it be bigger? If your answer to both of those questions is 'no' then that leaves you a choice between A and D.
> • If both factors halve the field what is going to happen?

# Current, magnetism and force

1  When a current-carrying wire is placed in a uniform magnetic field it experiences a force.
Explain why it experiences a force and how the force can be increased.

The current has a magnetic field around it. This magnetic field interacts with the

magnetic field of the magnet. .................................................................

.............................................................................................. **(3 marks)**

> Don't forget to mention that the wire has to be
> perpendicular to the field for the maximum force.

2  Calculate the force acting on a wire when it is placed at right angles to a uniform
magnetic field of 2.5 mT. The current in the 10 cm wire is 0.5 A.

$F = ?$, $B = 2.5$ mT $= 2.5 \times 10^{-3}$ T, $I = 0.5$ A, $L = 10$ cm $=$

$F = B \times I \times L$

.......................... **(2 marks)**

> • Must convert mT to T.
> • Must convert cm to m.

3  The diagram shows a current-carrying wire in a magnetic field. The wire will:

☐  **A**  move up

☐  **B**  move down

☐  **C**  stay in the same position

☐  **D**  move sideways

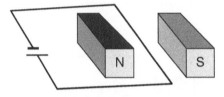

**(1 mark)**

> Remember, conventional current flows from the positive
> terminal to the negative terminal of the cell.

**Maths
skills**

4  A straight piece of wire 0.55 m long is placed at right angles to a uniform magnetic
field of 0.8 T. The force on the wire is 0.98 N. Calculate the current flowing in the wire.
Give your answer to two significant figures.

$F = 0.98$ N, $B = 0.8$ T, $I = ?$, $L = 0.55$ m

$F = BIL$

.......................... **(3 marks)**

> • First, divide both sides by $B$.
> • Second, divide both sides by $L$.

**Maths
skills**

5  A straight piece of wire 75 cm long is placed at right angles to a uniform magnetic field.
The current flowing in the wire is 4.5 A and the force experienced by the wire is 0.16 N.
Calculate the magnetic field. Give your answer in mT to two significant figures.

.......................... **(3 marks)**

> Look carefully at the tips in the previous questions before rearranging this equation.

# Extended response – Magnetism and the motor effect

**Practical skills**

Describe how to show that a current can create a magnetic effect. Your experiment should include how to show that the direction of the field depends on the current direction. Describe the field pattern and how it will vary with distance from the wire.

> It might be easier to draw a labelled diagram to explain how to use plotting compasses.

Showing the field:

Place a piece of card around a vertical current-carrying wire.

...............................................................................................................................

...............................................................................................................................

...............................................................................................................................

...............................................................................................................................

...............................................................................................................................

Showing the direction:

...............................................................................................................................

...............................................................................................................................

...............................................................................................................................

...............................................................................................................................

Describing how field varies with distance:

...............................................................................................................................

...............................................................................................................................

...............................................................................................................................

...............................................................................................................................

...............................................................................................................................

...............................................................................................................................

...............................................................................................................................

...............................................................................................................................

...............................................................................................................................

...............................................................................................................................

...............................................................................................................................

...............................................................................................................................

................................................................................................................. **(6 marks)**

# Electromagnetic induction and transformers

**1** The diagram shows a magnet moving into a coil of wire. The coil of wire is connected to a sensitive ammeter. The needle on the centre zero ammeter has moved to the right.

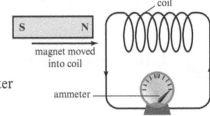

(a) Describe what would happen to the reading on the ammeter if the magnet were pulled out of the coil of wire.

The needle would ............................................................................................ **(1 mark)**

(b) Describe what would happen to the reading on the ammeter if the south pole of the magnet was moving into the coil of wire.

The needle would ............................................................................................ **(1 mark)**

(c) Describe what happens to the reading on the ammeter if the magnet is left inside the coil.

.................................................................................................................... **(1 mark)**

(d) Explain why the ammeter shows a reading.

> To induce a potential difference in the wire either the magnetic field or the coil have to be moving.

The moving ........................ induces a ........................ across the wire. This causes a current to flow. The current sets up a magnetic field that opposes the magnetic field that caused it. **(3 marks)**

(e) Describe how you could increase the potential difference across the wire.

....................................................................................................................

.................................................................................................................... **(2 marks)**

**2** A laptop charger is plugged into a 230 V a.c. supply in a home. The laptop has a label on the back stating '16 V 3.65 A'.

(a) Describe how the charger is constructed to allow it to give this output.

The charger must contain a transformer. A transformer consists of a primary and

.................................................................................................................... **(3 marks)**

(b) Calculate the current drawn from the mains supply.

$V_p = 230$ V, $I_p = ?$, $V_s = 16$ V, $I_s = 3.65$ A

Assuming the transformer is 100% efficient,

$V_p I_p = V_s I_s$

> To rearrange the equation divide both sides by $V_p$.

> • Is this transformer stepping up or stepping down the voltage?
> • Which coil will have more turns?

........................ **(2 marks)**

(c) The laptop requires the current to be direct current. Suggest a component that must also be in the charger and explain where in the circuit it should be connected.

....................................................................................................................

.................................................................................................................... **(3 marks)**

> • Which component allows current to only flow in one direction?
> • Should it be connected before the primary coil or after the secondary coil?
> • Can a transformer work on d.c.?

# Transmitting electricity

**1** Describe the National Grid.

The National Grid is the wires and ...................................................................

................................................................................................................ **(1 mark)**

**2** The diagram below includes the National Grid system.

(a) State the type of transformer X is and explain why it is needed in the system.

X is a step-up transformer. Stepping up the voltage decreases the current: this

is an advantage because ...........................................................................

................................................................................................................

> • Remember if a transformer is 100% efficient the power in equals the power out.
> • If the voltage is stepped up what happens to the current?
> • Why would that be an advantage?

**(3 marks)**

(b) State the type of transformer Y is and explain why it is needed in the system.

Y is a step-down transformer. .....................................................................

................................................................................................................ **(2 marks)**

(c) Explain why the National Grid system uses alternating current rather than direct current.

Direct current flows in one direction only. Alternating current continuously changes

direction, this means the magnetic field around a direct current ........................

................................................................................................................

> • To induce a potential difference either the coil or the magnetic field has to be moving.
> • What would the magnetic field around a d.c. current be like?

**(3 marks)**

(d) The power station generates 60 MW of power. The electricity is transmitted at 400 kV. Calculate the current in the transmission cables.

$P = 60$ MW = ........... W, $V_s = 400$ kV = ........... V, $I_s = ?$ ...........

........................................................................

........................................................................

> • The prefix M stands for $1 \times 10^6$.
> • The prefix k stands for $1 \times 10^3$.

**(3 marks)**

(e) Suggest whether the actual current will be the same as this. Explain your answer.

................................................................................................................

................................................................................................................ **(2 marks)**

# Extended response – Electromagnetic induction

A 2 W electric toothbrush operates at 12 V. The charger is plugged into 230 V a.c. Use the diagram to help you explain how an electric toothbrush can be charged even though there is no direct metallic contact between the base and the toothbrush.

The charger and toothbrush together make a transformer. In any transformer the primary and secondary coils are not electrically connected. They just need to be linked by an iron core. Since the magnetic fields can pass through the plastic the transformer

still works. .....................................................

> • This is a good start to the answer, but would not score full marks. The question is really asking how a transformer works, whereas this student has concentrated just on how it can work with the plastic there.
> • Finish the answer by explaining how a transformer works, including what type of transformer this is.

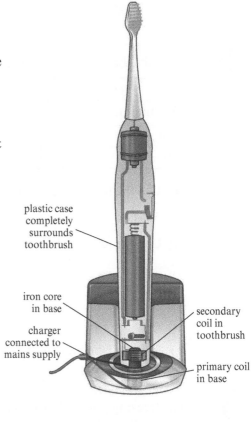

plastic case completely surrounds toothbrush

iron core in base

charger connected to mains supply

secondary coil in toothbrush

primary coil in base

.............................................................................

.............................................................................

.............................................................................

.............................................................................

.............................................................................

.............................................................................

.............................................................................

.............................................................................

.............................................................................

.............................................................................

.............................................................................

.............................................................................

.............................................................................

.............................................................................

.............................................................................

.............................................................................

.............................................................................

.............................................................................

.............................................................................

............................................................................. **(6 marks)**

# Changes of state

1 A change of state is a physical change. State one similarity and one difference between physical and chemical changes.

Mass is conserved in both physical and chemical changes. ............................

................................................................................................................ **(2 marks)**

2 The table below gives the melting and boiling points of some elements.

| Element | Melting point (°C) | Boiling point (°C) |
|---------|--------------------|--------------------|
| Aluminium | 660 | 2450 |
| Chlorine | −101 | −34 |
| Mercury | −39 | 357 |

(a) Use the table to determine the state of each element at room temperature (20 °C).

Aluminium is a solid, chlorine is a ....................................................... **(1 mark)**

(b) Use the table to determine which element condenses at the highest temperature.

................................................................................................................ **(1 mark)**

> Condensing is when a gas becomes a liquid. This will be at the same temperature as the boiling point.

(c) Use the table to determine the state of each element at −45 °C.

Aluminium is a solid, chlorine is a ....................................................... **(1 mark)**

3 The freezing point of carbon dioxide is −78.5 °C. At normal atmospheric pressure, when solid carbon dioxide reaches a temperature of −78.5 °C it starts to sublimate.

(a) Describe the movement and arrangement of the particles in carbon dioxide below −78.5 °C.

The particles are fixed in position in regular patterns and are able to ..................

................................................................................................................ **(2 marks)**

(b) Describe the movement and arrangement of the particles in carbon dioxide above −78.5 °C.

................................................................................................................ **(2 marks)**

> 'Sublimate' means to change from a solid directly to a gas.

(c) Describe how the force of attraction between the particles changes as the carbon dioxide sublimates.

................................................................................................................ **(2 marks)**

4 Explain whether the thermal energy is transferred to or away from ice cream as it is taken out of the freezer and served in a bowl.

Particles gain kinetic energy with increasing temperature. At a change of state,

energy is ................................................................................................ **(4 marks)**

> • Think about the arrangement and movement of the particles as they change state.
> • What happens at a change of state?
> • Make sure your answer states clearly whether thermal energy has been transferred to or away from the ice cream.

# Density

1  Complete the table by calculating the density of the different materials.

| Mass (kg) | Volume (m³) | Density (kg/m³) |
|---|---|---|
| 400 | 0.8 | $\rho = m \div V = 500$ |
| 4800 | 2 | $\rho = m \div V =$ |
| 2 | $2 \times 10^{-3}$ | |

(2 marks)

2  The base for a statue has a width of 1.5 m, a height of 2 m and a length of 5 m.

(a) Calculate the volume of the base.

Volume = $w \times l \times h$

........................ (1 mark)

(b) The density of concrete is 2400 kg/m³. Calculate the total mass of the base.

$\rho = 2400$ kg/m³, $m = ?$ , $V =$

$\rho = m \div V$

........................ (2 marks)

> • To make mass the subject, multiply both sides of the equation by V.
> • Don't forget you can always use the equation triangle.

3  The density of solid gold is 19.3 g/cm³ and the density of liquid gold is 17.3 g/cm³.

(a) Explain why liquid gold has a lower density than solid gold.

The particles in a liquid are further apart than in a solid; this means there ............

..............................................................................................................

.............................................................................................................. (2 marks)

(b) The mass of a gold bar is 12.5 kg. Calculate the volume of the gold bar. Give your answer to two significant figures.

$\rho = 19.3$ g/cm³, $m = 12.5$ kg = .................... g, $V = ?$

$\rho = m \div V$

$V =$                                        ........................ (3 marks)

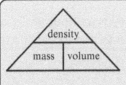

> • Remember, the mass has to be in g as you know the density in g/cm³.
> • To make volume the subject multiply both sides of the equation by V.
> • Then divide both sides by $\rho$.
> • You can always use the equation triangle.

(c) Explain whether the mould for a gold bar has to have a bigger or smaller volume than your volume calculated in part (b).

..............................................................................................................

.............................................................................................................. (2 marks)

> You might want to calculate the new volume using the density of liquid gold to help you answer this question.

241

Had a go ☐   Nearly there ☐   Nailed it! ☐

# Investigating density

Practical skills

A student has been asked to determine the density of a wooden block, a stone and a sample of a vegetable oil.

(a) Describe how the student could determine the volume of the block.

Use a ruler to measure the length, width and height. The volume can be calculated by multiplying ................................................................................ **(2 marks)**

(b) Describe how the student could determine the volume of the stone.

Fill a displacement can with water until water just starts to come out of the spout. Place a measuring cylinder .................................................................

.................................................................... Remember 1 ml = 1 cm³. **(3 marks)**

(c) Describe how the student could determine the volume of the vegetable oil.

Pour the oil into a measuring cylinder. Read the volume by looking at eye level at the bottom ................................................................................

................................................................................ **(2 marks)**

> You must read the volume at eye level to avoid parallax error – if you look down, the volume will be too low, if you look up the volume will be too high!

(d) Describe how the student could measure the mass of the vegetable oil.

................................................................................

................................................................................ **(2 marks)**

The student's final results table is shown below.

|  | Mass (g) | Volume (cm³) | Density (g/cm³) |
|---|---|---|---|
| **Wooden block** | 12.0 | 24 | 0.5 |
| **Stone** | 94.5 | 35 | 2.7 |
| **Vegetable oil** | 128.6 | 20 |  |

Maths skills

(e) Calculate the density of the vegetable oil.

$\rho = ?$, $m = 128.6$ g,    $V = 20$ cm³

$\rho = m \div V$ ........................ **(2 marks)**

Maths skills

(f) The student forgot to zero the scales when they were finding the mass of the vegetable oil. The mass of the measuring cylinder is 110 g. Calculate the actual density of the vegetable oil.

........................ **(2 marks)**

Maths skills

(g) The student looks up a value for the density of wood and discovers that it is 560 kg/m³. Compare the two answers and suggest a reason why they are different.

................................................................................

................................................................................ **(3 marks)**

> This density is in a different unit. First convert to g/cm³:
> × 1000 (kg to g)
> ÷ (100 × 100 × 100) (m³ to cm³)

# Energy and changes of state

**1** (a) Define specific heat capacity.

The energy required to change the temperature of 1 kg ...................................

........................................................................................................... **(1 mark)**

(b) Define specific latent heat.

........................................................................................................... **(1 mark)**

(c) Explain the difference between specific heat capacity and specific latent heat.

Specific latent heat involves changes of state and the .....................................

........................................................................................................... **(2 marks)**

**2** Steam from a kettle condenses on a cupboard in the kitchen. The mass of water collected on the cupboard was 5 g. The steam was at a temperature of 100 °C.

(a) Explain whether energy was transferred to the water or to the surroundings as the steam condensed.

...................................................

................................................... 

> In which state do the particles have more energy, liquid or gas?

**(2 marks)**

(b) Calculate the energy transferred as the steam condensed. Specific latent heat of evaporation is 2257 kJ/kg. Give your answer to three significant figures.

$Q = ?$, $m = 5g = $ ............... kg, $L = 2257 \times 10^3$ J/kg

$Q = mL$

> • This formula will be on the formula sheet.
> • Don't forget the mass must be in kg.
> • Also convert from kJ to J.

...................... **(3 marks)**

(c) Calculate the energy transferred as the water cooled to the room temperature of 20 °C. Specific heat capacity of water = 4200 J/kg °C.

$Q = ?$, $m = 5g = $ ......... kg, $c = 4200$ J/kg°C $\Delta\theta = (100 - 20) = $ ...............

$Q = mc\Delta\theta$

> This formula will be on the formula sheet.

...................... **(2 marks)**

**3** A 50 W heater takes 3 minutes to melt 30 g of ice.

(a) Calculate the specific latent heat of fusion of ice.

$Q = ?$, $m = 30 g = $ ......... kg, $L = ?$

To calculate $Q = Pt = $ ...................... **(3 marks)**

> • Remember $P = E \div t$.
> • This means energy transferred to the ice = $Pt$.
> • Don't forget the time must be in seconds.

(b) The actual value of specific latent heat of fusion of ice is 330 000 J/kg. Suggest why the experimental result is different.

........................................................................................................... **(1 mark)**

> The value is a bit low – what else could have been warming the ice?

# Thermal properties of water

**Practical skills**

A student is asked to obtain a temperature/time graph for melting ice and to use the data collected to calculate the specific heat capacity of water.

They are provided with the following equipment: ice, thermometer, electric heater, power supply, insulation, stopwatch, electronic balance.

(a) Describe how to set up the experiment to plot an accurate temperature/time graph for melting ice. Include a labelled diagram in your answer.

> • How often will you have to record the temperature to capture the change of state?
> • When should you stop heating?
> • How will you use the insulation?

Place the thermometer and heater directly into the ice and record the temperature

of the ice. ............................................................................................................

................................................................................................................................

................................................................................................................................ **(4 marks)**

(b) Sketch a prediction temperature/time graph for this investigation on the axes. Label clearly where the ice has melted.

*(graph with axes: Temperature in °C vertical, Time in seconds horizontal)* **(2 marks)**

**Maths skills**

(c) The student used their data after the ice had melted and recorded a temperature rise of 5 °C in 45 seconds. The mass of ice is 0.1 kg and the student used a 50 W heater. Calculate the specific heat capacity of water.

$Q = ?, \quad m = 0.1 \text{ kg}, \Delta\theta = 5 \text{ °C}, c = ?, \quad P = 50 \text{ W}, t = 45\text{s}$

$Q = mc\,\Delta\theta, P = E \div t$

.......................... **(3 marks)**

> Look back at page 243 Question 3 – how did you use the power of the heater to calculate the energy transferred?

(d) A second student argued that they could simply use the total temperature rise for the entire time of the experiment. Explain why this would not give an accurate value for specific heat capacity.

During the experiment the ice changed state. Some of ......................................

................................................................................................................................ **(2 marks)**

> • The heater might have been on for a few minutes. Did all the energy transferred go into raising the temperature of the ice?
> • Would the value for specific heat capacity be too high or too low?

# Pressure and temperature

**Maths
skills**

1 Convert the following temperatures.

(a) 300 K to degrees Celsius

- Kelvin to Celsius: subtract 273.
- Celsius to kelvin: add 273.

300 − 273 = ...........................................

(b) 210 K to degrees Celsius

...........................................................

(c) 20 °C to kelvin

20 + 273 = ...........................................

(d) −50 °C to kelvin

...........................................................    **(4 marks)**

2 Describe the term 'absolute zero'.

Absolute zero is −273 °C. At this temperature the ...........................................

................................................................................................................    **(2 marks)**

3 Explain how a gas exerts a pressure on the walls of its container using kinetic theory.

Remember, pressure is force ÷ area (from KS3).
Can you think how the particles can exert a force?

The particles in a gas are constantly moving around in random directions. The

particles will collide ........................................................................................

................................................................................................................    **(3 marks)**

**Maths
skills**

4 The graph shows how pressure varies with temperature for a fixed volume of gas.

(a) Describe and explain the relationship shown in the graph.

The graph shows a directly proportional relationship between pressure and temperature of a gas. This is

because as temperature increases the ..................

..................................................

..................................................

How will increasing the temperature change the number of collisions per second?

................................................................................................................    **(3 marks)**

(b) Suggest what happens to the pressure if the temperature decreases from 400 K to 200 K.

The temperature has halved so the pressure must have ...................................

................................................................................................................    **(1 mark)**

You have met proportional relationships before when you looked at how magnetic field strength varied with current – when you doubled the current, the magnetic field strength doubled.

# Extended response – Particle model

Explain why a burn caused by 100 °C steam is more damaging than a burn caused by boiling water. Your answer should include calculations.

Specific heat capacity of water = 4200 J/kg °C

Specific latent heat of evaporation for water = 2257 kJ/kg

Temperature change as water/steam comes into contact with skin = 60 °C

Mass of steam/water = 50 g

- Your answer should include an explanation **and** calculations.
- Remember, the equations for specific heat capacity and latent heat are given on the formula sheet.
- $Q = mL$.
- $Q = mc\Delta\theta$.
- Take care with units; kJ, J, kg, g.

..................................................................................................

..................................................................................................

..................................................................................................

..................................................................................................

..................................................................................................

..................................................................................................

..................................................................................................

..................................................................................................

..................................................................................................

..................................................................................................

..................................................................................................

..................................................................................................

..................................................................................................

..................................................................................................

..................................................................................................

..................................................................................................

..................................................................................................

..................................................................................................

..................................................................................................

..................................................................................................

..................................................................................................

..................................................................................................

..................................................................................................

**(6 marks)**

# Elastic and inelastic distortion

1 Describe **three** methods for distorting materials and state what they all have in common.

The three methods are bending, ...............................................................................

..............................................................................................................................

..............................................................................................................................

.......................................................................................................... **(4 marks)**

2 Give **two** examples of materials that behave:

(a) elastically

.......................................................................................................... **(1 mark)**

(b) inelastically.

.......................................................................................................... **(1 mark)**

3 Explain how a seatbelt can behave both elastically and inelastically.

> Seat belts have to be replaced if the car is in an accident.

Under a small force the seat belt will ..................................................................

..............................................................................................................................

..............................................................................................................................

.......................................................................................................... **(2 marks)**

4 Lycra® is used in athletic clothing. Describe the properties of a material such as Lycra® that make it so desirable for competitors.

> What is the advantage of Lycra® over a material such as cotton or wool when you are competing?

Lycra® is an elastic material: this means ...............

..............................................................................................................................

..............................................................................................................................

.......................................................................................................... **(3 marks)**

5 On the axes sketch a graph of a spring being stretched. After the forces are removed the spring is permanently deformed. Label the elastic limit.

> How might the graph show that the spring has been permanently deformed – will it be easier to stretch?

Force

Extension

**(2 marks)**

# Springs

**1** For linear elastic distortion you can use the equation $F = kx$. Explain what is meant by linear elastic distortion.

> Linear means straight line – what is the significance of a straight-line graph?

If the elastic distortion is linear the extension is ...........................................

.................................................................................................................... **(1 mark)**

**Maths skills**

**2** A spring is 5 cm long. When a weight of 4 N is hung from the spring, the spring measures 13 cm.

(a) Determine the extension of the spring.

Extension = new length – original length = ...................................................... **(1 mark)**

(b) Show that the spring constant for this spring is 50 N/m.

$F = 4$ N, $k = ?$, $x = $ .......................................................................................

$F = kx$ ................................................................................................................

$k = $ .................................................................................................................... **(2 marks)**

> • To rearrange the equation, simply divide both sides by $x$.
> • Don't forget $x$ must be in m!

(c) Calculate the extension if the spring is loaded with 8 N. State the assumption you made.

$F = 8$ N, $k = 50$ N/m, $x = ?$ ...........................

$F = kx$ .................................................

$x = $ .................................................................................................................... **(3 marks)**

> • To rearrange the equation simply divide both sides by $k$.
> • When can you use the equation $F = kx$?

(d) Calculate the work done stretching the spring 6 cm.

$E = ?$, $k = 50$ N/m, $x = 6$ cm = ........ m

$E = \frac{1}{2}kx^2$

> • This equation is provided on the formula sheet.
> • Don't forget to square the extension.

...................... **(1 mark)**

**3** Spring A has a much higher spring constant than spring B.

(a) On the axes sketch the force extension graph for **both** springs. Label them clearly.

> The spring constant tells you how many newtons it takes to stretch a spring 1 m. The higher the value, the harder the spring is to stretch.

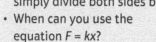

**(2 marks)**

(b) Explain which spring would store more elastic potential energy if they were both extended 4 cm.

....................................................................................................................

.................................................................................................................... **(2 marks)**

> Think of the equation for work done stretching the spring. This must be equal to the elastic potential energy stored in the spring.

# Forces and springs

**Practical skills**

A student investigates the extension and work done when applying forces to a spring.

The student is provided with: a clamp stand, G-clamp, 100 g masses, spring, ruler.

(a) Describe how the student safely increased the mass and measured the extension of the spring. Include a labelled diagram in your answer.

> Make sure you have included how the student takes each measurement.

Measure the length of the unstretched spring using a ruler or pair of callipers. ......

...................................................................................................................

................................................................................................................... **(4 marks)**

The student achieved the following results:

| Weight (N) | Extension (cm) |
|:----------:|:--------------:|
| 1 | 5 |
| 2 | 10 |
| 3 | 14 |
| 4 | 20 |
| 5 | 25 |

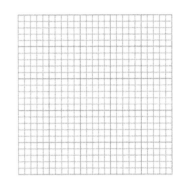

**Maths skills**

(b) Plot the graph on the graph paper provided. **(2 marks)**

(c) The student writes in their conclusion that these results show extension is directly proportional to length. Comment on their conclusion.

................................................................................................................... **(2 marks)**

> How can you tell from a graph that the relationship is directly proportional? There are two marks so think of two things to point out about the graph.

**Maths skills**

(d) Calculate the spring constant of the spring.

$F = 5$ N, $k = ?$, $x = 25$ cm $= 0.25$ m

$F = kx$

$k =$ ..................... **(2 marks)**

> • These values were taken from the graph – not the table. You should always use the graph because individual results might be anomalies.
> • To rearrange the equation, divide both sides by the extension.
> • The gradient of your graph is also equal to the spring constant.

**Maths skills**

(e) Calculate the work done stretching the spring 20 cm.

> • This equation will be on the formula sheet.
> • Don't forget to square the extension!

$E = ?$, $x = 20$ cm $= 0.2$ m, $k = ?$

$E = \frac{1}{2}kx^2$ ..................... **(2 marks)**

# Extended response – Forces and matter

**Practical skills**

A student is asked to investigate the extension of a spring and an elastic band, and to compare their behaviour. Describe how the student could safely and accurately carry out this investigation, and how they could compare the behaviour of the spring with that of the elastic band. Your answer should include an apparatus diagram.

> • To compare the behaviour you will have to see if they are linear or non-linear relationships. How can you tell that from your results?
> • Don't forget to write a clear method, explain how to compare the data, and explain how to be safe and accurate.

..................................................................

..................................................................

..................................................................................

..................................................................................

..................................................................................

..................................................................................

..................................................................................

..................................................................................

..................................................................................

..................................................................................

..................................................................................

..................................................................................

..................................................................................

..................................................................................

..................................................................................

..................................................................................

..................................................................................

..................................................................................

..................................................................................

..................................................................................

..................................................................................

..................................................................................

..................................................................................

..................................................................................

..................................................................................

.................................................................................. **(6 marks)**

# Answers

## Biology

**1. Plant and animal cells**

1  C **(1)**
2  D **(1)**
3  (a) 1 Cell membrane **(1)**, 2 Ribosome **(1)**,
    3 Nucleus **(1)**, 4 Mitochondria **(1)**
   (b) 1 The cell membrane controls the movements of substances into and out of the cell **(1)**. 2 The ribosomes are where proteins are made (protein synthesis takes place) **(1)**. 3 The nucleus controls all the activities of the cell and contains the genetic material/DNA **(1)**. 4 The mitochondria are where cellular respiration takes place, releasing energy for the cell. **(1)**
4  (a) A chloroplast is an organelle in a plant cell which absorbs light for photosynthesis. **(1)**
   (b) Root cell **(1)** It does not have chloroplasts because the roots are underground so there is no light **(1)** and they don't photosynthesise. **(1)**

**2. Different kinds of cell**

1  B **(1)**
2  (a) A Cytoplasm **(1)**         B Mitochondria **(1)**
   (b) A The nutrients in the cytoplasm provide the egg with the nutrients it needs to start dividing if it is fertilised **(1)**. B The mitochondria provide the energy needed for the sperm to swim towards the egg. **(1)**
   (c) The egg cell **(1)**
   (d) The egg needs to be big to contain the nutrients, and all the structures needed to grow and divide after fertilisation. **(1)**
       The sperm are small because they need to be able to swim through the female reproductive system. **(1)**
3  In non-smokers the ciliated epithelial cells move mucus containing trapped bacteria, viruses, dust and dirt away from the lungs to be removed from the body **(1)**. This prevents many pathogens getting into the body **(1)**. If the ciliated epithelial cells are not working, pathogens get into the lungs where they can cause infectious diseases. **(1)**

**3. Microscopes and magnification**

1  D **(1)**
2  (a) Image X **(1)**
   (b) This cell does not have a nucleus, it has a single chromosome, but cell Y has a nucleus. **(1)** Eukaryotic cells have a nucleus and prokaryotic cells do not **(1)**. This cell is an order of magnitude smaller than cell Y **(1)**. Prokaryotic cells are much smaller than eukaryotic cells. **(1)**
   (c) 2.5 cm = 25 000 μm **(1)**
       Magnification = $\frac{\text{image size}}{\text{real size}}$ = 25 000/10 = x2500 **(1)**
3  (a) Resolution is the smallest distance between two points that can still be seen as two separate points. **(1)**
   (b) They have a much higher magnification **(1)** and much higher resolution **(1)**

4  (a) 5 × 40 = ×200 magnification **(1)**
   (b) Any three from: one uses light to form image, other uses a beam of electrons **(1)**, electron microscope has greater magnification than light microscope **(1)**, electron microscope has greater resolution than light microscope **(1)**, can only view living specimens under light microscope **(1)**, any other valid observation

**4. Dealing with numbers**

1  D **(1)**
2  
| Length of plant cell; | 100 μm; | $1 \times 10^2$ μm | **(1)** |
| Diameter of cell nucleus; | 10 μm; | $1 \times 10^1$ μm | **(1)** |
| Diameter of a rose; | 9 cm   90 000 μm; | $9 \times 10^4$ μm | **(1)** |

3  (a) 1000 nanometres = 1 micrometre **(1)**
   (b) 1000 micrograms = 1 milligram **(1)**
   (c) 0.000000000001 metres = 1 picometre **(1)**
4  (a) 6.0/1 000 000 = 0.000006 mm = $6.0 \times 10^{-9}$ m **(2)**
   (b) 4.5/0.0000075 **(1)** = ×600 000 **(1)**

**5. Using a light microscope**

1  (a) A the eyepiece lens **(1)** B the objective lens **(1)**
       C the stage for the specimens **(1)**
   (b) You multiply the magnification of the eyepiece lens by the magnification of the objective lens to give the overall magnification (eyepiece lens × objective lens). **(1)**
   (c) Never point the mirror directly at the Sun **(1)** because it could burn or damage my eyes. **(1)**
   (d) Never use the coarse focusing wheel with a high power lens **(1)** as it moves the lens too much and may break the slide or damage the lens. **(1)**
2  (a) Add a drop of named stain to the drop of water so the cells show up more clearly. **(1)**
       Lower the coverslip slowly and carefully to avoid trapping air bubbles, which form black circles on the slide, making it harder to see the cells. **(1)**
   (b) Put the low power lens in place **(1)**. Clip the slide securely to the stage of the microscope using the clips provided **(1)**. Adjust the light source so light goes up through the slide (**never** point the mirror directly at the Sun) **(1)**. Look down the microscope, using the coarse focusing wheel and then the fine focusing wheel to focus on the slide. **(1)**

**6. Drawing labelled diagrams**

1  So that if you make a mistake you can rub it out carefully and redraw it. **(1)**
2  (a) It is drawn in pencil **(1)**, it is clearly labelled **(1)**, it has a title. **(1)**
   (b) It does not focus on the main cell in the centre of the image (all the cells are drawn in detail) **(1)**, it does not have a scale bar. **(1)**
   (c) Single main cell drawn in detail **(1)**, clean, sharp pencil lines **(1)**, clear labels **(1)**, scale bar **(1)**
3  Single main cell drawn in detail **(1)**, clean, sharp pencil lines **(1)**, clear labels **(1)**, scale bar **(1)**

## 7. Enzymes

1  (a) An enzyme is a biological catalyst which brings about a specific reaction in the body. **(1)**

   (b) Proteins/amino acids **(1)**

   (c) A active site **(1)**    B substrates **(1)**    C product **(1)**

   (d) The shape of the active site matches the shape of the substrate molecules and holds them close together so they react more easily **(1)**. Once the product is formed it no longer fits the active site and so it moves away **(1)**. The shape of the active site of an enzyme only fits the shape of specific substrates so the enzyme will only catalyse specific reactions. **(1)**

2  D **(1)**

3  A   At lower temperatures molecules move relatively slowly so substrate molecules take more time to fit into the active site of the enzyme and the reaction rate is relatively slow. **(1)**

   B   At the optimum temperature (which is around 40 °C) substrate molecules are binding to the active site as fast as the enzyme can process them so it is working as fast as it can. **(1)**

   C   At higher temperatures the protein structure of the enzyme is affected and the active site starts to change shape. It can't bind to the substrate as well so the rate of reaction starts to slow down. **(1)**

   D   At very high temperatures the shape of the active site is destroyed, the enzyme is denatured and can no longer catalyse the reaction. **(1)**

## 8. pH and enzyme activity

1  (a)

| pH | Volume of gas produced in 5 min (cm³) | Rate of catalase reaction (cm³ oxygen/min) |
|----|----|----|
| 4 | 0 | 0 |
| 5 | 5 | 1 |
| 6 | 20 | 4 |
| 7 | 15 | 3 |
| 8 | 2 | 0.5 |

**(3)**

   (b)

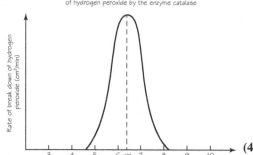

Graph to show the effect of pH on the breakdown of hydrogen peroxide by the enzyme catalase

**(4)**

   (c) Keep the temperature of the reacting mixture constant as temperature also affects the rate of enzyme reactions. **(1)**

## 9. The importance of enzymes

1  (a) Break down large, complex molecules into small molecules **(1)** which can be absorbed into the blood. **(1)**

   (b)

| Enzyme | Where it is found | Reaction catalysed |
|----|----|----|
| amylase | Saliva and the small intestine | Breaking down starch into small sugars |
| catalase | Most cells especially liver | Breaking down hydrogen peroxide to water and oxygen |
| **protease** | Stomach, small intestine | Breaking down proteins to amino acids |
| **lipase** | Small intestine | Breaking down lipids into fatty acids and glycerol |

**(4)**

2  (a) The enzyme catalyses **(1)** the synthesis (building up) of large DNA molecules from smaller subunits. **(1)**

   (b) Inside cells **(1)**

3  Food contains proteins (in egg, meat, etc.), lipids in fatty foods and carbohydrates (starches) **(1)**. If these food molecules get stuck on plates, the enzymes will break them down into small, soluble molecules, which will be washed off in the water. **(1)**

4  (a) Digesting food molecules in the digestive system. Building up and breaking down molecules in the cells

   (b) All reactions in the body controlled by enzymes **(1)**. Enzymes are proteins and are affected by temperature **(1)**. Body temperature low − substrate molecules moving more slowly, bind to active sites more slowly − reactions of body become too slow **(1)**. High temperatures − the active site changes shape so substrate molecules either bind less well or won't bind at all − reactions slow down or stop. **(1)**

## 10. Getting in and out of cells

1  C **(1)**

2  (a) The net movement of molecules from an area of high concentration to an area of low concentration **(1)** down a concentration gradient. **(1)**

   (b) Osmosis is a type of diffusion **(1)**. It involves the net movement of water molecules across a partially permeable membrane/It is the diffusion of water molecules down a concentration gradient, through a semi-permeable membrane. **(1)**

3  This process is called osmosis **(1)**. At the beginning of the experiment, there were more water molecules in the water in the beaker than in the same volume of sucrose solution in the Visking tubing bag **(1)**, so more water molecules moved into the bag than moved the other way out into the beaker **(1)**. This gave a net movement of water into the tubing, so the bag filled and the level in the tube went up **(1)**

4  (a) They are all methods of transport in cells **(1)**

   (b) The net movement of water molecules down a concentration gradient across a partially permeable membrane **(1)**

   (c) Active transport requires energy from respiration **(1)** to move molecules against a concentration gradient **(1)**. The other two processes are passive and do not need energy from respiration to move substances down a concentration gradient. **(1)**

## 11. Osmosis in potatoes

1  (a) C   Blot a piece of potato dry, measure and record its mass, then place it into one of the tubes, recording which tube **(1)**. Repeat for all tubes. **(1)**

       D   After 20 minutes, remove the pieces of potato, blot them dry and re-measure the mass **(1)**. Record all the final masses, making sure you know exactly which piece of potato was in which tube. **(1)**

   (b) It removes surface water **(1)** and so helps to increase the accuracy and reliability of the results.

2  (a)

| Solute concentration (mol dm⁻³) | Initial mass (g) | Final mass (g) | Change in mass (g) | Percentage change in mass (%) |
|----|----|----|----|----|
| 0.0 | 16.52 | 20.15 | 3.63 | 21.97 |
| 0.2 | 15.90 | 16.70 | 0.8 | <u>5.03</u> |
| 0.4 | 17.06 | 15.69 | −1.37 | <u>−8.03</u> |
| 0.6 | 16.88 | 14.36 | −2.52 | <u>−14.93</u> |
| 0.8 | 16.23 | 12.32 | −3.91 | <u>−24.09</u> |

**(2)**

   (b) (i)   Look for clear labels and title, sensible scale, well-drawn graph. **(3)**

       (ii)  Approximately 0.28 mol dm⁻³ **(1)**

## 12. Extended response – Key concepts

Answers could include the following **(6)**:

- Collect five test tubes and fill with the different strength sugar solutions and one with water, using the same volume of liquid for each;
- Label the tubes;
- Cut five equal cylinders of sweet potato, dry and record the mass of each/cut cylinders into small sections/ measure the length and diameter of each/any other sensible suggestion and place one into each of the tubes;
- Dry them to remove surface water and increase accuracy and reliability of results;
- Make sure you record which cylinder went into which tube;
- After 20–30 minutes remove the pieces of sweet potato, blot them dry and re-measure their mass;
- Record all the final masses – making sure you know which cylinder was in which tube;
- Plot the results on a graph – should show when the external solution is the same concentration as the cell contents and show that water moves by osmosis more when the concentration difference is greater.

## 13. Mitosis

1  C **(1)**
2  (a) They have two sets of chromosomes. **(1)**
   (b) They get one set of chromosomes from the mother and one from the father. **(1)**
   (c) They are both identical to the parent cell **(1)**
3  (a) A prophase **(1)**
      B metaphase **(1)**
      C anaphase **(1)**
      D telophase **(1)**
      E cytokinesis **(1)**
   (b) In stage A the nuclear membrane starts to break down around the chromosome copies and spindle fibres appear **(1)**. In stage C the chromosome copies are separated and move to either end of the cell on the spindle fibres **(1)**. In stage E new nuclear membranes have formed around the chromosomes to make two new nuclei and a cell surface membrane forms to separate the two cells **(1)** giving two genetically identical daughter cells. **(1)**

## 14. Cell growth and differentiation

1  D **(1)**
2  (a) The zygote **(1)**
   (b) Mitosis **(1)** so all the cells of the new organism are genetically identical **(1)**
   (c) The cells differentiate to form different types of specialised cells **(1)**. This is important because different types of cells are needed to do different jobs in the body. **(1)**
3  Cancer is the result of changes in cells which lead to uncontrolled cell division **(1)** and the formation of tumours **(1)**. If the noni fruit juice interferes with the stages of mitosis and stops it **(1)** it might be useful as a drug to stop uncontrolled mitosis (cell division) in cancer. **(1)**
4  (a) The region near the tip of a root or shoot where unspecialised cells are found and where cell division/mitosis takes place **(1)**
   (b) Elongation **(1)** and differentiation **(1)**
   (c) For example, red blood cell has no nucleus to give more room for oxygen-carrying haemoglobin molecules **(1)** and their biconcave shape gives a large surface area for maximum diffusion of gases **(1)**; xylem cell – loss of cell contents and end walls to make a hollow tube for water movement **(1)**; spiral lignin walls for strength and to withstand pressure. **(1)**

## 15. Growth and percentile charts

1  (a) A permanent increase in size **(1)**
   (b) Increase in length/height **(1)** increase in mass **(1)**
2  (a) (i)  $1500 - 245 = 1{,}255\,\text{g}$ (units must be given) **(1)**
      (ii) $1950 - 250 = 1{,}700\,\text{g}$ **(1)**
   (b) (i)  $1255/245 \times 100$ **(1)** $= 512\%$ **(1)**
      (ii) $1700/250 \times 100$ **(1)** $= 680\%$ **(1)**
   (c) $680 - 512 = 168\%$ **(1)**
   (d) The plants in set B are grown at 20 °C which is 10 degrees warmer than the other set **(1)**. An increase in temperature means the reactions take place faster, so the plants make more food and grow faster. **(1)**
3  (a) Growth **(1)**     (b) 75th percentile **(1)**
   (c) That it is not growing properly – it is either too heavy or too light **(1)**

## 16. Stem cells

1  B **(1)**
2  (a) Unspecialised cells which divide to produce many different types of cell **(1)**
   (b) Embryonic stem cells and meristem cells can both produce any type of adult cell needed in the body. **(1)** Embryonic stem cells are found in animals, meristem cells are found in plants. **(1)**
   (c) Embryonic stem cells and meristem cells can form any body cell **(1)**, but adult stem cells can only form a limited number of cell types. **(1)**
3  (a) Replacing or repairing damaged cells in the body, for example, in the brain to treat Parkinson's, in the retina to reverse blindness **(1)**; growing new tissues in the lab to use for transplants or drugs testing **(1)**
   (b) Stem cells are good at dividing. Sometimes they do not stop dividing and so may cause cancer in a patient instead of making them better **(1)**. An early human embryo is destroyed when the stem cells are removed. Some people think this is wrong and that the embryo has a right to life. **(1)**
4  The adult stem cells used in human medicine are usually extracted from the patient or from a willing donor, so no embryos are destroyed in the process **(1)**. This removes the ethical issue of using human embryos for some people **(1)**. Also, using adult stem cells extracted from the patient themselves removes any problems of tissue rejection **(1)**. In theory this means it will be safer for the patient and avoids the need to take lifelong anti-rejection/immunosuppressant medication. **(1)**

## 17. Neurones

1  (a) A specialised cell that carries electrical impulses/ nervous impulses **(1)**
   (b) Motor neurones carry impulses away from the central nervous system to effector organs **(1)**. Sensory neurones carry impulses to the central nervous system **(1)**. Relay neurones are found only in the central nervous system linking neurones in the CNS. **(1)**
2  (a) A – Nerve ending, B – axon, C – myelin sheath, D – dendrite **(2)**
   (b) (i)  Part B carries the electrical impulse over long distances around the body. **(1)**
      (ii) Part C insulates the neurone, **(1)** making the impulse jump along the axon, speeding up transmission of the impulse. **(1)**

3

| Motor neurone | Sensory neurone | Relay neurone |
|---|---|---|
| Impulse travels away from CNS | Impulse travels towards CNS | Impulse travels within CNS |
| Cell body at one end | Cell body between the axon and the dendron | Cell body central |
| Has sensory receptor at one end | Has nerve endings in an effector at one end | Links only to other neurones |

**(3)**

**4** (a) Electrical impulses from the receptor cells in the eye are transmitted through sensory neurones to the brain which processes the impulses and you see the fruit **(1)**.

The brain sends impulses through the motor neurones to the muscles of the arm and hand **(1)**. When the effectors receive the impulses, they contract and you pick up the fruit. **(1)**

(b) The myelin sheaths protect the neurones **(1)** and they make the transmission of the electrical impulse faster **(1)**. As the myelin sheath is lost, the signals weaken and travel more slowly until eventually the signals do not reach the muscles, so they cannot contract. **(1)**

## 18. Responding to stimuli

**1** (a) A gap between two neurones **(1)**

(b) A: An electrical impulse travels along the neurone and reaches the end, **(1)** causing a chemical neurotransmitter to be released from vesicles in the neurone into the synapse (gap). **(1)**

B: The neurotransmitter diffuses across the synapse/gap **(1)** and fits into the receptors on the membrane of the neurone on the other side. **(1)**

C: A new electrical impulse starts up and travels along the second neurone. **(1)**

**2** They allow new impulses to be generated in many neurones connected to the one initial neurone, without the electrical signal being split and weakened. **(1)** Neurotransmitters are only released from axon terminals into a synapse so they make sure impulses only flow in one direction along a neurone. **(1)**

**3** (a) Automatic, very rapid response to a stimulus **(1)**

(b) Reflex arcs only involve three neurones **(1)**. If the impulses went to the conscious areas of the brain to be processed it would involve many more synapses which would slow the response down. **(1)**

(c) They protect the body from harmful stimuli **(1)**. They allow basic functions of the body such as breathing to take place without conscious thought. **(1)**

**4** Stimulus (e.g. pinprick) → sensory receptor in skin → impulse in sensory neurone to synapse in spinal cord → synapse with relay neurone in spinal cord → impulse travels along relay neurone to synapse → synapse with motor neurone in spinal cord → impulse travels along motor neurone to effector (e.g. muscle in arm) → muscle contracts to move away from pinprick. **(4)**

## 19. Extended response – Cells and control

Answers could include the following **(6)**:

- Motor neurones carry electrical impulses from the central nervous system to the muscles. The impulse causes a neurotransmitter to cross the synapse from the end of the axon of the motor nerve to the muscle cells.
- When these neurotransmitter chemicals reach the muscle cells they stimulate them to contract. Muscle contraction causes many different responses in the body – for example, they move the limbs so an animal can move around and move the ribs so an animal can breathe.
- Synapses are tiny gaps between two neurones or between a motor neurone and a muscle cell (effector) When an electrical impulse arrives at the end of the axon of the motor nerve, it causes a chemical transmitter to be released from vesicles in the neurone into the gap between the neurone and the muscle cell.
- The neurotransmitter diffuses across the gap and fits into receptors in the membrane of the muscle cell and this stimulates it to contract.
- The poison curare binds to the receptors in the synapse between a motor neurone and a muscle cell.
- As a result, when an impulse travels down the motor nerve and causes neurotransmitter to be released into

the synapse, the neurotransmitter cannot bind to the receptors on the muscle cell. They are already taken up with curare.
- So, the nerves cannot stimulate the muscle cells, the muscle cells cannot contract and the animal is paralysed. Because the breathing muscles are also paralysed, the animal will die.

## 20. Meiosis

**1** A **(1)**

**2** (a) Diploid means a cell has two sets of chromosomes and haploid means a cell has one set of chromosomes. **(1)**

(b) Because two gametes join together to form a new diploid cell. **(1)**

(c) The original cell is diploid, but the daughter cells are haploid. **(1)**

**3** Cell A is the cell which is going to divide to make the gametes. It is diploid – it has two sets of chromosomes **(1)**. The chromosomes replicate (make copies of themselves) and the copies stay stuck together (see Stage B) **(1)**. The cell divides in two, rather like mitosis, producing two cells with two sets of chromosomes (Stage C) **(1)**. Then these two cells immediately divide again. Each of the final four daughter cells is haploid/ has only one set of chromosomes (see Stage D). **(1)**

## 21. DNA

**1** C **(1)**

**2** A chromosome consists of a long molecule of DNA tightly coiled up and held together by proteins **(1)**. A gene is a section of DNA which codes for a protein **(1)**. DNA is the genetic material making up the chromosomes in the nuclei of cells. **(1)**

**3** (a) The structure formed as the two strands of a DNA molecule coil around each other is known as a double helix. **(1)**

(b) A phosphate group **(1)** B sugar **(1)** C complementary base pairs **(1)**

(c) X is a hydrogen bond **(1)**. Hydrogen bonds are formed when the slightly negatively charged part of one base is attracted to the slightly positive part of another base **(1)**. These weak forces of attraction hold the DNA molecule together. **(1)**

**4** (a) It is made up of many monomers/small units joined together. **(1)**

(b) The same bases always link together, for example, A with T. **(1)**

(c) Complementary base to adenine is thymine (T) **(1)** and to guanine is cytosine (C). **(1)**

(d) DNA makes up the chromosomes which are held inside the nucleus of the cell **(1)**. Both the nucleus and the cell are surrounded by membranes **(1)** so to extract the DNA from the nucleus you need to use detergent to break open both the cell and nuclear membranes. **(1)**

## 22. Genetic terms

**1** Base, gene, chromosome, genome **(2)**

**2** (a) A short piece of DNA on a chromosome which codes for a particular characteristic **(1)**

(b) Alleles are different forms of the same gene **(1)**, which code for different variations of the same characteristic. **(1)**

**3** Genotype: the alleles present in an organism for a particular characteristic **(1)**. Example: the mouse in the photograph will have inherited an allele for brown coat from its mother and an allele for white coat from its father **(1)** so its genotype is Bb. **(1)**

Phenotype: the characteristics of an individual as a result of its genotype, including its physical appearance **(1)**. Example: the mouse in the photograph is brown. **(1)**

Dominant allele: the characteristic coded for appears in the phenotype even if only one allele is present in the genotype **(1)**. Example: the mouse in the photo has one brown allele and one white allele, but it has a brown coat **(1)** so the brown allele B is dominant. **(1)**
Recessive allele: the characteristic coded for only appears in the phenotype if two copies of the allele are present in the genotype **(1)**. Example: the mouse in the photo has one brown allele and one white allele, but it has a brown coat **(1)** so the white allele b does not show up in the phenotype − it is recessive. **(1)**

**4** (a) Homozygous means both alleles are the same, **(1)** heterozygous means the alleles are different. **(1)**

   (b) (i)  RR Homozygous, has round peas **(1)**
      (ii)  Rr Heterozygous, has round peas **(1)**
      (iii) rr Homozygous, has wrinkled peas **(1)**

### 23. Monohybrid inheritance

**1** (a)

|   | T | t |
|---|---|---|
| t | Tt | tt |
| t | Tt | tt |

**(1)**

½ of the kittens will have the genotype Tt and so their phenotype will be Manx/tailess. This is $\frac{2}{4} \times 100 = 50\%$ **(1)**

½ of the kittens will have the genotype tt and so their phenotype will be to have a tail. This is $\frac{2}{4} \times 100 = 50\%$ **(1)**

   (b) Manx cat genotype Tt **(1)**

   (c) The ratio of kittens with a dominant allele which gives the Manx form to kittens who inherit homozygous recessive alleles is 3:1. **(1)**

|   | T | t |
|---|---|---|
| T | TT | Tt |
| t | Tt | tt |

   (d) 2:1 **(1)**, because any kittens born with the homozygous TT will die before they are born **(1)**

**2** Cross 1: Purple flowers are homozygous dominant, RR, and white flowers are homozygous recessive, rr.

|   | R | R |
|---|---|---|
| r | Rr | Rr |
| r | Rr | Rr |

**(1)**

100% of the offspring have the genotype Rr and the phenotype purple flowers. **(1)**

Cross 2: Purple flowers are heterozygous, Rr, and white flowers are homozygous recessive, rr.

|   | R | r |
|---|---|---|
| r | Rr | rr |
| r | Rr | rr |

**(1)**

50% of the offspring have the genotype Rr and the phenotype purple flowers. 50% of the offspring have the genotype rr and the phenotype white flowers. **(1)**

### 24. Family pedigrees

**1** (a) C **(1)**

   (b) They both have the dominant phenotype so must have at least one dominant allele A **(1)**. They have an albino child so they must both have carried and passed on a recessive albino allele a **(1)**. So, they must both be heterozygotes (Aa). **(1)**

   (c) Individual 4 is aa. Individual 3 does not have albinism **(1)**. The allele for normal colouring A is dominant. So, the genotype of individual 3 could be AA or Aa. **(1)**

|   | A | A |
|---|---|---|
| a | Aa | Aa |
| a | Aa | Aa |

AA × aa: All the children are unaffected by albinism, which is what we see. **(1)**

|   | A | a |
|---|---|---|
| a | Aa | aa |
| a | Aa | aa |

Aa × aa: There is a 1 in 2 chance that a child will have albinism **(1)** but in this case they all inherited a normal allele from their father and all are unaffected. **(1)**

**2** The combination of alleles from the mother and father that combine to form a zygote is always a matter of chance **(1)**. In both couples, one parent has a dominant Huntington's allele but is heterozygous (Hh) [you can see this by looking at the genotype of their parents, couple 1 and 2] and the other does not, so the genetic cross is the same in both cases. **(1)**

Hh × hh
Each time one of these couples conceives, there is a 50% chance their baby will be affected by Huntington's

|   | H | h |
|---|---|---|
| h | Hh | hh |
| h | Hh | hh |

and a 50% chance it will be healthy **(1)**. Couple 3 and 4 were lucky both times they had a child, couple 8 and 9 were lucky twice, but in one case the sperm which fertilised the egg was carrying the dominant allele for Huntington's and so the child was affected. **(1)**

### 25. Sex determination

**1** D **(1)**

**2** C **(1)**

**3** (a)

|   | X | Y |
|---|---|---|
| X | XX | XY |
| X | XX | XY |

**(2)**

   (b) Each baby gets one set of chromosomes from the mother and one from the father **(1)**. Each time a baby is conceived there is a 50% chance it will be a boy and a 50% chance it will be a girl **(1)**. The outcome is not affected by the sex of any other children a couple may have so the new baby has a 50:50 chance of being a boy or a girl **(1)**. Both sets of friends are wrong. **(1)**

**4** Gametes produced by meiosis which gives haploid cells (with a single set of chromosomes). As the sex chromosomes in a woman's diploid body cell are both X, all the eggs she produces will contain one X chromosome so they can all form half of a female zygote **(1)**. The sex chromosomes in a man's diploid body cells are XY, so when they divide by meiosis to form the gametes **(1)** 50% of his sperm will contain one X chromosome so they can form a female zygote **(1)** and the other 50% will contain one Y chromosome so they can form a male zygote. **(1)**

### 26. Variation and mutation

**1** Genetic variation, for example, eye colour, natural hair colour: environmental variation, for example, scars, being able to drive **(1)**

**2** B **(1)**

**3** (a) A change in the sequence of bases in the DNA which forms a new allele **(1)**

   (b) Mistakes made when a cell divides, **(1)** radiation damage **(1)**

   (c) The sequence of bases in the DNA codes for the amino acids which are joined together in protein synthesis to make a protein **(1)**. If a mutation affects the base sequences so that different amino acids are joined in the protein chain **(1)**, this will affect the properties of the protein which in turn may affect the phenotype of the organism. **(1)**

**4** (a) The number of times it appears in a population **(1)**

   (b) That the characteristic it is measuring shows continuous variation **(1)**

**5**

**(4)**

# Answers

(b) Age of child within the class – there can be as much as a year difference in Year 6 – environmental **(1)**. How well the child is fed – environmental **(1)**. Parents may be very tall/have big feet – genetic. **(1)**

## 27. The Human Genome Project
1 (a) The human genome is all of the bases in all the DNA in a human cell. **(1)**
 (b) A collaboration between scientists set up to decode the complete human genome. **(1)**
 (c) It enables them to look at how the genome of the person interacts with the medicine **(1)** as some alleles make people more or less affected by a particular drug. **(1)**
2 (a) Advantage 1: A person who is at risk from a genetic condition or has a genetic tendency towards a particular condition such as heart disease can make lifestyle changes to minimise their risks. **(1)** Advantage 2: Doctors may be able to tailor treatments to an individual when their alleles mean they are particularly sensitive to or affected by a medicine/can distinguish between different forms of a disease so the best medicine can be used. **(1)**
 (b) If you know you have an increased risk of developing something like heart disease or breast cancer you may have to pay more for life insurance. **(1)**
3 If you know you have a number of alleles increasing your risk of developing heart disease you can try to protect yourself, for example, lifestyle changes such as low fat diet and plenty of exercise, regular check-ups, monitoring weight and blood pressure, etc. **(1)**. So a test could give you the power to reduce your risks as much as you can **(1)**. However, you would have the stress of knowing you had a higher risk which could increase the risk further **(1)**. Life insurance could be expensive **(1)**. Knowing you don't have the high risk alleles for heart disease could lead to you living a very unhealthy lifestyle and getting other problems, for example, type 2 diabetes. **(1)**

## 28. Extended response – Genetics
Answers could include the following points **(6)**:
- A mutation is a change in the arrangement of the bases in the DNA, which may or may not affect the phenotype. The mutated allele H is dominant, which means if you inherit the allele from just one parent you will develop the disease. In the case of Huntington's disease, it causes changes which usually appear in middle age and lead to serious illness and death.
- Key: h = normal, H = Huntington's disease

| | H | h |
|---|---|---|
| h | Hh | hh |
| h | Hh | hh |

- Or: If one of your parents has the allele, you have a 50% chance of inheriting it/If you have the allele, you have a 50% chance of passing it on to your children.
- The HGP enables us to identify the faulty allele that causes Huntington's disease and develop a test to show if someone has the allele. The main advantage of having the test for the Huntington's mutation is that you know what is coming. If you don't have the allele you can forget about it. If you do have the allele, although there is nothing you can do to stop the disease developing, you can plan your life, make choices about whether to have children or, if you do have children, choose whether to use pre-implantation diagnosis to be sure your children are not going to be affected. You can plan your finances, etc.
- The disadvantages of having the test include the fact that other members of your family, for example, your parents may not want to be tested, but your result could tell them if they have the allele. Also, it is an incurable

disease and the knowledge you are going to become ill could be difficult to deal with as there is nothing you can do to reduce the risk.

## 29. Evolution
1 Adult organisms usually produce more offspring than the environment can support. As a result, there is competition between the young to survive and reproduce. **(1)**
↓
Some of the offspring inherit advantageous variations making them better adapted to survive in a particular environment. Others inherit variations which are less well suited to that particular environment. **(1)**
↓
Individuals with the advantageous variations are more likely to survive and reproduce, passing the advantageous variations on to their offspring. **(1)**
↓
The number of individuals with the advantageous variations in the population will increase. **(1)**
2 Darwin's theory of evolution by natural selection states that the individuals which survive to reproduce will be the ones with the most advantageous variations for a particular environment **(1)**. Those advantageous characteristics will become more common. Eventually, if populations are separated, they will become separate species adapted for different environments **(1)**. Aloes and agaves both live in very similar desert environments. They both show characteristics which help them survive in a desert/fleshy leaves, ability to store water, spines to stop animals eating them **(1)**. As a result of natural selection, these characteristics will have survived and become more and more common in each generation, so the different species have ended up looking very similar even though they are in very different parts of the world **(1)**. They may have had a common ancestor, but have evolved/changed due to the separation of land mass. **(1)**

## 30. Human evolution
1 (a) Fossils **(1)** (b) The lack of fossils **(1)**
 (c) The volume of the skull gives us a measure of the brain volume, **(1)** and the big increase in the size of the brain in relation to the size of the body was an important factor in human evolution. **(1)**
2 The layers of rock where stone tools were found have been dated. Earliest stone tools found (about 3.3 million years old) are relatively simple (when human ancestors had relatively small brains) **(1)**. More modern stone tools are more sophisticated – scientists think this reflects increasing brain volume – thought and coordination improved. **(1)**
3 Any four, for example: Species have got taller (Ardi was only 1.2 m tall, each successive species taller) **(1)**. Skull volume and therefore brain volume has increased from 350 cm³ to 1450 cm³ **(1)**. The relative length of the arms has reduced **(1)**. The arrangement of the toes has changed from big toes sticking out for gripping in trees to modern toes aligned to the front **(1)**. Teeth have changed – got smaller and less specialised **(1)**. Dome of the skull has got bigger and rounder to accommodate the brain **(1)**. Brow ridge has reduced. **(1)**

## 31. Classification
1 D **(1)**
2.

| Kingdom | Characteristics |
|---|---|
| Animals | 1 multicellular<br>2 cells have nuclei<br>3 no cell walls |

| Kingdom | Characteristics |
|---------|-----------------|
| Plants | 1 multicellular/cell have nuclei<br>2 chloroplasts for photosynthesis<br>3 cellulose cell walls |
| Fungi | 1 multicellular (apart from yeasts)/cells have nuclei<br>2 all feed off dead matter or other living organisms/ saprophytes or parasites<br>3 cell walls contain chitin, but **not** cellulose |
| Protists | 1 mostly unicellular<br>2 cells have nuclei<br>3 some cells have cell walls, but not made of chitin or cellulose |
| Prokaryotes | 1 unicellular<br>2 cells do not have nuclei<br>3 cell walls are flexible, not made of chitin or cellulose |

(5)

3  (a) A system of classifying all living organisms into one of three domains **(1)**

(b) Archea − cells with no nucleus, genes contain unused sections of DNA **(1)** Bacteria − cells with no nucleus and no unused sections in the genes **(1)** Eukaryota − cells with a nucleus and unused sections in the genes **(1)**

(c) The three domain classification system is based on differences in the way the DNA of the different organisms is organised and how it works **(1)**. It is also based on chemical differences in the ribosomes **(1)**. These differences could not be detected until the technology needed to read the DNA code and analyse cell organelles had been developed and this only happened from the 1970s onwards. **(1)**

## 32. Selective breeding

1  D **(1)**

2  (a) It is when plants or animals with desirable characteristics are chosen to breed together so the offspring produced inherit the favourable characteristics. **(1)**

(b) Any three from: disease resistance **(1)** increased yield **(1)** faster growth **(1)** better flavour **(1)** ability to cope with difficult conditions **(1)**

3  The breeder would choose two cats − male and female − with very little hair **(1)**. Then they would choose the kittens with the least hair and when they grew up, breed them with other cats with very little fur **(1)**. This would be repeated for many generations until a breed of cats with little or no hair is produced. **(1)**

4  (a) They remained stable and relatively low until after 1945−50 **(1)**. Then the yields increased steadily and significantly from just over 2 tonnes per hectare to over 8 tonnes per hectare until around 1980 **(1)**. Since then yields have stabilised and continued to increase, but very slowly. **(1)**

(b) Selective breeding − artificial selection of the wheat which gives the highest yield and breeding it for generations **(1)** adding high quality fertilisers **(1)**

(c) If the wheat ears become too heavy, they break the stalk and then they can't be harvested or they stop growing **(1)**. So, have to find a balance between wheat which gives a big yield and wheat which doesn't get blown over if there is a storm **(1)**. Can selectively breed for shorter, stronger stems and well as high yield to get the maximum crop. **(1)**

## 33. Genetic engineering

1  (a) Genetic engineering is changing the DNA of an organism, often by inserting genes (sections of DNA) from another organism. **(1)**

(b) The gene for a desired characteristic is cut out of a chromosome using enzymes **(1)**. The gene is inserted into a chromosome inside the nucleus of a cell in a different organism. **(1)** The cell of the engineered organism now produces the characteristic coded for by the new gene. **(1)**

2  (a) An organism which has had its DNA altered, often by having a gene from a different organism added **(1)**

(b) Advantage: they can be very useful to humans, for example, make chemicals we need, resist pests and help us identify pollutants, etc. **(1)**. Disadvantage: Some people feel it is wrong because it is not natural/ if genetically modified organisms breed with wild organisms it could upset the balance of nature. **(1)**

3  (a) No bacteria contain the human gene to make human insulin **(1)**. They only have bacterial genes. They had to genetically modify the bacteria to add the human gene they needed. **(1)**

(b) The gene for making insulin was identified and cut out of a human chromosome **(1)**. It was then inserted into the bacterial chromosome, so that the bacterium made insulin **(1)**. When the bacterium divides, it makes new copies of the human gene in its DNA so the offspring can also make human insulin. **(1)**

## 34. Stages in genetic engineering

1  D **(1)**

2  (a) Specific enzymes called restriction enzymes cut the required gene out of the DNA of a human cell **(1)**. They leave staggered ends on the DNA fragments − these are called sticky ends. **(1)**

(b) The same restriction enzymes are used to cut open a plasmid in the bacterial cell **(1)**, leaving matching sticky ends (plasmids are small circles of DNA found in bacterial cells). **(1)**

(c) The pieces of DNA containing the human growth hormone gene are mixed with the cut plasmids **(1)**. The complementary bases on the sticky ends pair up. **(1)** An enzyme called DNA ligase joins the ends together **(1)**. The plasmids act as vectors when they are inserted back into the bacteria, carrying the new genes. **(1)**

(d) The bacteria reproduce and divide making huge numbers of bacteria all carrying the new human gene so they can make a lot of human growth hormone. **(1)**

3  Restriction enzymes cut the DNA in specific places, leaving sticky ends **(1)** − sequences of bases which will line up with the complementary bases of the host DNA **(1)**. They are used to both cut out the desired gene and to open up the host DNA **(1)**. DNA ligase enzymes join together sections of DNA with complementary sticky ends **(1)**, so they are used to attach to desired gene into the host DNA. **(1)**

## 35. Extended response − Genetic modification

Answers could include the following points **(6)**

- Evolution is a process of natural selection which often takes place over long periods of time. The organisms with alleles which give them adaptations suited to their environment are most likely to survive and reproduce, passing on their alleles until a new species arises.
- Selective breeding is when the characteristics selected for are chosen by people and only organisms with the desired characteristics are allowed to breed. It can take many years.
- In genetic engineering scientists choose specific alleles and insert them in organisms to give them desired characteristics. It can be very rapid.
- Selective breeding has produced many very useful organisms for people over time, but the organisms can only interbreed with organisms of the same species so the changes that can be achieved are limited.

- Genetic engineering makes it possible to take genes from one type of organism and place them in an entirely different type of organism in a relatively fast process. This means we can make some extremely useful organisms, but there are some ethical issues about moving genes between species, and so far, there are limits to what can be engineered.

### 36. Health and disease
1 (a) A disease which can be passed from one person to another **(1)**
  (b) Pathogens **(1)**     (c) B **(1)**
2 (a) Being free from disease **(1)**
  (b) Getting on well with other people/having a good social network supporting you **(1)**
  (c) Feeling good about yourself **(1)**
3 (a) A microorganism which causes communicable disease **(1)**
  (b)

| Pathogen | How do they make you ill? |
|---|---|
| Bacteria | May release toxins in their host/damage body cells |
| Viruses | Take over the DNA of a body cell, so the cell makes new viruses which damage the cell when they are released |
| Fungi | Eukaryotic organisms which dissolve and damage cells |
| Protists | Eukaryotic organisms which can live in the body and damage cells |

**(4)**

4 If you have a disease which affects the immune system, you will be more likely to get other infectious diseases as the immune system will not be able to fight them **(1)**. If you have a disease which stops one organ working properly you will be unwell and so more likely to get another infectious disease/if you have a disease due to poor nutrition your whole body will be affected and you may be more likely to get both communicable and non-communicable diseases. **(1)**

### 37. Common infections
1 C **(1)**
2 (a) 8000 **(1)**     (b) $\frac{6000}{8000} \times 100 = 75\%$ **(2)**
  (c) HIV is a viral infection which attacks the immune system **(1)**. When the immune system is not working properly people are much more likely to pick up another infection such as TB **(1)** because their immune system cannot fight the infection. **(1)**
3

| Pathogen | Disease | Symptoms |
|---|---|---|
| Bacterium | Cholera/tuberculosis/stomach ulcers | Diarrhoea/lung damage/damage to stomach lining |
| Virus | HIV/ Ebola | Mild infections followed by damage to immune system and many other infections/internal bleeding, fever, severe headaches, diarrhoea |
| Protist | Malaria | Fever, weakness, chills, sweating |

**(6)**

### 38. How pathogens spread
1 D **(1)**
2 (a) Bacteria **(1)**
  (b) Large amounts of pale, watery diarrhoea **(1)**
  (c) The bacteria that cause cholera pass out of the body in diarrhoea **(1)**. If there is a good sewage system, the bacteria do not come into contact with other people so the disease does not spread **(1)**. After natural disasters sewage systems are often destroyed so diarrhoea gets into water used for drinking, washing, etc. and so the bacteria spread rapidly from one person to another **(1)**.

3 A pathogen is a microorganism which causes an infectious disease. **(1)**
  A vector is a living organism (e.g. mosquito) which carries a pathogen from one host to another. **(1)**
4 (a) Pathogens pass out of the body in the faeces **(1)**. Washing your hands removes the pathogens so you cannot pass them on to someone else. **(1)**
  (b) Pathogens from bodily waste can find their way into the drinking water if there is poor sewage treatment **(1)**. Boiling water kills pathogens such as bacteria and protists and prevents the spread of disease. **(1)**
  (c) The pathogens causing the disease are trapped in the tissue and then thrown away, avoiding droplet infection in the air **(1)**. Washing your hands then removes any pathogens which might be left so if you touch surfaces you won't pass the pathogens to other people who touch the surfaces and then put their fingers in their mouths. **(1)**

### 39. STIs
1 D [STIs are usually curable; HIV is the exception] **(1)**
2 (a) STIs are spread by contact with sexual fluids containing the pathogens **(1)**. If a man wears a condom, it prevents him coming into contact with the sexual fluids of his partner **(1)** and prevents his partner coming into contact with his semen which will contain pathogens if he is infected with an STI. **(1)**
  (b) A woman can have these STIs without knowing **(1)**. The pathogens can be passed from a mother to her unborn child and cause damage to the child **(1)**. If the infection is picked up by screening it can be treated which protects the baby, or the baby can be treated as soon as it is born. **(1)**
3 *Using condoms during sexual intercourse*: Prevents sexual/bodily fluids from an infected person coming into contact with a healthy person and infecting them **(1)**. *Screening blood transfusions for STIs*: The pathogens causing STIs can be passed into a healthy person through an infected blood transfusion **(1)**. Screening blood for STIs before it is used prevents that happening **(1)**. *Increasing sex education for young people*: Many people do not understand much about STIs, for example, that you can have an STI without knowing, or that they can be passed from mother to baby **(1)**. They also do not know how to treat or prevent STIs **(1)**. Better education would mean people who are likely to have different sexual partners would be better informed and better able to protect themselves from STIs and get appropriate treatment if they become infected **(1)**. *Supplying intravenous drug users with sterile needles*: If someone infected with an STI uses a needle to inject drugs, and someone else who does not have an STI then uses the same needle, that person may become infected with the STI **(1)**. If drug users are all provided with sterile needles, they will not need to share needles and the spread of STIs will be reduced. **(1)**

### 40. Human defences
1 C **(1)**
2 (a) Unbroken skin forms a physical barrier between pathogens and the inside of the body **(1)** because it is too thick and tough for most pathogens to get through **(1)**
  (b) The acid in the stomach acts as a chemical barrier to pathogens **(1)** – it destroys most of the pathogens you take into your body in food and drink or you swallow in your mucus. **(1)**
  (c) Tears act as a chemical barrier to pathogens **(1)** as they contain the enzyme lysozyme which breaks

down the cell walls of bacteria and destroys them. **(1)** (They also wash bacteria out of the eyes.)

3  (a)  A  mucus **(1)**          B  cilia **(1)**
        C  ciliated epithelial cell **(1)**
    (b)  Mucus in the nose and tubes leading to the lungs traps pathogens such as bacteria **(1)**. Some of the cells lining the nose and the tubes in the breathing system have cilia. The cilia beat and move mucus away from the lungs to the throat where it is swallowed and the pathogens are destroyed by the stomach acid. **(1)**
    (c)  Chemicals in cigarette smoke paralyse/damage the cilia in the nose and trachea **(1)**. The paralysed/damaged cilia cannot move the mucus to the back of the throat to be swallowed **(1)**. The mucus travels down to the lungs, taking the pathogens with it. The pathogens can cause chest infections. **(1)**

## 41. The immune system

1  A **(1)**
2  (a)  White blood cells called lymphocytes have antibodies on their surface **(1)**. The shape of each antibody matches the shape of the antigens on a specific pathogen **(1)**. If the pathogen is present, a lymphocyte with the right antibody will attach to it. **(1)**
    (b)  A lymphocyte is activated when an antigen from a pathogen fits into the antibodies on the surface of the lymphocyte **(1)**. It then divides over and over again to produce clones of identical lymphocytes **(1)**. These cloned lymphocytes release large amounts of antibodies which bind to the antigens on the pathogens and destroy them. **(1)**
    (c)  Some of the activated lymphocytes form memory cells **(1)**. When you meet the same pathogen again, they can make the right antibodies and destroy the pathogens before you develop symptoms of the disease. **(1)**
3  (a)  The person has a second infection with the same pathogen **(1)**
    (b)  A is the primary response to the pathogen **(1)**, B is the secondary response to the same pathogen. **(1)**
    (c)  After the primary response, memory cells are formed which have the right antigens ready for that particular pathogen. They remain in your system **(1)**. If that pathogen enters your body for a second time, there is an immediate production of antibodies and an immediate rapid cloning of activated cells to make even more antibodies **(1)**. This is why the response is both faster and results in more antibodies being made. **(1)**

## 42. Immunisation

1  (a)  Immunisation is when you give a person a vaccine to prevent them from becoming ill from a particular disease in the future. **(1)**
    (b)  A vaccine is a medicine made of inactivated pathogens injected into the body of a person, or taken by mouth **(1)**, to produce immunity to the disease caused by that type of pathogen. **(1)**
2  Natural immunity results from your exposure to a live pathogen, when you get a disease **(1)**. In artificial immunity, inactivated pathogens are injected into the body (or taken by mouth/nose), so you never get the disease **(1)**. In both natural and artificial immunity, the antigens on the pathogens/inactivated pathogens trigger an immune response and so the body builds up memory cells carrying the antibodies for the antigens on the pathogens/inactivated pathogens **(1)**. If you then

meet the live pathogen, a normal secondary immune response takes place, with the rapid production of many antibodies which will destroy the pathogen before it can cause disease. **(1)**
3  (a)  It contains the inactivated pathogens of five different diseases **(1)**
    (b)  When a lymphocyte becomes activated, it produces many cloned lymphocytes making many antibodies **(1)**. These attach to the antigens on a particular type of pathogen and destroy it **(1)**. The antigen-antibody reaction depends on the exact shape of the antigen and the antibody **(1)**. Antibodies produced against one pathogen would not fit onto the antigens on the surface of a different type of pathogen **(1)**, and so would not be able to destroy it and prevent disease. **(1)**

## 43. Treating infections

1  D **(1)**
2  (a)  Because they affect bacterial cells but do not affect human cells **(1)**
    (b)  They can kill bacteria **(1)** or they can inhibit their cell processes, which stops them growing and reproducing **(1)**
    (c)  Colds are caused by viruses **(1)**. Antibiotics do not have any effect on viruses so they would not help the child get better. **(1)**
3  (a)  875/100 000 live births **(2)**
    (b)  The beginning of widespread use of antibiotics to treat infections in women after they gave birth **(1)**
    (c)  The over-use of antibiotics has led to an increase in antibiotic resistance in pathogens **(1)**. This means they are no longer harmed by the antibiotics **(1)**. If the number of antibiotic-resistant bacteria keeps increasing, the time will come when antibiotics are no longer effective against them, and so people will once more die in large numbers from infectious diseases **(1)**.
        On the other hand, new medicines are being developed all the time, and doctors and scientists are working to reduce the development of antibiotic resistance so this may never happen. **(1)**

## 44. New medicines

1  C **(1)**
2  (a)  Because they don't know exactly which chemical is doing what. There may be side effects **(2)**
    (b)  (i)   Testing new medicines in the laboratory **(1)** to check that the drugs are taken into the cells and seem to have the desired effect **(1)**
        (ii)  Testing on cultures of cells **(1)**; Testing on cultures of tissues **(1)**; Testing on whole living animals **(1)**
    (c)  It goes into clinical testing **(1)**. First it is tried on a small number of healthy people to make sure the drug is not toxic **(1)**, and then it is tried on a larger number of people with the disease the drug is intended to treat, to see if it has the desired effect. **(1)**
3  (a)  In case they have unexpected side effects which may be harmful **(1)**
    (b)  A measure of how well it works **(1)**
    (c)  The best dose to give the patient – usually the lowest dose that treats the disease **(1)**
    (d)  It means it is harmful to the patient **(1)**
    (e)  Because there is always a limit to the number of people in clinical trials **(1)**. Once the medicine is being prescribed by doctors, thousands of people will be using the drug **(1)** and so there is more chance of picking up any adverse side effects. **(1)**

### 45. Non-communicable diseases

1  (a) They cannot be passed directly from one person to another. **(1)**

   (b) Genes **(1)**, age **(1)**, lifestyle **(1)**, environment/sex **(1)**

2  (a) 51 − 2 = 49% **(1)**

   (b) 87% risk for breast cancer compared with 63% risk for ovarian cancer **(1)**

   (c) (i) Age **(1)**

      (ii) It increases the risk **(1)** – from around 51% by the age of 50 to around 87% by the age of 70 **(1)**. Over those 20 years the gene stays the same, but the risk increases. **(1)**

3  Age: e.g. the older you get, the more likely it is that cells will develop mutations leading to cancer/any other sensible answer **(1)**. Lifestyle factors: e.g., if we don't get enough to eat we may develop deficiency diseases such as lack of vitamin C (scurvy)/any other sensible answer **(1)**. Environmental factors: e.g. air pollution/asbestos can cause lung disease/any other sensible answer **(1)**. Gender: e.g., breast cancer rates are 100 times higher in women than men/any other sensible answer **(1)**.

### 46. Alcohol and smoking

1  B **(1)**

2  (a) Brazil, USA, Australia, Russia/UK, UK/Russia **(1)**

   (b) Australia, USA, UK, Brazil, Russia **(1)**

   (c) A  Russia is one of the countries which drinks the most alcohol per person per year, and also has the most deaths from liver disease, which is linked to drinking alcohol. **(1)**

      B  The UK appears to drink a similar amount of alcohol to Russia, but far fewer people die of liver diseases, Australia drinks a lot of alcohol, but has the lowest number of deaths from liver disease **(1)** – facts like these suggest that other factors are also important. **(1)**

3  (a) A disease which is caused by particular aspects of the way we live such as diet, smoking, alcohol, etc. **(1)**

   (b) Carbon monoxide reduces the amount of oxygen which can be carried by the blood **(1)**. Nicotine is an addictive drug **(1)**. Tar contains chemicals which can cause cancers **(1)**. Chemicals in the smoke can make the blood vessels narrow, which increases blood pressure and can lead to cardiovascular disease. **(1)**

### 47. Malnutrition and obesity

1  (a) When someone eats too little or too much of a nutrient in their diet **(1)**

   (b) For example, anaemia through lack of iron in the diet/rickets through lack of vitamin D or calcium in the diet **(1)**

2  (a) Body mass index **(1)**      (b) $\text{BMI} = \dfrac{\text{weight (kg)}}{(\text{height (m)})^2}$ **(1)**

   (c) $\text{BMI} = \dfrac{70}{1.6^2} = \dfrac{70}{2.56}$ **(1)** = 27.34 **(1)**

   A BMI of over 30 is obese, so this man is not obese. **(1)**

3  (a) An alternative way to BMI of measuring obesity **(1)**, where the waist measurement is divided by the hip measurement **(1)**

   (b) They show that an increase in obesity appears to increase the risk of death from cardiovascular disease **(1)**, although a very low BMI also seems to be linked to a slight raise in the risk of death from cardiovascular disease. **(1)**

   (c) Waist : hip ratio gives reliable estimate of obesity levels regardless of the activity levels **(1)** and body makeup of an individual **(1)**. BMI can be an unreliable indicator of obesity in people who are very fit and muscular, when they may be heavy but as a result of muscles not fat. **(1)**

### 48. Cardiovascular disease

1  Substances from tobacco smoke damage the artery lining. **(1)**
   Fat builds up on the artery wall at the site of the damage **(1)**, making the artery narrower. **(1)**
   A blood clot may block the artery where it is damaged **(1)**, or break off and block an artery in another part of the body **(1)**, causing a heart attack or stroke. **(1)**

2  (a) Lose weight **(1)**, give up smoking **(1)**, take more exercise **(1)**, eat a healthy diet (low fat, salt and sugar) **(1)**

   (b) Advantages (two of these): no side effects **(1)**, cheap **(1)**, may help prevent other diseases. **(1)**
   Disadvantages (one of these): may not work **(1)**, may be too late **(1)**

3

| Advantages of taking drugs to treat cardiovascular disease | Disadvantages of taking drugs to treat cardiovascular disease |
|---|---|
| Have an immediate effect | Need to be taken long term |
| Relatively cheaper than surgery/less risky than surgery | Can have side effects/may not work well with other medication |

   **(4)**

4  (a) The coronary arteries supply blood to the heart **(1)**. If they become narrowed or blocked the heart muscle cannot get enough oxygen, the cells die **(1)** and the person has a heart attack. **(1)**

   (b) A wire frame inserted into an artery to hold it open **(1)**

   (c) A blood vessel taken from somewhere else in the body is inserted to bypass blocked coronary arteries. **(1)**

   (d) Surgery carries a risk that the patient will die **(1)** or may develop an infection after surgery **(1)**. It is more difficult and time-consuming than giving medication **(1)** and it is also more expensive **(1)**. Lifestyle changes or medication are cheaper and less risky so they are usually tried first. **(1)**

### 49. Extended response – Health and disease

Answers could include the following points **(6)**

- The risk of any individual developing a non-communicable disease, such as lung cancer and heart disease, is the result of a number of different factors. These include age, sex, genetic inheritance, the environment you live in and the lifestyle you lead.
- Strong scientific evidence from many studies shows that smoking regularly increases the risk of developing a number of diseases, such as lung cancer and heart disease.
- Based on statistics, most smokers live less long than most non-smokers.
- Similar evidence shows that drinking relatively large amounts of alcohol regularly over time increases the risk of a person developing liver or brain diseases.
- In an individual like the woman in the newspaper reports, she has lifestyle factors, such as smoking and drinking, which increase her risk of developing lung cancer, heart disease, liver disease, etc. She is also old, which increases her risk of developing many diseases including different types of cancers.
- However, she is a woman, which may have protected her against some diseases, for example, heart disease for many years until she was over the menopause. Most importantly, she may have inherited alleles which mean she is very unlikely to develop certain cancers and heart disease, whatever her lifestyle or environment.

### 50. Photosynthesis

1  (a) C **(1)**

   (b) carbon dioxide + water **(1)** → glucose + oxygen **(1)**

   (c) Chloroplasts **(1)**

(d) The products of the reaction have more energy than the reactants **(1)** so energy is transferred from the surroundings during the reaction. **(1)**

2 (a) To make sure the plant had used up all of the starch stored in its leaves **(1)**, so any starch detected in the investigation is the result of new photosynthesis. **(1)**

(b) A is blue-black indicating the presence of starch because the leaf had been in the light and photosynthesising during the day **(1)**, so it has made glucose which has been converted to starch. **(1)**

(c) B is orange because the black card stops light reaching the leaf **(1)** so it cannot photosynthesise and make starch. **(1)**

(d) C is orange where the black card has covered the leaf and it couldn't photosynthesise **(1)**, with a blue-black circle where light reached the leaf and it could photosynthesise and produce starch.

(e) Test several of each type of leaf for starch instead of just one of each type. **(1)**

### 51. Limiting factors

1 Any three from: Light intensity **(1)**, carbon dioxide concentration **(1)**, temperature **(1)**, water. **(1)**

2 (a) At point A, light intensity is limiting the rate of photosynthesis **(1)**. As the light intensity increases, the rate of photosynthesis also goes up. **(1)**

(b) Light is no longer the limiting factor on the rate of photosynthesis **(1)**. However much the light intensity increases, the rate of photosynthesis will not change **(1)**. Another factor (temperature or carbon dioxide) is limiting the rate of photosynthesis. **(1)**

3 (a) Because carbon dioxide is a reactant of photosynthesis **(1)** and so the more there is, the more photosynthesis can potentially take place. **(1)**

(b) Initially, as the temperature increases the kinetic energy of the molecules goes up, increasing the rate of the enzyme-controlled reactions so the rate of photosynthesis goes up **(1)**. Once the temperature goes above a certain level the enzymes controlling photosynthesis will start to be denatured, so photosynthesis will slow **(1)**. If the temperature gets too high the enzymes will be permanently denatured and the plant will no longer be able to photosynthesise. **(1)**

4 (a) A – carbon dioxide concentration **(1)**, B – light intensity **(1)**, C – carbon dioxide concentration **(1)**

(b)

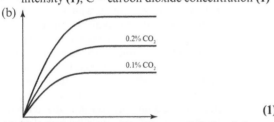

0.2% CO₂

0.1% CO₂

**(1)**

(c) (i) Light intensity **(1)** – because light levels low in morning/temperature – it can be cool in the morning **(1)**

(ii) Carbon dioxide concentration **(1)** as light intensity and temperature close to maximum at midday **(1)** (although these could fluctuate and so still be limiting factors)

### 52. Light intensity

1 (a) The effect of light intensity on the rate of photosynthesis **(1)**

(b) By counting the number bubbles/volume of oxygen produced **(1)** in a measured time interval **(1)**

(c) Make sure that the temperature of the water stays the same/use a water bath to keep the temperature constant. **(1)**

2 (a)

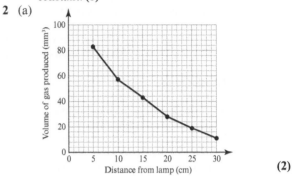

**(2)**

(b) 37 mm³ or 38 mm³ **(1)**

(c) The distance of the light from the lamp is a simple measurement. However, light intensity decreases with distance from the lamp following the inverse square law – so the light intensity is 1/distance² **(1)**. So light intensity decreased faster than might be expected. **(1)**

### 53. Specialised plant cells

1 (a) Xylem **(1)**       (b) Water **(1)**

(c) Four from: Dead cells **(1)** – more space for water containing minerals to move through **(1)**. Walls strengthened with lignin rings **(1)** – makes them strong and prevents collapsing **(1)**. No end walls **(1)** so they form continuous tubes for water transport. **(1)**

2 (a) The uptake of water and mineral ions from the soil **(1)**

(b) The root hair has a big surface area **(1)** for absorbing water and mineral ions **(1)**. The root hair has a thin cell wall **(1)** to make it quicker for water and ions to move into the cell. **(1)**

(c) Structure B is a mitochondrion. They provide the energy needed **(1)** for the root hair cell to move mineral ions into the cell against a concentration gradient. **(1)**

3 (a) Phloem **(1)**

(b) Sieve tube elements which have very little cytoplasm so there is a lot of space to transport sucrose **(1)** Companion cells with lots of mitochondria to supply energy for the active transport of sucrose into and out of the phloem vessels **(1)**

### 54. Transpiration

1 D **(1)**

2 (a) The movement of water from the roots of a plant to the leaves and into the air **(1)**

(b) Water enters the roots by osmosis through the root hair cells

↓ **(1)**

Water is drawn up the stem through the xylem from the roots

↓ **(1)**

Water is drawn into the leaves and evaporates from the leaf cells into the air spaces

↓ **(1)**

Water diffuses out through the stomata down a concentration gradient      **(1)**

3 (a) They allow carbon dioxide to diffuse into the leaf **(1)**, and oxygen and water vapour to diffuse out of the leaf down concentration gradients. **(1)**

(b) A – guard cells, B – stoma, C – vacuole, D – chloroplast **(2)**

(c) In the light chloroplasts make sugar and water which moves into the guard cells by osmosis, making them swell and become rigid (**1**). The cell wall is thicker on one side of the cell than on the other, so when the cell swells, an opening appears between the two guard cells. This is the stoma (**1**). At night, when there is no photosynthesis, water moves out of the guard cells by osmosis (**1**). They lose their rigidity and the stoma closes. (**1**)

## 55. Translocation

**1** B (**1**)

**2** (a) Translocation is the movement of sucrose around a plant in the phloem. (**1**)

(b) Translocation of sucrose depends on sucrose being moved by active transport into and out of the phloem sieve tubes by the companion cells (**1**). If the poison inhibits active transport, the companion cells will no longer be able to move sucrose into and out of the sieve tubes and translocation will stop. (**1**)

**3**

|  | **Transpiration** | **Translocation** |
|---|---|---|
| **Tissue where it takes place** | Xylem | Phloem |
| **Substances transported** | Water | Sucrose dissolved in water |
| **Direction of transport** | From the roots to the leaves | From the leaves, both up and down the plant |

(**3**)

**4** (a) Cellular respiration in growing regions, for example, the bud (**1**). Converted to starch and stored in leaves and storage organs for use when needed. (**1**)

(b) Carbon dioxide is taken into the leaf and used to make glucose by photosynthesis. In the experimental leaves, this glucose contains radioactive carbon which the scientists can detect (**1**). The glucose is converted into sucrose to be transported around the plant, so the sucrose produced by the experimental leaf will also be radioactive (**1**). Scientists can also detect the radioactive water as it travels up the plant (**1**). Scientists can show that radioactive water is found above the ring of dead tissues, showing that the movement of water up the plant in the xylem is not affected by killing the cells in the stem, as the xylem cells are already dead (**1**). Radioactive carbon is only found in areas below the ring of dead tissue, showing that the movement of sucrose is an active process which relies on living phloem cells, and it does not take place if the cells are killed. (**1**)

## 56. Water uptake in plants

**1** (a) The uptake of water from a cut stem (**1**)

(b) (i) The air flow moves across the leaf increasing the concentration gradient between the inside and the outside of the leaf (**1**). This increases the loss of water by evaporation and diffusion from the plant (**1**) and so the air bubble moves across the scale faster. (**1**)

(ii) Water vapour diffuses out of the leaf through the stomata (**1**). Most of the stomata are on the underside of the leaf. If the underside of the leaf is covered in petroleum jelly, gases will not be able to leave the leaf (**1**) so the rate of water loss will slow down and the bubble will move very slowly or stop. (**1**)

**2** (a)

| Movement of air bubble in 5 minute interval (mm) | Plant A at 15 °C | Plant B at 25 °C | Plant C at 25 °C with a fan blowing at the leaves |
|---|---|---|---|
| Reading 1 | 50 | 80 | 105 |
| Reading 2 | 45 | 84 | 106 |
| Reading 3 | 55 | 91 | 104 |
| Mean result | 50 | 255/3 = 85 | 315/3 = 105 |
| Mean rate of water uptake (mm/min) | 50/5 = 10 | 85/5 = 17 | 105/5 = 21 |

(**4**)

(b) To make sure the experiment is repeatable and the data is as precise as possible (**1**)

(c) (i) Plant A is photosynthesising at 15 °C and the rate of uptake of water as measured by the distance moved by the air bubble is 10 mm/min (**1**). Plant B was at 25 °C and the rate of uptake of water was 17 mm/min (**1**). As the temperature increases, water molecules move around faster and so more water evaporates from the cells in the leaves (**1**) so more water was taken up by plant B in the transpiration stream. (**1**)

(ii) The rate of water uptake in plant B is 17 mm/min (**1**). Plant C is also at 25 °C, **but** it takes up 21 mm water/min (**1**). The difference is that a fan is blowing on plant C. This blows away the water vapour from the surface of the leaf, increasing the concentration gradient between the inside and the outside of the leaf (**1**). This increases the water lost from the leaf by evaporation and diffusion, so more water is pulled up into the shoot by the transpiration stream. (**1**)

## 57. Extended response − Plant structures and functions

Answers could include the following points (**6**)

- Plants make their own food through the process of photosynthesis. They trap energy from the Sun in their chloroplasts and convert carbon dioxide from the air and water from the soil into glucose and oxygen. The more a plant photosynthesises, the faster it will grow. Lack of any of these factors can limit the rate of photosynthesis, and a suitable temperature is also needed.

- Early in the morning there will be plenty of carbon dioxide because the plants have been respiring all night, but not using it in photosynthesis. The temperature will be relatively low. Computers switch the heating on so temperature does not limit the rate of photosynthesis. If it is a dull morning (or winter) lights will come on so light intensity doesn't limit the rate of photosynthesis.

- During the morning, temperatures will rise and light levels increase naturally, so the heating and lighting will be switched off. But as the carbon dioxide which has built up overnight is used up, more is pumped into the greenhouse so a low carbon dioxide concentration does not become a limiting factor. If the temperature gets too high it can reduce the efficiency of the enzymes in the plants or even denature them completely, so if the temperature gets too high, cooling fans are switched on to keep the temperature in the optimum range.

- Towards the end of the day, the temperature and light levels may fall, so cooling fans are switched off and heating may come on again. Similarly, lights may be used to maintain light levels. Carbon dioxide levels are maintained high all day until darkness falls when the plants again respire, but do not use carbon dioxide in photosynthesis.

## 58. Hormones

**1** B (**1**)

**2** A hormone is a compound produced by an endocrine gland and released directly into the blood (**1**). It travels around the body in the blood until it reaches its target organ or organs **(1)**. It causes a response in the target organ. **(1)**

3 (a) Hypothalamus **(1)**, produces TRH (thyrotropin-releasing hormone) or CRH (corticotropin-releasing hormone). **(1)**

(b) Thyroid gland **(1)**, produces thyroxine. **(1)**

(c) Testes **(1)**, produce testosterone. **(1)**

4

| Hormone | Produced in | Target organ/s and tissues |
|---|---|---|
| TSH | Pituitary gland | Thyroid gland |
| Insulin | Pancreas | Liver, muscles and fatty tissue |
| Adrenaline | Adrenal glands | Heart, liver, skin, other organs |
| Oestrogen | Ovaries | Ovaries, uterus, pituitary gland |

**(4)**

### 59. Adrenaline and thyroxine

1 (a) To help control the metabolic rate of the body **(1)**

(b) If a factor in the internal environment increases or decreases **(1)**, changes take place to restore the original level. **(1)**

(c) If the concentration of thyroxine in the blood falls too low, the hypothalamus secretes more TRH **(1)**. This stimulates the pituitary to secrete more TSH **(1)**. This TSH is carried in the blood to the thyroid gland which responds by producing more thyroxine **(1)**. If the level of thyroxine in the blood increases, the hypothalamus secretes less TRH so the pituitary makes less TSH **(1)** and the thyroid gland makes less thyroxine, so levels return to normal. **(1)**

2 (a) Adrenaline is released when an individual is threatened or in a dangerous situation **(1)**. It brings about changes, for example, to the heart, the blood vessels and the muscles which prepare the individual to run away or defend themselves. **(1)**

(b) Makes the heart beat more rapidly and contract more strongly **(1)**, so it increases the volume of blood pumped by the heart and the rate at which blood is pumped around the body. **(1)**

(c)

| Type of blood vessel | Effect on the blood vessel | Impact on the body |
|---|---|---|
| Supplying blood to the skeletal muscles | Diameter widens/blood vessels dilate | Blood flow to skeletal muscles increased, carrying more oxygen and food for flight or fight |
| Supplying blood to organs such as the gut | Diameter narrows/blood vessels constrict | Blood flow to gut reduced – reducing activity during flight or flight so food and oxygen available for skeletal muscles and heart |

**(4)**

3 If you don't have enough iodine in your diet you can't make enough thyroxine **(1)**. This is detected and so the negative feedback system involving the hypothalamus and the pituitary gland keep producing lots of TRH and TSH **(1)**. The TSH stimulates the thyroid gland and it grows bigger to try to make more thyroxine, even though it can't due to lack of iodine. **(1)**

### 60. The menstrual cycle

1 D **(1)**

2 (a) When the ovary releases an egg cell in the middle of the menstrual cycle **(1)**

(b) The event which marks the start of a new menstrual cycle, when the thickened part of the uterus lining and the unfertilised egg cell are lost during the monthly bleed or period **(1)**

(c) When a sperm meets and fuses with an egg cell in the oviduct **(1)**

3 (a) The thickened lining of the uterus and the unfertilised egg are lost through the vagina if pregnancy has not occurred (period). **(1)**

(b) An egg is released from the ovary/ovulation. **(1)**

(c) The lining of the uterus thickens ready to receive a fertilised egg. **(1)**

4 (a) A method used to try to prevent fertilisation/the joining of the egg and sperm **(1)**

(b) Days 14–16 **(1)** when the egg is released **(1)**

(c) Condoms **(1)** – barrier methods put a physical barrier between the egg and the sperm to stop them meeting. **(1)**

(d) They release hormones which interfere with the menstrual cycle **(1)** and prevent ovulation and/or change the mucus at the cervix, making it difficult for sperm to get through. **(1)**

(e) Barrier contraception is easily available and doesn't involve medical professionals **(1)**. Used properly with spermicides it is very reliable, **but** can go wrong – split, come off, etc. which increases the risk of pregnancy **(1)**. Hormonal contraception requires prescribing by a medical professional **(1)**. Oral tablets have to be taken daily (or injections received regularly at the correct time in your cycle), it is 99.9% effective when taken properly, **but** if tablets/injections are missed or if not all of the hormone is absorbed, for example, due to diarrhoea or vomiting, it can be ineffective. **(1)**

### 61. Control of the menstrual cycle

1 D **(1)**

2 (a) FSH: Made in the pituitary gland **(1)**, target organ the ovaries **(1)**

(b) Oestrogen: Made in the ovaries **(1)**, target organs the pituitary gland, ovaries and uterus **(1)**

(c) Progesterone: Made in the corpus luteum in the ovaries **(1)**, affects the pituitary gland and uterus **(1)**

3 (a) FSH is secreted by the pituitary gland **(1)**. This causes a follicle in the ovary to mature **(1)**. As the follicle matures it secretes oestrogen, so initially as FSH levels rise, oestrogen levels rise **(1)**. The oestrogen in turn inhibits the production of FSH from the pituitary, so as oestrogen levels rise, FSH levels fall. **(1)**

(b) A high level of oestrogen triggers a surge of LH from the pituitary which in turn triggers ovulation. **(1)**

(c) LH triggers ovulation and the remains of the follicle form the corpus luteum **(1)**. The corpus luteum secretes progesterone **(1)**. Progesterone affects the pituitary and suppresses the secretion of LH. **(1)**

(d) (i) The end of a woman's fertile life when there are no more eggs released from her ovaries and the periods stop **(1)**

(ii) FSH triggers the ovary to produce oestrogen **(1)** which causes the lining of the uterus to build up and the follicles to ripen, and also triggers the production of LH **(1)**. If these hormones are no longer being produced, the menstrual cycle is failing and the woman is probably in the menopause. **(1)**

### 62. Assisted Reproductive Therapy

1 A **(1)**

2 (a) The release of an egg from the ovary **(1)**

(b) Patient A **(1)** She has low levels of FSH and LH **(1)**. These are hormones made in the pituitary gland which are needed for an egg to mature in the ovary and then be released at ovulation **(1)**. Clomifene helps increase the levels of FSH and LH in the blood, increasing the chances that the woman will ovulate and so may get pregnant. **(1)**

(c) Patient B has normal hormone levels, but no eggs in her ovaries **(1)**. Increasing the levels of FSH and LH in her blood would not increase her chances of getting pregnant as there are no eggs to release. **(1)**

3 (a) IVF/in vitro fertilisation **(1)**

(b) Fertility drugs such as Clomifene are used to stimulate the formation of as many mature follicles as possible. **(1)**
Eggs are collected from the ovary and sperm cells are collected from the man. **(1)**
They are mixed together in a dish for the sperm to fertilise the eggs. **(1)**
The fertilised eggs are kept in ideal conditions for a few days and the cells divide to form embryos. **(1)**
One or two of the embryos are replaced in the woman's uterus where, if all goes well, they will develop to form a healthy baby. **(1)**

## 63. Blood glucose regulation

1 D **(1)**

2 (a) It is broken down in the cells during respiration; this reaction enables energy to be transferred **(1)**

(b) The pancreas **(1)**

(c) When carbohydrates are digested in the gut, glucose is released **(1)**. It passes from the gut into the blood by diffusion and active transport so the blood glucose levels rise. **(1)**

(d) Insulin and glucagon **(1)**

(e) If the blood glucose levels/concentration are too low, the cells will not have enough glucose for respiration and the body will not function effectively and will eventually die **(1)**. If the blood glucose levels/concentration get too high it can damage organs and cause coma and death. **(1)**

3 A − Pancreas detects rise in blood glucose concentration **(1)**. B − Pancreas increases secretion of insulin **(1)** and decreases secretion of glucagon **(1)**. C − Insulin causes muscle and liver cells to remove glucose from the blood **(1)** and store it as glycogen **(1)**. D − Pancreas detects fall in blood glucose concentration **(1)**. E − Pancreas decreases secretion of insulin **(1)** and increases secretion of glucagon **(1)**. F − Glucagon causes liver cells to convert glycogen to glucose **(1)** and release it into the blood **(1)**

## 64. Diabetes

1 (a) At A the person has just had a meal **(1)**. The carbohydrates they have eaten are being digested (broken down) and the glucose produced is being absorbed into the blood so blood glucose levels rise **(1)**. At B insulin has been released from the pancreas **(1)**. This causes the liver and muscles to convert glucose to glycogen so the blood glucose concentration falls. **(1)**

(b) The blood glucose level would rise and continue to rise until it reached a plateau/levelled out. **(1)**

(c) The blood glucose concentration increases after a meal as normal, but the pancreas does not release insulin **(1)**. As a result, the blood glucose is not converted into glycogen in the liver and muscles **(1)**. The level continues to rise until all of the glucose from the meal has been absorbed into the blood **(1)**, and then it will stay the same as the glucose cannot get into the cells. **(1)**

(d) An insulin injection replaces the natural insulin **(1)** and allows the liver and muscle cells to store glycogen so the blood glucose levels fall. **(1)**

2

| | Type 1 diabetes | Type 2 diabetes |
|---|---|---|
| Cause | Immune system damages insulin-producing pancreatic cells so they cannot produce insulin **(1)** | Person produces insulin **(1)**, but the liver and muscle cells have become resistant to it **(1)** |
| Control | Injecting the right amount of insulin at regular intervals to keep the blood glucose concentration within safe limits **(1)** | Most people can control type 2 diabetes by losing weight, eating low-carbohydrate foods and exercising more **(1)**. There are medicines available if needed **(1)** |

3 (a) There appears to be a correlation between BMI category and type 2 diabetes in women **(1)**. In men, there is a higher percentage of normal BMI men than overweight men with type 2 diabetes **(1)**. Being obese appears to correlate closely with type 2 diabetes in both men and women. **(1)**

(b) The data covers all adults in the UK so should be reliable **(1)**. In each BMI category given, a higher percentage of men have type 2. So, the claim could seem reasonable **(1)**. **But** − don't know what happens in other BMI categories **(1)**, don't know if there are any other factors involved, for example, smoking, drinking, etc. So, can't make that claim without qualifying it. **(1)**

## 65. Extended response − Control and coordination

Answers could include the following points **(6)**

- In fertilisation, a sperm penetrates an egg to form a new cell. Contraception aims to prevent the sperm and the egg fusing. Barrier methods put a layer between the sperm and the eggs (condoms are placed over the penis, diaphragms are placed across the cervix). Hormonal contraception uses female sex hormones or similar chemicals to interfere with the menstrual cycle so ovulation does not take place. They also affect the mucus around the cervix so it is harder for sperm to get to the egg.

- From the data given, hormone-based contraception appears several percentage points more effective than barrier contraception, with a mean effectiveness of over 99% compared with a mean effectiveness of 96% for barrier methods. The percentage effectiveness of a method of contraception is measured by the number of women who would get pregnant out of 100 women using the method of contraception correctly for a year − so 98% effective means two women out of the hundred using it correctly for a year would get pregnant.

- To use a contraceptive correctly, the instructions must be followed exactly every time, for example, no pills forgotten, spermicide used with condoms, etc. In real life, many people do not use contraception correctly every time and so real life failure rates are probably higher than those shown in the data.

- Although hormone methods are more effective, barrier methods have several advantages − they do not require a visit to medical professionals, they have no associated health risks and they are available at any time. Both forms of contraception meet people's needs.

## 66. Exchanging materials

1 C **(1)**

2 (a) Smaller organism SA = $6 \times 1\,\mu m^2 = 6\,\mu m^2$
Volume = $1 \times 1 \times 1 = 1\,\mu m^3$
sa:vol = 6:1 or 6
Larger organism SA = $6 \times 36\,\mu m^2 = 216\,\mu m^2$
Volume = $6 \times 6 \times 6 = 216\,\mu m^3$
sa:vol = 1:1 or 1 **(2)**

(b) Substances are transported into and out of cells through the outer surface (1). As an organism gets bigger, the surface area to volume ratio gets smaller and it would take too long for materials to diffuse in or out (1). So large multicellular organisms need exchange surfaces with large surface areas to move substances in and out and transport systems to carry substances to and from where they are needed. (1)

3  (a) Any two from: Lungs (1) small intestine (1) kidneys (1)
   (b) The circulatory system (1)
   (c) Large surface area (1), thin/short distances to travel (1)

4

| Substance | Site of exchange | Reason for exchange |
|---|---|---|
| Oxygen | Alveoli in lungs | Needed for respiration |
| Carbon dioxide | Alveoli in lungs | Waste product of respiration |
| Dissolved food molecules | Small intestine | Needed for respiration/cell metabolism |
| Mineral ions | Small intestine | Needed for cells to function properly |
| Urea | Nephrons in kidney | Waste product of breakdown of amino acids/metabolism |

(5)

## 67. Alveoli

1  (a) The movement of air in and out of the lungs (1)
   (b) Oxygen diffuses from the air in the alveoli of the lungs into the blood (1). Carbon dioxide diffuses from the blood into the air in the alveoli. (1)
   (c) It removes air relatively high in carbon dioxide and replaces it with air relatively high in oxygen (1). This maintains a steep concentration gradient between the air and the blood (1) so diffusion of gases in and out of the blood is as fast and efficient as possible. (1)

2  Large surface area – lots of area over which gas exchange can take place (1). Good blood supply – constantly delivers carbon dioxide-rich blood to the alveoli and removes oxygen-rich blood (1). This maintains steep concentration gradients for diffusion of gases (1). Thin walls – give short diffusion distances between the air and the blood, making diffusion more efficient. (1)

3  (a) The larger air sacs will have a smaller surface area:volume ratio (1), so there will be less gas exchange and so less oxygen will get into the blood and less carbon dioxide will be removed, causing breathlessness. (1)
   (b) The tumour takes up the space of the lung tissue made up of alveoli, greatly reducing the surfaces available for gas exchange by diffusion (1). This makes the person breathless and lowers blood oxygen concentration. (1)
   (c) The blood cannot get into the capillaries around the alveoli of the lungs, there is little or no gas exchange between the air in the lungs and the blood (1). As a result, the person becomes breathless with low blood oxygen. (1)

## 68. Blood

1  D (1)
2  (a) A: plasma; B & C: white blood cells and platelets; D: red blood cells (2)
   (b) Plasma: transport of dissolved substances/food/carbon dioxide/mineral ions (1); white blood cells: attack pathogens in the body (1); platelets: help clotting the blood to prevent bleeding/protect

damaged skin (1) red blood cells: carry oxygen around the body (1)

3  Red blood cells contain haemoglobin which binds with oxygen in the lungs and carries it around the body to the tissues (1). Their biconcave shape gives a big surface area for gas exchange so oxygen can diffuse in and out easily (1). They have no nucleus which makes more space for haemoglobin in the cell so more oxygen can be carried. (1)

4  (a) Some white blood cells called phagocytes (1) surround foreign cells/pathogens and digest them. (1) White blood cells called lymphocytes (1) produce chemicals called antibodies that stick to foreign cells/pathogens and help to destroy them. (1)
   (b) White blood cells protect us against infection by engulfing pathogens or producing antibodies (1). Children with SCID don't produce healthy white blood cells (1) so any pathogens which enter their body can easily cause an infection as they are not attacked by the white blood cells of the immune system. (1)

## 69. Blood vessels

1  (a) A = vein, B = artery, C = capillaries (2)
   (b) Blood pressure is highest in blood vessel B (1) because the heart squeezes blood into these vessels at high pressure with each heartbeat. (1)

2  (a) Walls thinner than arterial walls, (1) large space in the middle, valves (1)
   (b) Thin walls allow flow of blood which is not under high pressure so don't need to be thick (1), wide lumen allows high volume of blood to flow (1), valves prevent backflow of blood. (1)

3  (a) Blood is squeezed into the arteries by the heart at high pressure (1). The elastic walls of the arteries stretch so they are not damaged (1). After they have been stretched, the muscles and elastic fibres contract, returning the artery to its original size and helping the blood to flow smoothly. (1)
   (b) As you move, your muscles squeeze the blood along the veins towards the heart (1). The valves open to allow the blood to flow towards the heart, but close to stop it flowing backwards. (1)

4  (a) Capillaries are very small blood vessels with walls which are only one cell thick. (1) (They are so narrow red blood cells move through them in single file.)
   (b) Because capillaries transport food and oxygen to the cells and remove waste products (1); they are the site of exchange between the blood and the cells (1)
   (c) They have a very large surface area as they are so small and there are so many of them (1). Their walls are only one cell thick so the diffusion distances for dissolved food, oxygen and waste products are very short, allowing for rapid, efficient exchange (1). Blood flows through them continually from the arteries to the veins, maintaining concentration gradients between the blood and the cells, so diffusion takes place as quickly and efficiently as possible. (1)

## 70. The heart

1  C (1)
2  (a) A = right and left atria (1), B = right and left ventricles (1)
   (b) Valves (1) – prevent the blood flowing backwards through the heart (1)
   (c) Muscle wall of the left ventricle is thicker than the muscle wall of the right ventricle (1). It pushes blood all around the body whilst the right side pushes it only to the lungs. (1)

3 (a) Blood returns to the heart from <u>the organs</u> in <u>the veins</u> **(1)** → the <u>atria</u> contract forcing <u>blood into the ventricles</u> **(1)** → the <u>valves</u> close preventing <u>blood flowing the wrong way</u> through the heart **(1)** → the <u>ventricles</u> contract, forcing <u>blood out of the heart</u> into <u>the arteries</u> which carry it to the organs. **(1)**

(b) The right-hand side of the heart contains deoxygenated blood and the left-hand side of the heart contains oxygenated blood **(1)**. The two sides are kept apart by the muscle wall between the two sides **(1)**. If there is a hole in this wall of muscle, the deoxygenated and oxygenated blood will mix and the cells of the body will not get all the oxygen they need **(1)**. This will make the child breathless and weak **(1)**. If surgeons can mend the hole, the deoxygenated and oxygenated blood will be kept separate again and the child's body will function normally. **(1)**

## 71. Aerobic respiration

1 (a) It is a chemical reaction that releases energy from glucose for use in cellular activities **(1)**, using oxygen. **(1)**

(b) glucose + oxygen **(1)** → carbon dioxide + water **(1)**

(c) Mainly in the mitochondria **(1)**

(d) Glucose comes from digested food **(1)**, oxygen from the air in gas exchange in the lungs. **(1)**

2 (a) For metabolic processes/to build larger molecules from smaller ones for growth **(1)**; to enable muscle contraction **(1)**; in mammals to help maintain a steady body temperature **(1)**

(b) Building larger molecules from smaller molecules **(1)**. For example, using sugars and nitrates to build amino acids to make proteins **(1)**

3 (a) Enzymes are biological catalysts made of protein **(1)**. Protein is denatured if the temperature gets too high (above 40 °C) **(1)** or if the pH is not in the ideal range **(1)**. If the enzymes controlling cellular respiration are denatured, there will be no energy available for the cells so it is important to control the environment. **(1)**

(b) The poison affects the enzymes of the mitochondria and prevents aerobic respiration **(1)** so, energy is not released for cell metabolism **(1)**. Supplying useable energy provides the cells with what they need even though cellular respiration is not taking place, so the normal reactions of metabolism can take place. **(1)**

## 72. Anaerobic respiration

1 B **(1)**

2 (a) Anaerobic respiration is the incomplete breakdown of glucose **(1)** when there is not enough oxygen for aerobic respiration to take place. **(1)**

(b)

| Advantages of anaerobic respiration | Disadvantages of anaerobic respiration |
|---|---|
| 1 Anaerobic respiration is useful to muscle cells because it can release energy to allow muscle cells to continue contracting even when the heart and lungs cannot deliver oxygen and glucose fast enough for aerobic respiration<br>2 Respiration can continue in organisms that have no, or a very limited supply of, oxygen | 1 Anaerobic respiration releases much less energy from each molecule of glucose than aerobic respiration<br>2 Lactic acid is not removed from the body. It builds up in the muscles and blood, and must be broken down using oxygen after exercise |

**(4)**

3 (a) They respire aerobically, using oxygen to breakdown glucose to release energy **(1)**, forming carbon dioxide and water as waste products. **(1)**

(b) The muscles respire anaerobically, so glucose is not completely broken down **(1)**. Lactic acid is formed **(1)** and much less energy is released for the cells to use. **(1)**

(c) The heart rate falls back to normal relatively quickly **(1)**, but the breathing rate remains raised for some time. **(1)**

(d) The lactic acid produced by the muscles during anaerobic respiration cannot be removed from the body **(1)**. It needs to be broken down using oxygen **(1)**. After exercise stops the breathing rate remains high to bring extra oxygen into the body until all the lactic acid has been broken down **(1)**. The heart rate falls back to normal although the amount of blood it pumps may remain raised to get the blood containing extra oxygen to the muscles where it is needed. **(1)**

## 73. Rate of respiration

1 (a) Soda lime absorbs the carbon dioxide produced by the seeds during respiration so it doesn't affect the respirometer reading, which measures uptake of oxygen. **(1)**

(b) As the peas absorb oxygen from the air as they respire, the liquid moves along the scale **(1)**. If the distance the liquid moves in given intervals of time is measured, the rate of respiration can be calculated indirectly by dividing the distance travelled by the time. **(1)**

(c) No movement of the liquid/no uptake of oxygen **(1)**. Boiling the peas kills them so they no longer respire. **(1)**

2 (a) Carbon dioxide **(1)**

(b) The mealworms must be handled very carefully to minimise any trauma or damage **(1)**. Changes in temperature must be relatively small and never up to a level that would damage the animals. **(1)**

(c) Mealworms would respire at a faster rate than germinating peas. **(1)**

(d) Mealworms are animals so they move around which requires energy from respiration **(1)**. They are active and so respire relatively fast **(1)**. Germinating peas are actively growing, but they do not move. Their energy needs are lower **(1)** and so respiration rate would be slower. **(1)**

## 74. Changes in heart rate

1 B **(1)**

2 (a) The volume of blood pushed out of the heart into the aorta with each heartbeat **(1)**; measured in litres **(1)**

(b) The number of times the heart beats in a minute **(1)** measured in beats/minute **(1)**

(c) The volume of blood pushed into the aorta per minute **(1)**; measured in litres/minute **(1)**

(d) Cardiac output = stroke volume × heart rate **(1)**

3 (a) Person C is the fittest **(1)** because they had the highest cardiac volume, fitter people have larger stroke volumes and pump more blood to the muscles during exercise. **(1)**

(b) Person A **(1)** – people who are unfit usually have small stroke volumes and their hearts beat very fast during exercise to try to get enough blood to the muscles to supply them with the food and oxygen they need. **(1)**

(c) B = 0.095 × 120 = 11.4 litres/min **(1)**<br>C = 0.15 × 100 = 15.0 litres/min **(1)**

(d) 3.6/11.4 × 100 = 31.6% more blood per minute **(1)**

**75. Extended response – Exchange**

Answers could include the following points **(6)**

- The muscles need a good supply of glucose and oxygen to carry out aerobic respiration to release as much energy as possible for muscle contraction.
- If the muscles don't get enough oxygen, they will undergo anaerobic respiration, where glucose is broken down without oxygen to form lactic acid, releasing very little energy. This also makes the muscles hurt because lactic acid builds up in the muscles.
- In the gas exchange system of the lungs, oxygen needed by the muscles moves from the air to the blood down a concentration gradient by diffusion, and waste carbon dioxide produced in aerobic respiration diffuses from the blood into the air in the alveoli of the lungs to be removed from the body.
- During exercise Tom will breathe faster and more deeply to supply more oxygen for aerobic respiration in the contracting muscles and to remove more carbon dioxide.
- As the race progresses, Tom's heart beats faster and the stroke volume of the heart at each beat increases, increasing the cardiac output.
- This increases the flow of blood to the muscles, carrying oxygen and food to the contracting cells, and removing the waste carbon dioxide, carrying it to the lungs to be removed from the body.

**76. Ecosystems and abiotic factors**

1  D **(1)**
2  (a) A single, living individual **(1)**
   (b) All of the organisms of the same species in an area **(1)**
   (c) All of the different populations in an area **(1)**
   (d) All the living organisms/communities in an area along with all the non-living components which affect them **(1)**
3  (a) Three from: light levels **(1)**, average temperature **(1)**, average rainfall **(1)**, oxygen levels in water **(1)**
   (b) The soil of bogs is very poor with few mineral ions/ low nitrate levels **(1)**. The sundew gets mineral ions/ nitrates from the insects it digests **(1)**. Ordinary plants cannot do this so they can't survive. **(1)**
   (c) Baby birds eat a lot of caterpillars **(1)**. If the weather is cold it will kill the caterpillars, so there are fewer available for the parents to find **(1)**. Heavy rain can wash small caterpillars and insects off leaves, again making them harder to find. There is less food and some of the chicks starve to death. **(1)**

**77. Biotic factors**

1  C **(1)**
2  (a) Territory **(1)** and mates **(1)**   (b) Competition **(1)**
   (c) Any species with explanation: for example, rabbits and sheep both eat grass and compete for it in fields **(1)**, beavers and elk compete for trees in America **(1)**, puffin and haddock both eat sand eels and compete for them, any other sensible answer. **(1)**
3  In early spring, the trees have no leaves, so the light the ground plants need to grow reaches them and they grow fast and flower, avoiding competition with the trees **(1)**. As the leaves open on the trees, less light reaches the ground plants and they die back because there is not enough light for them to continue photosynthesising **(1)**. By summer the trees have many leaves and very little light reaches the ground beneath them so other plants cannot compete and grow. **(1)**
4  (a) An animal which hunts and eats other animals **(1)**
   (b) An animal which is hunted and eaten by other animals **(1)**
   (c) As snowshoe hare numbers fall, they are followed by a fall in the lynx numbers **(1)**. Then as snowshoe hare numbers rise, this is followed by a rise in lynx numbers. **(1)**

(d) The hare numbers fall because they are being eaten by the lynxes **(1)**. But once the number of hares gets too low, there isn't enough food for all the lynxes so the lynx numbers fall **(1)**. Once there are fewer predators, the hare numbers go up as they reproduce and fewer are eaten **(1)**. But when there is more prey, the lynx do better and so their numbers go up again. **(1)**

**78. Parasitism and mutualism**

1  D **(1)**
2  (a) An organism that benefits from feeding off a host organism **(1)** and causes harm to the host **(1)**
   (b)

| Parasite | How it feeds |
|----------|--------------|
| Flea | Sucks blood after piercing skin with sharp mouthparts |
| Tapeworm | Live in intestines, attach to gut wall, absorb digested nutrients through body |
| Mistletoe | Grows roots into host tree and absorbs water and nutrients |

**(3)**

3  Hooks and suckers on the head to attach it firmly to the intestine wall of the host **(1)**. A thin flattened body so food from the host can be absorbed over the whole body with no need for a digestive system or circulatory system **(1)**. Segments contain male and female sex organs so fertilisation can take place inside the body of the host. **(1)**
4  (a) A relationship between two different types of organisms where both organisms benefit **(1)**
   (b) The leguminous plant gets nitrogen compounds which it needs to grow and make proteins from the bacteria **(1)**. The nitrogen-fixing bacteria are protected from the environment and get food from the plant. **(1)**
   (c) The clown fish is protected from predators by the stinging tentacles **(1)**. The clownfish chase off fish which would eat the anemone and their faeces provide the anemone with nutrients. **(1)**

**79. Fieldwork techniques**

1  (a) $\frac{10 + 2 + 15 + 9 + 3 + 22 + 14 + 12 + 20}{9} = \frac{107}{9}$ **(1)**

   $= 11.9$ nests/100 m² **(2)**
   (b) A good year compared to the previous years as there were more nests per 100 m² of beach **(1)**, 11.9/100 m² compared to 5.6/100 m² and 8.4/100 m² **(1)**
   (c) Biotic factor: food supply/numbers of predators **(1)** Abiotic factor: temperature/amount of heavy rain **(1)**
2  (a) A measure of how common something is in an area **(1)**
   (b) Mean number of slugs in 1 m² $= \frac{10 + 6 + 5 + 9 + 2}{5}$ $= \frac{32}{5} = 6.4$ slugs/m² **(2)** Garden is 100 m² in area so approximate slug population of the garden is $6.4 \times 100 = 640$ slugs. **(1)**
3  (a) The distribution of plants describes where they are found in an ecosystem. **(1)**
   (b) A quadrat is a square frame with a known area, used to take samples of organisms in the field. **(1)**
   (c) Students are investigating the effect of abiotic factors on the distribution of plants in a park so a belt transect will give them the best results **(1)**. They need to sample organisms in relation to changes in abiotic factors which can be recorded and correlated with changes in plant numbers **(1)**. Random quadrats might all land in areas with similar abiotic factors **(1)** and so make it much more difficult to relate the abiotic factors of the environment to the distribution of plants. **(1)**

### 80. Organisms and their environment

1  (a) Transect A $= \frac{1+3+1+4}{8} = \frac{9}{8} = 1$ plant/0.25 m² (to the nearest whole number) **(1)**

Transect B $= \frac{4+6+8+10+10+5+3}{8} = \frac{46}{8} = 5.75$ or 6 plants/0.25 m² (to the nearest whole number) **(1)**

(b) Transect A has very few sundew plants so it is probably not through a bog **(1)**. However, there are a few sundews so it probably borders onto a bog **(1)**. Transect B has lots of sundew plants. Most are in the middle of the transect, so it probably goes across the middle of a bog, with the lowest numbers of sundews at the edges. **(1)**

(c) Carry out more transects/indicate where the transects are taken on a map/use larger quadrats for sampling/do the samples closer together **(1)**, for example, space quadrats every metre instead of every two metres. **(1)**

2  Need to be organised to start when tide is at its lowest **(1)**. Peg out a long tape measure from low tide to high tide mark up the beach **(1)**. Decide on the intervals at which to place quadrats to count crabs, for example, 1 m apart and decide on the size of quadrat to use, for example, 0.25 m², 1 m² **(1)**. Start at low tide and work up the tape counting the numbers of mussels on the rocks in each quadrat. Record numbers **(1)**. Record any abiotic factors – most important is distance from low water. **(1)**

### 81. Human effects on ecosystems

1  B **(1)**

2  (a) Introduction of new non-indigenous species **(1)**

(b) A new species can out-compete indigenous species and take over an ecosystem very quickly, damaging the balance of the indigenous species **(1)**. New species can easily become pests. **(1)**

(c) New species may be introduced to control another species – indigenous or non-indigenous – which has got out of control **(1)**. They can be very effective as long as they only eat the pest species. **(1)**

3  (a) Fish farming involves growing fish in pens **(1)** where they can be fed and monitored as they grow. **(1)**

(b) Three from: The fish grow faster because they have plenty of food **(1)**, fish are protected from predators and disease **(1)**, fishermen don't have to risk their lives catching fish **(1)**, gives a reliable source of fish and more fish for people to eat. **(1)**

(c) Uneaten food and faeces sink to the bottom of the sea/lake and change the environment **(1)**. Disease can spread from farmed fish to wild stock. **(1)**

4  Excess fertiliser on farmer's fields **(1)** → nitrates and phosphates washed into water of lake by rain **(1)** → many plants grow as a result of fertiliser in the water **(1)** → surface plants block sunlight so plants in water die and stop producing oxygen **(1)** → bacteria break down dead materials and use up more oxygen **(1)** → aquatic animals, such as fish, die due to lack of oxygen. **(1)**

### 82. Biodiversity

1  (a) The variety of species in an area **(1)**

(b) Three from: To maintain the structure of ecosystems as organisms are interdependent/to maintain the food chains in an ecosystem **(1)**, some species are useful to people, for example, for potential medicines **(1)**, because morally people should respect other organisms **(1)**, people enjoy seeing a variety of different organisms in different habitats. **(1)**

2  (a) Deforestation removes trees from an area **(1)**. This also removes the habitat of many different species and may remove the food source for some animals, so it reduces biodiversity in an area. **(1)**

(b) When an area where the trees have been removed in the process of deforestation is allowed to return to woodland/forest **(1)**; can be by natural re-growth or replanting **(1)**

(c) Rainforests contain about 500 species of tree per hectare when UK woodlands have around 12 species per hectare/rainforests have two orders of magnitude more species than UK forests **(1)**. Trees in both places will support huge numbers of other plants, fungi, bacteria and animals/organisms **(1)**. But, in terms of numbers of species lost, deforestation of a rainforest will lose more species than deforestation in the UK. **(1)**

3  Four from: Providing suitable habitat by planting conifer woodlands **(1)**; connecting one conifer woodland with another by conifer corridors **(1)**; feeding red squirrels to improve breeding success and killing grey squirrels in the feeding area **(1)**; producing a vaccine against squirrelpox and giving it to red squirrels **(1)**; keeping grey squirrels out of red squirrel strongholds **(1)**

### 83. The carbon cycle

1  A **(1)**

2  (a) Decomposers respire using dead plant and animal material and animal waste products, releasing carbon dioxide into the air. **(1)**

(b) In combustion, the wood and other material reacts with oxygen, and carbon dioxide is produced and released into the air **(1)**. Trees take a lot of carbon dioxide from the air by photosynthesis **(1)**. If they are destroyed by burning, they can no longer remove carbon from the air **(1)** or act as carbon stores. **(1)**

3  (a) The carbon cycle is the movement of carbon through the biotic and abiotic components of the environment. **(1)**

(b) (i)  Process A is respiration **(1)**. Respiration takes place in plants, animals and decomposers/ all organisms **(1)**. It releases carbon back into the air as carbon dioxide **(1)**, a waste product formed when glucose is broken down using oxygen to release energy. **(1)**

(ii)  Process B is photosynthesis **(1)**. During photosynthesis, plants absorb carbon dioxide gas **(1)** and convert it to carbon compounds, for example, glucose. **(1)**

(iii) Process C is feeding **(1)**. Carbon compounds in plants are passed to animals when they eat plants, and from animal to animal along a food chain **(1)**. This provides the glucose for respiration. **(1)**

(iv) Process D is combustion **(1)**. In combustion, fossil fuels or plant material reacts with oxygen to burn **(1)**. Carbon dioxide is produced as a waste product and released into the air. **(1)**

### 84. The water cycle

1  (a) A model of how water moves through the abiotic (and some biotic) parts of an ecosystem **(1)**

(b) Two from: water makes up a large percentage of the body mass of most organisms **(1)**, most of the reactions in cells take place in water **(1)**, we are constantly losing water to the environment and need to replace it **(1)**

(c) A = evaporation, B = transpiration, C = condensation, D = cooling **(2)**

2  (a) Sea water contains lots of salt and this would upset the balance of our bodies. **(1)**

(b) Desalination **(1)**

(c) Water containing salt is heated until the water evaporates, forming steam **(1)**. The steam is condensed in another container to give pure water **(1)**.

The salt and any other impurities are left behind in the very salty water remaining. **(1)**

3 Water evaporates from the surface of seas, rivers, lakes and the land **(1)**. The water vapour condenses as it rises and forms clouds **(1)**. The water continues to cool as it rises to form precipitation (rain or snow) that returns the water to the Earth **(1)**. Some of the water evaporates again, but some runs off the land into the sea or enters rivers and flows back into the sea, and the process continues **(1)**. Some of the water filters down to underground natural reservoirs. **(1)**

### 85. The nitrogen cycle

1 D **(1)**
2 (a) Plants need nitrates to make proteins and DNA so they can grow properly **(1)**. Growing crops every year can mean the nitrate levels in the soil get low **(1)**. Adding nitrate fertilisers means the growing crops have all the nitrates they need. **(1)**
   (b) Different types of plants take different combinations of minerals out of the soil **(1)** so by rotating the types of crops grown the farmer reduces the chances of the soil being low in the minerals a crop needs. **(1)**
   (c) Peas and clover have root nodules containing bacteria that can fix nitrogen from the air and convert it into nitrogen compounds in the soil **(1)**. They have a mutualistic relationship so the bacteria are protected in the plant roots **(1)** and the plants get nitrogen compounds directly from the bacteria **(1)**. If a farmer grows these crops and then digs the roots into the soil, the following year a different crop will benefit from the additional nitrogen compounds in the soil. **(1)**
3 (a) Bacteria **(1)**
   (b) A: Nitrogen fixation by bacteria in the root nodules of plants such as peas and clover **(1)** B: Nitrogen fixation – nitrogen in the air being joined with other chemicals to form nitrogen-containing compounds by bacteria in the soil and by lightning **(1)** C: Denitrification – breakdown of nitrogen-containing compounds to nitrogen by bacteria in the soil **(1)** D: Breakdown of proteins and urea in animals and animal products by decomposers including soil bacteria **(1)** E: Absorption of nitrates from the soil by plants **(1)**

### 86. Extended response – Ecosystem and material cycles
Answers could include the following points **(6)**
• Panda numbers fell as a result of hunting and loss of habitat. As the bamboo forests, which were home to pandas, were destroyed there would have been a general loss of biodiversity.
• The lowest recorded panda population was 1114 in the 1980s. Since then the populations have increased with a 16.8% increase in the last 10 years (1864 − 1596 = 268, 268/1596 × 100 = 16.8%).
• Numbers are still not up to the population in 1974−7 (2459).
• Ways of increasing panda numbers could include protecting the habitat by preventing the destruction of the bamboo forests, stopping the hunting and killing of pandas for their body parts by making it illegal, and perhaps captive breeding programmes to help increase the population to release in the wild.
• By conserving the bamboo forests for the pandas, the biodiversity of the whole area would be conserved and will possibly increase as all the plants and other animals which thrive in that habitat will be able to grow and reproduce successfully again.

# Chemistry
### 87. Formulae
1 D **(1)**
2 Water, $H_2O$ **(1)**
   Magnesium sulfate, $MgSO_4$ **(1)**
   Sodium hydroxide, NaOH **(1)**
   Potassium chloride, KCl **(1)**
   Methane, $CH_4$ **(1)**
   Iron oxide, $Fe_2O_3$ **(1)**
   Sodium carbonate, $Na_2CO_3$ **(1)**
3 (a) Copper, sulfur, oxygen **(1)**
   (b) Lithium, oxygen **(1)**
   (c) Hydrogen, chlorine **(1)**
4 (a) Magnesium oxide **(1)**
   (b) Sodium chloride **(1)**
   (c) Hydrogen fluoride **(1)**
5 (a) 5 **(1)**        (b) 2 **(1)**        (c) 5 **(1)**
6 Nitrogen, $N_2$, only contains atoms of nitrogen, and hydrogen gas, $H_2$, only contains atoms of hydrogen so these are elements **(1)**. Ammonia contains one atom of nitrogen and three atoms of hydrogen chemically bonded – it contains different elements so is therefore a compound. **(1)**

### 88. Equations
1 Incorrect **(1)**, incorrect **(1)**, correct **(1)**, incorrect **(1)**
2 (a) lead chloride + magnesium **(1)** → magnesium chloride + lead **(1)**
   (b) sulfuric acid + magnesium **(1)** → magnesium sulfate + hydrogen **(1)**
3 Solid – calcium carbonate **(1)**
   Aqueous – hydrochloric acid and calcium chloride **(1)**
   Liquid – water **(1)**
   Gas – carbon dioxide **(1)**
4 (a) Sulfuric acid and copper carbonate **(1)**
   (b) Carbon dioxide **(1)**
   (c) sulfuric acid + copper carbonate **(1)** → copper sulfate + water + carbon dioxide **(1)**
   (d) $H_2SO_4(aq) + CuCO_3(s) \rightarrow CuSO_4(aq) + H_2O(l) + CO_2(g)$ **(3)**
   (correct; balanced; state symbols)

### 89. Ionic equations
1 B **(1)**
2 (a) $Na^+$ and $Cl^-$ **(1)**        (b) $H^+$ and $SO_4^{2-}$ **(1)**
   (c) $Cu^{2+}$ and $OH^-$ **(1)**        (d) $NH_4^+$ and $NO_3^-$ **(1)**
3 (a) $Ba^{2+}$ and $Cl^-$ **(1)** $Na^+$ and $SO_4^{2-}$ **(1)**
   (b) $BaSO_4$ **(1)**
   (c) $Na^+$, $Cl^-$ **(1)**
   (d) $Na^+$ **(1)** and $Cl^-$ **(1)**
   (e) $Ba^{2+}(aq) + SO_4^{2-}(aq) \rightarrow BaSO_4(s)$ **(1)**
4 (a) $OH^-$ **(1)**        (b) $H^+$ **(1)**
   (c) $H^+ + OH^- \rightarrow H_2O$ **(1)**

### 90. Hazards, risk and precautions
1 (a) Two from: The Bunsen burner could topple over and cause a fire **(1)**, Flammable gas **(1)**, heat **(1)**
   (b) Two from: Fire or explosion **(1)**, burns – hands, face, hair **(1)**, gas leak from faulty hose **(1)**,
   (c) Two from: Tie long hair back **(1)**, check hose for leaks **(1)**, use appropriate equipment to handle hot surfaces **(1)**, use in ventilated lab **(1)**
2 Hazard **(1)**, corrosive **(1)**, oxidising **(1)**, explosive **(1)**
3

| Hazard | Risk | Precaution |
|---|---|---|
| Flammable gas (1)/heat Bunsen burner (1) | Fire (1)/ burns (1) | Use safety glasses (1), tie hair back (1), check Bunsen connected properly (1) |
| Suck back lime water (1) | Broken glass cutting face and hands (1) | Wear safety glasses (1) remove limewater before heating is stopped (1) |

### 91. Atomic structure

1   2 electrons on outer circle **(1)**
2 protons **(1)** and 2 neutrons **(1)**
inside inner circle

2  (a)

| Particle | Relative mass | Relative charge |
|----------|---------------|-----------------|
| Neutron | 1 | 0 |
| Electron | 1/1835 | −1 |
| Proton | 1 | +1 |

**(3)**

(b) Atoms contain positive protons and negative electrons in equal numbers therefore the charges cancel out. **(1)**

3  $3.33 \times 10^4$ **(1)**

4  Since 1800 subatomic particles have been discovered so we now know the atom is made up of smaller parts so can be split. **(1)**

5  (a) These particles did not hit anything because most of an atom is made up of empty space. **(1)**
(b) The positive alpha particles were being deflected by the positive nucleus. **(1)**
(c) A few of the alpha particles hit the gold nuclei and so bounced back. **(1)**

### 92. Isotopes

1  (a) X **(1)**
(b) (i) The atomic number which tells us the number of protons **(1)**
(ii) Atomic masses **(1)**
(iii) Carbon-14 **(1)**

2  (a)

**(3)**

(b) Both isotopes have the same number of electrons. It is the electrons that determine the chemical properties of an element. **(1)**
(c) $(20/100 \times 10) + (80/100 \times 11)$ **(1)** = 10.8 **(1)**

### 93. Mendeleev's table

1  B **(1)**

2  (a) Hydrogen is a gas not a metal **(1)** it does not behave the same as the other elements in the group **(1)**
(b) They had similar physical properties **(1)** They had similar chemical properties **(1)**
(c) He realised some elements had not been discovered **(1)**
(d) The properties of iodine fitted better with group 7 **(1)**

3  Noble gases **(1)** They were not discovered yet **(1)** (as are inert and difficult to find)

### 94. The periodic table

1  (a) Cl – different group  (b) N – different period
(c) O – not a metal    (d) Mg – not a non-metal **(1)**

2  (a) Halogens **(1)**
(b) Transition metals **(1)**
(c) 3, 11, 19 **(1)**
(d)

| Atomic number | Group number | Period number |
|---------------|--------------|---------------|
| 12 | 2 | 3 |
| 14 | 4 | 3 |
| 9 | 7 | 2 |
| 17 | 7 | 3 |
| 19 | 1 | 4 |

3  (a) The number of protons in the nucleus of an atom of an element **(1)**
(b) Between hydrogen and lawrencium the atomic numbers increase by 1 each time **(1)**; as you can't get part of half a proton it means there are no gaps. **(1)**

4  They are in order of atomic number **(1)** not mass **(1)**

### 95. Electronic configurations

1  C **(1)**

2  (a) Sodium: 2,8,1 **(1)** Lithium: 2,1 **(1)**
(b)

**(3)**

(c) Sodium and lithium both have one electron in their outer shell **(1)** so must belong to the same group. **(1)**

3  Boron has the electronic configuration 2,3. Carbon is 2,4, but aluminium is 2,8,3 **(1)**. This means that aluminium has one extra shell and belongs in a different period. **(1)**

4  Magnesium: 2,8,2 **(1)**, sulfur: 2,8,6 **(1)**, neon: 2,8 **(1)**

### 96. Ions

1  (a) 10 **(1)**    (b) 2,8 **(1)**    (c) cation **(1)**

2  (a) C **(1)** because it has more protons than electrons **(1)**
(b) B **(1)** because it has more electrons than protons **(1)**
(c) Anions **(1)**

3  (a) 8 protons **(1)**
(b) 8 protons, 6 electrons **(1)**
(c) 8 protons, 9 electrons **(1)**

4

|  | Atomic Number | Mass Number | Protons | Electrons | Neutrons |
|--|---------------|-------------|---------|-----------|----------|
| $Mg^{2+}$ | 12 | 24 | 12 | 10 | 12 |
| $F^-$ | 9 | 19 | 9 | 10 | 10 |
| $O^{2-}$ | 8 | 16 | 8 | 10 | 8 |
| $Li^+$ | 3 | 7 | 3 | 2 | 4 |
| $Al^{3+}$ | 13 | 27 | 13 | 10 | 14 |

**(5)**

### 97. Formulae of ionic compounds

1  (a) B **(1)**
(b) Phosphide only contains phosphorus atoms **(1)** whereas phosphate contains phosphorus and oxygen. **(1)**

2

|  | $Cl^-$ | $NO_3^-$ | $SO_4^{2-}$ | $CO_3^{2-}$ | $OH^-$ |
|--|--------|----------|-------------|-------------|--------|
| $Na^+$ | $NaCl$ | $NaNO_3$ | $Na_2SO_4$ | $Na_2CO_3$ | $NaOH$ |
| $Ca^{2+}$ | $CaCl_2$ | $Ca(NO_3)_2$ | $CaSO_4$ | $CaCO_3$ | $Ca(OH)_2$ |
| $Al^{3+}$ | $AlCl_3$ | $Al(NO_3)_3$ | $Al_2(SO_4)_3$ | $Al_2(CO_3)_3$ | $Al(OH)_3$ |
| $NH_4^+$ | $NH_4Cl$ | $NH_4NO_3$ | $(NH_4)_2SO_4$ | $(NH_4)_2CO_3$ | $NH_4OH$ |

**(20)**

3  (a) 2+ **(1)** (b) The charges must cancel each other out. **(1)**

4  (a) They both contain sodium and chlorine. **(1)**
(b) Only sodium chlorate contains oxygen. **(1)**

5  It is made up of 3 magnesium ions **(1)** and 2 phosphate ions **(1)**. These ions bond together by ionic bonding. **(1)**

### 98. Properties of ionic compounds

1  (a) Ionic bonding **(1)** giant ionic lattice **(1)**
(b) Electrostatic **(1)** interactions between oppositely charged ions are strong **(1)** and they all need to be broken for melting to take place. **(1)**

2  (a) No reading on ammeter **(1)**. Ions in solid sodium chloride are fixed in place **(1)** so it cannot conduct electricity and complete the circuit. **(1)**
(b) The ammeter would now give a reading **(1)** because the ions are now free to move. **(1)**

3  C because it has a high melting point **(1)** and only conducts electricity when molten. **(1)**

4  When potassium bromide is either molten or dissolved in water the ionic lattice breaks down and the ions are free **(1)** to move and carry charge. **(1)**

### 99. Covalent bonds

1  (a) Non-metals **(1)**    (b) Shared **(1)**
(c) 2 **(1)**    (d) Double bond **(1)**

**2** (a) 5.7 **(1)**    (b)

 **(2)**

**3** (a) To obtain a full outer shell of electrons

(b)

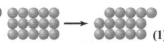 **(1)**

(c) Both share electrons **(1)**, but each oxygen shares 2 and each hydrogen shares 1. **(1)**

**4** Formula: $CH_4$ **(1)**

**(2)**

### 100. Simple molecular substances

**1** C **(1)** as it has a low melting point and does not conduct electricity when molten or solid **(1)**

**2** (a)    (b) Covalent **(1)**

**(1)**

(c) There are weak intermolecular forces between molecules of ammonia **(1)** so not much energy is needed to break the intermolecular forces. **(1)**

**3** Melting point increases as you go down the group **(1)**. The intermolecular force between the molecules is increasing. **(1)**

### 101. Giant molecular substances

**1** C **(1)**

**2** (a) Both made of carbon **(1)**

(b) In diamond each carbon makes four bonds, in graphite three **(1)**. Or, graphite forms in layers. **(1)**

(c) Giant molecular structures **(1)**

(d) There are weak intermolecular forces between the layers in graphite **(1)**, the layers can therefore easily slide over each other and act as a lubricant. **(1)**

**3** (a) They both have four electrons in their outer shell **(1)**

(b) Two from: Hard **(1)** high melting point **(1)** does not conduct electricity when molten or solid **(1)** does not conduct electricity **(1)**

(c) Hard **(1)** − can be used for drill bits **(1)**

### 102. Other large molecules

**1** (a) Propene **(1)**    (b) Covalent **(1)**

**2** (a) Weak intermolecular forces between each fullerene **(1)** therefore not much energy is needed to break the bond between molecules **(1)**

(b) Weak intermolecular bonds between molecules **(1)**

(c) Lubricants **(1)**

**3** (a) Each carbon makes three bonds **(1)** to three other carbons. **(1)**

(b) Each carbon is bonded to three others **(1)** by covalent bonding **(1)** covalent bonding is very strong **(1)**

(c) Each carbon has one delocalised electron **(1)** and delocalised electrons conduct electricity. **(1)**

### 103. Metals

**1** A **(1)**

**2** (a) Malleable **(1)**    (b)

**(1)**

**3** (a) The greater the charge on the metal ion **(1)** the higher the electrical conductivity. **(1)**

(b) The greater the charge on a metal ion the more delocalised electrons it produces **(1)** so a sodium ion produces one delocalised electron whereas an aluminium ion produces three. The more delocalised electrons there are, the greater the electrical conductivity. **(1)**

### 104. Limitations of models

| Advantage | Type of model | Disadvantage |
|---|---|---|
| Shows three-dimensional arrangement as well as size relationships between atoms. | Space fill | Bonding between atoms can sometimes be difficult to distinguish. |
| Shows three-dimensional arrangement of atoms and bonds. | Ball and stick | Identification of atoms requires a key of colour representations. |
| Shows how electrons are shared between atoms. | Dot cross | Only shows two-dimensional shape and gets very crowded with larger molecules. |
| Shows all the bonds that are present. | Structure | Only shows two-dimensional shape and no indication about type of bonding. |

**(4)**

**2** Dot cross **(1)** as this is the only model that shows electrons **(1)**

**3** They allow you to see the bonding between elements **(1)** and visualise the molecules. **(1)**

**4** The positive metal ions are not fixed in place, they vibrate on the spot and the model can not show them vibrating **(1)**. The electrons are able to move within the structure, but the model implies they are fixed in position. **(1)**

### 105. Relative formula mass

**1** (a) Magnesium **(1)**    (b) 8 **(1)**    (c) Nitrogen **(1)**

**2** (a) 32 **(1)**    (b) 44 **(1)**    (c) 17 **(1)**    (d) 18 **(1)**

**3** (a) 30 **(1)**    (b) 208 **(1)**    (c) 78 **(1)**

(d) 142 **(1)**    (e) 149 **(1)**    (f) 148 **(1)**

(g) 46 **(1)**

### 106. Empirical formulae

**1** $C_6H_{12}$ **(2)**

**2** (a) HO **(1)**    (b) $CH_2O$ **(1)**

(c) $CH_2O$    (d) $P_2O_5$

**3** (a) $N_2O$ **(1)**    (b) $CH_3$ **(1)**

**4** (a) 2.54 g **(1)**    (b) 0.64 g **(1)**

(c) 2.54/63.5 = 0.04    0.64/16 = 0.04
ratio is 1 : 1, Cu : O, formula is CuO

### 107. Conservation of mass

**1** (a) The system is open **(1)** The mass of the flask has changed because gas has escaped **(1)**

(b) Wear safety glasses **(1)**

(c) after 75 s **(1)**, no more gas is given off **(1)**

**2** (a) 1 mol of Mg **(1)**, 0.5 mol of $O_2$ **(1)**, 16 g oxygen **(1)**

(b) 0.2 mol of HCl **(1)**, 0.1 mol of zinc **(1)**, mass of zinc 6.5 g **(1)**

### 108. Reacting mass calculations

**1** (a) D **(1)**

(b) 1 mol of $CaCO_3$ reacts with 2 mol of HCl **(1)** limiting reagent is HCl **(1)**

**2** (a) 0.1 mol iron **(1)**, 0.2 mol sulfur **(1)**, excess reagent is sulfur **(1)**

(b) $0.1 \times (56 + 32)$ **(1)** 8.8 g **(1)**

**3** (a) $Ca(OH)_2 + H_2SO_4 \rightarrow CaSO_4 + 2H_2O$ **(1)**

(b) Moles of $Ca(OH)_2$ = 1.76 **(1)**, mass of $CaSO_4$ = 239.4 g **(1)**

### 109. Concentration of solution

**1** (a) 4 dm³ **(1)**    (b) 0.1 dm³ **(1)**

**2** (a) 250 cm³ **(1)**    (b) 2125 cm³ **(1)**

3  (a) 7.5 g dm⁻³ **(1)** (b) 0.2 g dm⁻³ **(1)**
   (c) 10 g dm⁻³ **(1)** (d) 500 g dm⁻³ **(1)**
4  Original mass = 0.4 g **(1)** 1 g dm⁻³ **(1)**
5  (a) 12.5 g **(1)**
   (b) To make sure the potassium nitrate dissolved fully **(1)**
   (c) It gets more concentrated **(1)** because a greater mass of potassium nitrate is dissolved in the same volume of water **(1)**

## 110. Avogadro's constant and moles

1  A **(1)**
2  (a) $6.02 \times 10^{23}$ **(1)** (b) $3.01 \times 10^{23}$ **(1)**
   (c) $1.806 \times 10^{24}$ **(1)**
3  (a) 1.35 **(1)** (b) 0.2 **(1)** (c) 3 **(1)**
4  $1.204 \times 10^{23}$ **(2)**
5  3 **(2)**
6  Moles of zinc = 0.33 **(1)**, mass of zinc = 21.7 g **(1)**

## 111. Extended response – Types of substance

Answers could include the following points: **(6)**
- Ions can move in molten sodium chloride
- Ions carry charge so conduct electricity
- Graphite (carbon) has four electrons in its outer shell
- Only three of the four outer electrons are used to bond to other carbons so one electron is delocalised
- Graphite contains delocalised electrons that conduct electricity
- Iron is a metal so has metallic bonding
- Positive metal ions are held together by delocalised electrons
- Delocalised electrons conduct electricity

## 112. States of matter

1  D **(1)**
2  Atoms in solids are fixed in place. Atoms in liquids are free to move but are very close together **(1)**. In both cases, there are no spaces between atoms **(1)**. In a gas, the atoms are spread out with spaces in between, so can be compressed. **(1)**
3  (a) Liquid: move around each other **(1)**
       Gas: move quickly in all directions – random **(1)**
   (b) Deposition **(1)**
   (c) Energy of the atoms increases **(1)**
   (d) Liquid **(1)**
4  Density is greatest when copper is a solid **(1)**

liquid (1)

solid (1)

## 113. Pure substances and mixtures

1  Pure: pure sugar, graphite electrode **(1)**, diamond **(1)**
   mixture: perfume, mud, smoke **(1)**
2  (a) A and C **(1)**
   (b) C **(1)** because it contains only one type of molecule **(1)**
3  Iron and sulfur are a mixture, yet iron sulfide is a compound as chemically bonded **(1)** so can no longer be separated. **(1)**
4  (a) B **(1)** (b) Higher **(1)**
   (c) Line on graph with no horizontal section, indicating the range of melting points in the components of the impure sample. **(1)**

## 114. Distillation

1  B **(1)**
2  (a) Add anti-bumping granules; clamp apparatus to a stand **(1)**
   (b) Alcohol **(1)**
   (c) Hot gas is cooled **(1)** by condenser and condenses **(1)** to a liquid **(1)**
3  A, C, D **(1)** – boil at a specific temperature not a range **(1)**

## 115. Filtration and crystallisation

1  (a) Filtration **(1)** (b) Water **(1)** (c) Flour **(1)**
2  Magnesium carbonate is a solid **(1)**, filter **(1)**
3  (a) To make sure all of the sulfuric acid reacts **(1)**
   (b) From top to bottom: (filter paper); residue; funnel; evaporating dish; (magnesium sulfate) **(3)**
   (c) Evaporate the solution with gentle heating until crystals start to form **(1)**. Allow concentrated solution to cool **(1)**. Filter crystals and dry on folds of filter paper. **(1)**
   (d) magnesium oxide + sulfuric acid → magnesium sulfate + water **(1)**
4  Filter sand **(1)** from salt and water then evaporate **(1)** water leaving salt crystals.

## 116. Paper chromatography

1  (a) A & C **(1)** (b) Pencil **(1)** (c) Paper **(1)**
   (d) Water **(1)** (e) D **(1)**
2  (a) B **(1)** (b) 1.19 **(1)**
   (c) How soluble the substance is in the mobile phase **(1)**

## 117. Investigating inks

1  (a) (i) So the solvent does not evaporate **(1)**
       (ii) To stop the liquid bumping **(1)**
       (iii) To identify the boiling point of the solvent **(1)** so he can compare with the bottle of ink **(1)**
   (b) (i) The ink needs to be soluble **(1)**
       (ii) So it does not interfere with the results **(1)**
       (iii) So $R_f$ values can be calculated **(1)**
       (iv) Keep clear of naked flames **(1)**, use safety glasses **(1)**
   (c) The centre point of each spot has moved up the paper to the same amount for both inks **(1)**. Therefore they could be guilty as the spots match. **(1)**

## 118. Drinking water

1  Drinking water **(1)**
2  Two steps and reasons from: Step: sedimentation **(1)**; Reason: to remove any large pieces of insoluble material from the water **(1)**
   Step: filtration **(1)**; Reason: remove small pieces of insoluble material **(1)**
   Step: chlorination **(1)**; Reason: kill microorganisms **(1)**
3  (a) Distillation **(1)**
   (b) Very expensive/cost **(1)**
   (c) Water boils and is turned into a gas **(1)**. The water then condenses **(1)** and turns back into a liquid **(1)**. Salt is left behind in the distillation flask. **(1)**

## 119. Extended response – Separating mixtures

Answers could include the following points: **(6)**
- Step 1. Filter the solid substance C from the soluble solutions A and B
- C is insoluble so stays in the filter paper
- Wash C with water
- Step 2 – distillation. A and B are both soluble, but B has a lower boiling point than A
- Set up distillation equipment and heat solutions A and B
- B will be collected first at 78 °C
- A will be collected second at 100 °C.

## 120. Acids and alkalis

1  B **(1)**
2  (a) Red **(1)** (b) Goes green, neutral **(1)** then blue, alkali **(1)**
3

|  | Acid | Alkali |
|---|---|---|
| Litmus | red **(1)** | blue **(1)** |
| Methyl orange | red **(1)** | yellow |
| Phenolphthalein | colourless | pink **(1)** |

4  (a) Hydrogen, $H^+$ **(1)**
   (b) $HNO_3(l) \rightarrow H^+(aq) + NO_3^-(aq)$ **(1)**
5  (a) $OH^-$ **(1)**          (b) increases **(1)**

### 121. Strong and weak acids
1  B **(1)**
2  Concentrated acids have greater number of hydrogen ions **(1)** in the same volume **(1)** when compared with a weak acid
3  (a) 2 **(1)** (b) The acid has been diluted by a factor of 10 and every tenfold dilution increases pH by 1 **(1)**
4  (a) Ethanoic **(1)**
   (b) Weak acids dissociate only partially **(1)** while strong acids dissociate fully in aqueous solution **(1)**
   (c) Hydrogen **(1)**
   (d) Squeaky pop test: lit splint at mouth of test tube filled with gas **(1)** burns with pop sound **(1)**

### 122. Bases and alkalis
1  C **(1)**
2  (a) Solution 2 as $10\,g\,dm^{-3}$ **(2)**        (b) Alkali **(1)**
3  (a) Green **(1)** as water is neutral **(1)**
   (b) (i)  2 **(1)** $CO_2$ **(1)**
       (ii) Bubble through limewater **(1)**, turns cloudy **(1)**
4  (a) X **(1)**          (b) W **(1)**          (c) Z **(1)**

### 123. Neutralisation
1  (a) Burette **(1)**
   (b) ammonia + nitric acid → ammonium nitrate **(1)**
2  (a) 10, 10
   (b) As the concentration of HCl **increases (1)**, the volume of acid required to neutralise the KOH **decreases. (1)**
   (c) $H^+ + OH^- \rightarrow H_2O$ **(1)**

### 124. Salts from insoluble bases
1  (a) (i)  Hydrochloric acid **(1)**
       (ii) $Zn(OH)_2 + 2HCl \rightarrow ZnCl_2 + 2H_2O$ **(1)**
   (b) (i)  To speed up the reaction **(1)** and make sure a saturated solution forms **(1)**
       (ii) Solid zinc hydroxide collecting at the bottom of the beaker **(1)**
       (iii) Filter
   (c)

evaporating dish — gauze — tripod — Bunsen burner
          **(1)**

   (d) Allow the remaining water to evaporate slowly **(1)**
2  (a) $ZnO(s) + H_2SO_4(aq)$ **(1)** $\rightarrow ZnSO_4(aq) + H_2O(l)$ **(1)**
   (b) $MgCO_3(s) + 2HNO_3(aq)$ **(1)** $\rightarrow Mg(NO_3)_2(aq) + H_2O(l) + CO_2(g)$ **(1)**

### 125. Salts from soluble bases
1  A **(1)**
2  (a) Hydrochloric acid **(1)**, ammonium hydroxide **(1)**
   (b) Hydrochloric acid **(1)**, sodium hydroxide/carbonate **(1)**
3  (a) Pipette **(1)**
   (b) 23.80 **(1)**, 17.60 **(1)**
   (c) To get an approximate value for the titration **(1)**
   (d) 3 **(1)**
   (e) $\frac{23.70 + 23.80}{2}$ **(1)** $= 23.75\,cm^3$ **(1)**
   (f) She wanted the potassium sulfate to be pure **(1)**

### 126. Making insoluble salts
1  Soluble: $NaCl$, $NaNO_3$, $KBr$; insoluble: $AgCl$, $CaSO_4$, $BaCO_3$ **(6)**
2  (a) Lead nitrate **(1)**, potassium iodide **(1)**

   (b) $Pb(NO_3)_2(aq) + 2KI(aq)$ **(1)** $\rightarrow PbI_2(s) + 2KNO_3(aq)$ **(1)**
   (c) $Pb^{2+}(aq) + 2I^-(aq) \rightarrow PbI_2(s)$ **(1)**
3  (a) Two from: the beaker that the solutions were in needs to be washed out with distilled water **(1)**, swirl the solutions together in a beaker till a precipitate forms **(1)**, filter using filter paper **(1)**, rinse beaker with water, wash the barium sulfate with water **(1)**, dry in a warm oven **(1)**
   (b) $Ba(NO_3)_2(aq) + Na_2SO_4(aq)$ **(1)** $\rightarrow BaSO_4(s) + 2NaNO_3(aq)$ **(1)**
   (c) $Ba^{2+}(aq) + SO_4^{2-}$ **(1)** $\rightarrow BaSO_4(s)$ **(1)**
   (d) Heat it in an oven **(1)**, squeeze between filter paper **(1)**

### 127. Extended response – Making salts
Answers could include the following points: **(6)**
• Dissolve magnesium hydroxide in water
• Place nitric acid in burette
• Magnesium hydroxide in conical flask
• Add indicator to flask
• Titrate – record value
• Repeat titration no indicator
• Transfer solution to evaporating basin
• Heat until crystals start to form
• Then leave to fully evaporate slowly to get large crystals

### 128. Electrolysis
1  B **(1)**
2  (a) Graphite **(1)**
   (b) So it is molten **(1)**, when molten the ions can move to the electrodes **(1)**
   (c) Bromine **(1)** as bromide ions are negative **(1)**
   (d) Bromine is toxic **(1)**, carry out in fume hood **(1)**
3  (a) $Cu^{2+}$, $Cl^-$ **(1)**
   (b) $Cu^{2+}(aq) + 2e^-$ **(1)** $\rightarrow Cu(s)$ **(1)**
   (c) Reduction **(1)**
   (d) $2Cl^-(aq) \rightarrow Cl_2(g) + 2e^-$

### 129. Electrolysing solutions
1  (a)

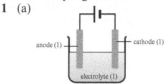
anode (1) — cathode (1) — electrolyte (1)

   (b) Dissolved in water **(1)**
   (c) The ions are free to move **(1)**
2  (a) $Na^+$, $Cl^-$ **(1)**, $OH^-$, $H^+$ **(1)**
   (b) Anode = chlorine **(1)**, cathode = hydrogen **(1)**
   (c) Bleaches damp litmus paper **(1)**
   (d) It becomes alkaline **(1)** as sodium hydroxide forms **(1)**
   (e) Start green **(1)** as neutral and end blue **(1)** to show alkali has been produced
3  (a) Anode = oxygen **(1)**, Cathode = hydrogen **(1)**
   (b) Per mole of water hydrolysed **(1)** there are twice as many hydrogen atoms as oxygen atoms. **(1)**

### 130. Investigating electrolysis
1  (a) Graphite/platinum **(1)**
   (b) Orange deposit on cathode **(1)**, electrolyte getting paler **(1)**, bubbles form on the anode **(1)**
   (c) Colour changes from blue to paler blue / colourless **(1)** because the copper ions are being used up / deposited on the cathode **(1)** in the reaction.
2  (a) $Cu(s) \rightarrow Cu^{2+}(aq) + 2e^-$ **(1)** $Cu^{2+}(aq) + 2e^- \rightarrow Cu(s)$ **(1)**
   (b) graph plotted accurately **(4)**
   (c) As the time increases **(1)** the mass of the electrode increases **(1)**
   (d) A trend line should be a straight line going through as many points as possible, with an equal number

of points above and below the line of points that do not directly fit on the line. **(1)** 10.6 g **(1)**

### 131. Extended response – Electrolysis
Answers could include the following points: **(6)**
- Brine contains $H^+$, $OH^-$, $Na^+$ and $Cl^-$ ions
- Hydrogen and sodium ions go towards the cathode
- Hydrogen ions are reduced/hydrogen ions gain electrons
- Hydrogen gas is discharged at the anode $2H^+ + 2e^- \rightarrow H_2$
- Hydroxide and chloride ions go towards the anode
- Chloride ions are oxidised/chlorine ions lose electrons
- Chlorine is discharged $2Cl^- \rightarrow Cl_2 + 2e^-$
- Sodium ions and hydroxide ions remain in the electrolyte and can join together to form sodium hydroxide $Na^+ + OH^- \rightarrow NaOH$

### 132. The reactivity series
1 (a) Water **(1)**      (b) Hydrogen **(1)**
  (c) Squeaky pop test: gas inside a test tube burns with a pop when lit splint is placed at the mouth of the tube **(1)**
2 copper<zinc<magnesium<calcium<potassium **(1)**
3 (a) $2K + 2H_2O \rightarrow 2KOH + H_2$
  (b) Add universal indicator; it will turn blue **(1)**
4 (a) zinc + hydrochloric acid → zinc chloride + hydrogen **(1)**
  (b) Platinum is less reactive than zinc **(1)**
  (c) Effervescence / bubbling / fizzing and the **(1)** piece of magnesium decreases in size / vanishes **(1)**

### 133. Metal displacement reactions
1 B **(1)**
2 (a) Blue colour of solution would fade **(1)**, brown solid would start to form **(1)**
  (b) Magnesium sulfate **(1)** and copper **(1)**
3 (a) calcium + copper oxide → calcium oxide **(1)** + copper
  (b) $Zn + PbO \rightarrow ZnO + Pb$ **(1)**
  (c) $Fe_2O_3(s) + 2Al(s) \rightarrow Al_2O_3(s) + 2Fe(s)$ **(1)**
4 (a) Potassium **(1)** and magnesium **(1)** because no displacement reaction occurs **(1)**
  (b) Aluminium or zinc **(1)**

### 134. Explaining metal reactivity
1 C **(1)**
2 (a) $Ag^+(aq) + e^- $ **(1)** $\rightarrow Ag(s)$ **(1)**
  (b) Oxidised **(1)**      (c) Zinc **(1)**
3 (a) Any two metals above hydrogen: e.g sodium/ calcium/magnesium **(2)**
  (b) Yes **(1)**
  (c) $2H^+ + 2e^- \rightarrow H_2$ **(1)**
  (d) calcium + hydrochloric acid → calcium chloride + hydrogen
  (e) $Ca(s) + 2HCl(aq) \rightarrow CaCl_2(aq) + H_2(g)$
  (f) $Ca \rightarrow Ca^{2+} + 2e^-$
  (g) $Ca + 2H^+ \rightarrow Ca^{2+} + H_2$

### 135. Metal ores
1 B **(1)**
2 They are very unreactive so do not combine with other elements **(1)**
3 (a) Carbon has been oxidised as it has gained oxygen **(1)**, lead reduced (loses oxygen) **(1)**
  (b) Oxidation is loss of electrons **(1)**, reduction is gain of electrons **(1)** (OIL RIG)
  (c) An orange **(1)** solid **(1)** would form
  (d) Wash with water to suspend the charcoal powder **(1)** then filter using a sieve **(1)**

### 136. Iron and aluminium
1 D **(1)**
2 (a) Carbon is more reactive than iron so can displace iron from iron oxide **(1)**
  (b) Any metal above carbon in the reactivity series: for example, magnesium/potassium **(1)**
  (c) Carbon **(1)** because it has gained oxygen **(1)**
3 (a) The ore must be molten **(1)** so the ions can move **(1)** during electrolysis
  (b) To reduce the melting point of the aluminium **(1)**; this saves energy **(1)**
  (c) Cathode: $Al^{3+}(aq) + 3e^- \rightarrow Al(s)$ **(1)**
    Anode: $2O^{2-} \rightarrow O_2 + 4e^-$ **(1)**
  (d) Oxygen is produced at the anode **(1)** and this reacts with the carbon electrodes at the higher temperatures involved **(1)** to produce carbon dioxide
  (e) The process needs to be heated to a high temperature **(1)**. Large amounts of electricity are needed because the aluminium ion is $Al^{3+}$ **(1)**

### 137. Biological metal extraction
1 (a) Plants burned **(1)**
  (b) Carbon dioxide is released **(1)** which adds to global warming. **(1)**
2 (a) An ore is a rock that contains enough of a compound to extract a metal for profit. **(1)**
  (b) Temperature **(1)**, pH **(1)**
  (c) Iron is more reactive than copper. **(1)**
  (d) iron + copper sulfate **(1)** → copper + iron sulfate **(1)**
3 Not suitable as the toxic chemicals in the leachate could run down the mountain **(1)** and enter the water in the reservoir. **(1)**

### 138. Recycling metals
1 One advantage and one disadvantage: Advantages: less mining / natural reserves last longer / less pollution / less energy used / less landfill waste / digging ores from ground is expensive / extracting from ores may use more energy overall **(1)**; Disadvantages: the metals need to be collected or taken to recycling centres / some metals may be difficult to process, for example, tins with lots of oily paint residue on them **(1)**
2 (a) Bauxite **(1)**    (b) 95% less energy needed **(1)**, 9 tonnes less $CO_2$ produced **(1)**
  (c) 6 **(1)**
3 (a) Considerable energy savings **(1)**, can make money from selling the recycled metal **(1)**
  (b) 40 **(2)**
  (c) £500 ÷ 5£/kg = 100 kg **(1)** 100 × 1000 = 100 000 g **(1)** 100 000 g ÷ 15 g = 6667 phones **(1)**

### 139. Life-cycle assessments
1 (a) C **(1)**
  (b) (i) Manufacturing product **(1)**
     (ii) Disposal of product **(1)**
  (c) The waste product can often be recycled **(1)** into the raw materials again. **(1)**
2 (a) 45 kg **(1)**
  (b) Any three from:
    Paper bags made from renewable material **(1)**;
    Plastic bags produce less greenhouse emissions **(1)**;
    Paper bags use less energy **(1)**; Plastic bags produce less waste – but will take years to decompose **(1)**; Less water to produce plastic bags **(1)**; Choices must be backed up with three pieces of evidence from the table.

### 140. Extended response – Reactivity of metals
Answers could include the following points: **(6)**
- Take a beaker and add $20\,cm^3$ of one of the nitrates
- Add a piece of metal to the metal nitrate and record any observations
- Do not add zinc to zinc nitrate as no reaction will occur
- If a reaction occurs, a displacement reaction has occurred and the metal is more reactive than the metal in the nitrate solution
- Repeat for all combinations of metals and metal nitrates
- The most reactive metal will carry out the most displacement reactions

### 141. The Haber process
1  (a) A **(1)**
   (b) None of the products and reactants can be lost **(1)**
2  (a) Hydrogen – methane **(1)** Nitrogen – air **(1)**
   (b) Iron **(1)** 450 °C **(1)** 200 atmospheres **(1)**
3  (a) 60 minutes **(1)**
   (b) They are siphoned off and re-reacted **(1)**

### 142. More about equilibria
1  (a) Graph line between the lines shown, but a bit closer to the 350 °C line **(1)**
   (b) Increasing pressure increases yield **(1)**. Increasing temperature decreases yield. **(1)**
   (c) At low temperatures the reaction is not fast enough **(1)** the conditions used are a trade-off between the temperature, pressure and costs. **(1)**
   (d) The gases are cooled **(1)** and ammonia turns liquid at the highest temperature. **(1)**
   (e) Increasing the temperature and pressure increases the rate of the reaction, but increasing the temperature decreases the yield **(1)**. The cost of producing a high pressure is also a factor. **(1)**
   (f) Catalysts only increase speed of the reaction **(1)** not the yield **(1)** of the reaction.

### 143. The alkali metals
1  (a) The melting points of the alkali metals (lithium, sodium and potassium) are lower than the melting point of iron **(1)**
   (b) Iron will sink, lithium, sodium and potassium will float **(1)**
   (c) Any number between 30 and 50 °C **(1)**
2  (a) $2Na + 2H_2O \rightarrow 2NaOH + H_2$
   (b) Sodium hydroxide is produced **(1)** which is an alkali. **(1)**
   (c) More vigorous reaction **(1)** bursts into flames **(1)**
3  (a) $Li \rightarrow Li^+ + e^-$ **(1)**
   (b) The atoms gain more shells as you go down the group so it becomes easier to lose an electron and become a cation. **(1)**

### 144. The halogens
1  Chlorine – green gas **(1)** Bromine – brown liquid **(1)** Iodine – black solid **(1)**
2  (a)

**(1)**

Halogens all have seven electrons in their outer shells **(1)**
   (b) Consists of two atoms **(1)**
   (c)

**(1)**

   (d) Makes damp blue litmus paper turn red, and then bleaches it white **(1)**

(e) Chlorine is toxic **(1)**, use only in fumehood, wear eye protection **(1)**
3  (a) The wool would catch fire / burn **(1)** Fluorine is the most reactive halogen **(1)**
   (b) As you go down the group there are more shells of electrons **(1)** This means the distance between the outermost shell and the nucleus increases **(1)** making it harder to attract an electron and form a negative ion **(1)**

### 145. Reactions of halogens
1  (a) Iron chloride **(1)**
   (b) $2Fe + 3Cl_2 \rightarrow 2FeCl_3$ **(1)**
   (c) More reactive reaction **(1)** iron wool bursts into flames **(1)**
2  (a) $H_2 + I_2 \rightarrow 2HI$ **(1)**      (b) Add it to water **(1)**
   (c) Reactivity decreases down the group **(1)** because there are more shells **(1)** so the nucleus is less able to attract an electron **(1)**
3  (a) $Cl_2 + 2e^- \rightarrow 2Cl^-$ **(1)**
   (b) To gain an electron **(1)** to complete its outer shell **(1)**
   (c) chlorine + potassium → potassium chloride
   (d) $Cl_2(g) + 2Na(s) \rightarrow 2NaCl(s)$

### 146. Halogen displacement reactions
1  C **(1)**
2

|  | Chlorine water | Bromine water | Iodine water |
|---|---|---|---|
| Sodium chloride | ✗ | ✗ | ✗ |
| Sodium bromide | ✓ | ✗ | ✗ |
| Sodium iodide | ✓ | ✓ | ✗ |

**(2)**

   (c) Sodium chloride and chlorine both contain chlorine so there will not be a reaction. **(1)**
3  (a) Redox reaction **(1)**
   (b) Oxidised: iodide ions **(1)**
       $2I^- \rightarrow I_2 + 2e^-$ **(1)**
       Reduced: bromine **(1)**
       $Br_2 + 2e^- \rightarrow 2Br^-$ **(1)**
4  (a) $2NaAt + Br_2 \rightarrow 2NaBr + At_2$
   (b) No **(1)**, as iodine is more reactive than astatine **(1)**

### 147. The noble gases
1  B **(1)**
2  (a) Argon **(1)** krypton **(1)**
   (b) They will float **(1)**; the gas is inert so the balloons will be safe to use **(1)**
   (c) Gas **(1)** density greater than air **(1)**
3  (a)

**(2)**

   (b) They have a full outer shell of electrons **(1)**, so they can't add any more electrons in a reaction with other atoms. **(1)**

### 148. Extended response – Groups
Answers could include the following points: **(6)**
- Alkali metals get more reactive as you go down the group, because the outer electron is more easily lost as more inner electron shells are added
- Halogens decrease in reactivity as you go down the group, as it is more difficult to attract the final electron into the outer electron shell as more inner electron shells are added to shield the nucleus
- Most reactive pair will be potassium and chlorine
- $K \rightarrow K^+ + e^-$
- $Cl_2 + 2e^- \rightarrow 2Cl^-$
- $2K + Cl_2 \rightarrow 2KCl$

## 149. Rates of reaction

1  (a) C (1)
   (b) Greater surface area (1) so more reactions (1)
2  (a) Highest temperature is line A > line B > line C (1)
   (b) It's the point at which the limiting reagent is used up (1)
   (c) At higher temperatures, particles have more energy (1) to move around so greater chance (1) of collisions with enough energy to overcome the activation energy. (1)
   (d) Increase the concentration of the HCl (1). Increase the surface area of the magnesium (1).

## 150. Investigating rates

1  (a) Measure decrease in mass of the flask over time (1), measure the volume of gas produced over time (1)
   (b) Calcium carbonate was in excess (1) so all of the hydrochloric acid was used before all of the calcium carbonate could be used up. (1)
2  (a) 10 times faster (1)
   (b) The mass remains unchanged (1). It speeds up the rate of reaction. (1)
3  (a) You watch for it to disappear so that you know when the reaction is over. (1)
   (b) To stop contamination – you need to remove all the precipitate as this would affect your reading in the next measurement. (1)
   (c) As the concentration of the acid is decreased, the rate of reaction will decrease (1) because there are fewer particles to react (1) so the chance of a collision is less. (1)

## 151. Exam skills – Rates of reaction

(a)
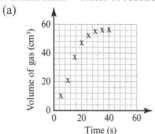
(3)
   (b) At the start, the reaction is fast up to around 20 s (1) it then slows down between 20 s and 30 s (1) and levels off from 35 s when the limiting reagent (sodium carbonate in this case) is used up. (1)
   (c) Steeper line (1) ending at same position (1)

## 152. Heat energy changes

1  (a) Endothermic        (b) Exothermic
   (c) Take up            (d) Release (1)
2  (a) Energy is transferred from stores of energy in chemical bonds (1) to the surroundings. (1)
   (b) The energy released when bonds are made is greater (1) than the energy needed to break the bonds. (1)
3  (a) Ammonium nitrate plus water (1)
   (b) To make sure all the solid dissolves/to make sure the temperature reading was accurate (1)
   (c) To prevent heat loss (1)

## 153. Reaction profiles

1  (a)
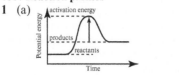
(1)
   (b) More energy is taken in to break the bonds in the reactants (1) than energy is released when bonds are formed in the products. (1)

2  (a) $Fe_2O_3 + 2Al \rightarrow Al_2O_3 + 2Fe$ (1)
   (b)
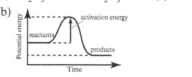
(3)
   (c) The flame supplies the reactants with the energy to overcome the activation energy. (1)
   (d) More energy is released from bond making (1) than is taken in to break the bonds for the reaction. (1)

## 154. Calculating energy changes

1  (a) C–H bonds = 1652 (1), O=O bonds = 996 (1), Total = 2648 kJ mol⁻¹ (1)
   (b) C=O bonds = 2 × 805 = 1610 (1)
       H–O bonds = 4 × 464 = 1856 (1)
       Total = 1610 + 1856 = 3466 kJ mol⁻¹ (1)
   (c) Total energy change = bonds broken − bonds formed = 2648 − 3466 (1) = −818 kJ mol⁻¹ (1)
   (d) Exothermic (1) because the energy change is negative (1)
2  Bonds broken = 1370 kJ mol⁻¹ (1)
   Bonds formed = 1856 kJ mol⁻¹ (1)
   Energy change = −486 kJ mol⁻¹ (1) exothermic (1)

## 155. Crude oil

1  C (1)
2  (a) Carbon (1) hydrogen (1)
   (b) Hydrocarbons (1)
3  (a) Methane (1)
   (b) Octane and cyclooctane probably, although to answer this question we also need the melting temperatures [they could be solids] (1)
   (c) Octane and cyclooctane (1)
4  (a) A resource that will run out (1) and cannot be replaced (1)
   (b) It is a raw material (1) that can be used to make lots of other chemicals (1), for example, after cracking of the longer fractions more desirable chain lengths are obtained (for example, petroleum), and the alkenes obtained in the process can be used to make plastics.

## 156. Fractional distillation

1  (a) The fractions have a range of boiling temperatures. (1)
   (b) Evaporating = the crude oil evaporates in the heating burner/boiler (1); Condensing = the hydrocarbons condense at a height in the fractionating column where the temperature matches their boiling points. (1)
   (c) The larger (1) the molecule, the higher the boiling point (1)
2  (a) How thick/runny the liquid is (1)
   (b) C>A>B (2)
3  Bitumen – road surfaces (1); Fuel oil – large ships/power station fuel (1); Kerosene – aircraft fuel (1)

## 157. Alkanes

1  (a) So the water vapour condenses (1)
   (b) The limewater will go cloudy. (1)
   (c) $C_5H_{12} + 8O_2 \rightarrow 5CO_2 + 6H_2O$
2  (a) All contain carbon (1) and hydrogen (1) and have only single bonds (1)
   (b) $C_4H_{10}$ (1)
   (c) $C_nH_{2n+2}$ (1)
3  (a) As the number of carbons increases (1) the boiling point increases. (1)
   (b) Any figure between 90–110 °C (1)

## 158. Incomplete combustion

1  (a)  Blue **(1)**
   (b)  Not enough oxygen gets to the fuel for complete combustion to take place. **(1)**
   (c)  Incomplete combustion takes place **(1)** so carbon forms, which is soot. **(1)**
2  (a)  propane + oxygen → water + carbon monoxide + soot **(1)**
   (b)  It binds to haemoglobin, the molecule in your red blood cells that bind to oxygen, much more strongly than oxygen, so your cells do not get enough oxygen. This can result in death. **(1)**
   (c)  It causes soot to build up in some appliances and can cause breathing problems. **(1)**
3  Yellow flame **(1)** soot **(1)**
4  $2C_4H_{10} + 13O_2 \rightarrow 8CO_2 + 10H_2O$ **(1)**
   $C_4H_{10} + 5O_2 \rightarrow CO + C + 2CO_2 + 5H_2O$ **(1)**

## 159. Acid rain

1  (a)  One sulfur **(1)** two oxygen **(1)**
   (b)  Sulfur impurities in the hydrocarbon **(1)**
   (c)  (i)  $H_2O(l) + SO_2(g) \rightarrow H_2SO_3(aq)$ **(1)**
       (ii)  $2H_2SO_3(aq) + O_2(g) \rightarrow 2H_2SO_4(aq)$ **(1)**
2  (a)  Kills trees **(1)** acidifies lakes **(1)**
   (b)  Corrodes metal **(1)** weathers limestone **(1)**
3  (a)  Nitric acid **(1)**  (b)  Nitrogen **(1)** oxygen **(1)**
   (c)  Fit a catalytic converter **(1)**

## 160. Choosing fuels

1  (a)  Renewable **(1)**      (b)  Renewable **(1)**
   (c)  Non-renewable **(1)**  (d)  Renewable **(1)**
   (e)  Non-renewable **(1)**
2  (a)  From fossil fuels **(1)**, electrolysis of water **(1)**
   (b)  $2H_2 + O_2$ **(1)** $\rightarrow 2H_2O$ **(1)**
   (c)  The only combustion product is water
   (d)  Compress gas **(1)** cool gas **(1)**
3  Three from − advantages: clean reaction, no greenhouse gases produced; disadvantages: difficult to store safely as it's highly explosive, takes up more space, energy needed to convert to liquid (at least one each from advantages and disadvantages; three in total)

## 161. Cracking

1  B **(1)**
2  (a)  (i)  Supply is 25 million, demand is 40 million **(1)**, 1.6 times greater **(2)**
       (ii)  Paraffin, fuel oil and bitumen **(1)**
   (b)  Used to fuel vehicles **(1)** lots of vehicles worldwide **(1)**
3  (a)  Ethene contains a double bond, butane only single bonds **(1)**
   (b)  $C_6H_{14}(l) \rightarrow C_4H_{10} + C_2H_4$ **(1)**
4  When large hydrocarbons are broken down **(1)** into two or more smaller alkanes and alkenes **(1)**

## 162. Extended response − Fuels

Answers could include the following points: **(6)**
• Hydrocarbons contain impurities of sulfur;
• When the hydrocarbons are burned sulfur dioxide is released as a gas into the atmosphere;
• The sulfur dioxide reacts with water in the clouds to form sulfurous acid;
• Sulfurous acid is oxidised to sulfuric acid, which then falls as acid rain;
• Since industrial revolution more industry;
• Greater use of fossil fuels so more hydrocarbons burned;
• More sulfur dioxide released into atmosphere;
• Acid rain damages trees;
• Acid rain acidifies lakes;
• Acid rain damages buildings by corroding metal work;
• Acid rain damages limestone.

## 163. The early atmosphere

1  A **(1)**
2  (a)  (i)  Earth cooled **(1)**
       (ii)  The gaseous water vapour cooled **(1)** and condensed **(1)** to form water.
   (b)  The concentration of carbon dioxide decreased **(1)** because it was dissolved **(1)** into the oceans.
   (c)  (i)  Ancient rocks contain pyrite that could not have formed in the presence of oxygen **(1)**, volcanoes do not release oxygen **(1)**
       (ii)  Relight a glowing splint **(1)**
       (iii)  Photosynthesis **(1)** of plants/microorganisms **(1)**

## 164. Greenhouse effect

1  (a)  Carbon dioxide **(1)** water vapour **(1)** methane **(1)**
   (b)  The earth absorbs solar radiation **(1)** and emits infrared radiation **(1)**. Greenhouse gases in the atmosphere absorb the infrared radiation and warm the Earth. **(1)**
2  Burning fossil fuels **(1)** deforestation **(1)**
3  (a)  The graph does show a correlation **(1)** as increased global temperatures are matched by increased carbon dioxide levels. **(1)**
   (b)  No **(1)**, there is not enough evidence **(1)**
   (c)  One of: This is historic data, so wasn't recorded at the time **(1)**, data has to be worked out from other things that can be measured **(1)**
   (d)  One from: Earth's temperature increases **(1)** ice caps melt **(1)** sea levels rise **(1)**

## 165. Extended response − Atmospheric science

Answers could include the following points: **(6)**
• Ice caps melt causing sea levels to rise and flooding
• Animals and plants may move to cooler climates
• Animals and plants may become extinct if they cannot survive the warmer temperatures
• More extreme weather events
• Oceans will become more acidic damaging the ecosystems
• Oceans will become warmer
• To reduce greenhouse gas emissions, use renewable energy
• Carbon capture technology
• Help people adapt to the changes

# Physics

## 166. Key concepts

1  6, 2, 4 **(1)**
2  93 s **(1)** 3896 s **(1)**
3  Hydroelectric power output = $2.1 \times 10^9$ W **(1)**
   Nuclear power output = $1860 \times 10^6$ W **(1)**
   $= 1.86 \times 10^9$ W **(1)**
4  60 km = 60 000 m **(1)** There are 3600 s in an hour **(1)**
   Speed = 60 000 ÷ 3600 = 16.67
   Speed = 17 m/s to 2 sf **(1)**
5  10 nm = $10 \times 10^{-9}$ m **(1)** 6 μm = $6 \times 10^{-6}$ m **(1)**
   Therefore, number = $6 \times 10^{-6}$ m ÷ $10 \times 10^{-9}$ m
   = 600 times **(1)**

## 167. Scalars and vectors

1  Scalars: Kinetic energy, Temperature, Mass, Potential energy **(4)** Vectors: Friction, Displacement, Acceleration, Air resistance **(4)**
2  Distance has size only **(1)**. Displacement has both size **and** direction. **(1)**
3  (a)  speed = 3300 ÷ 74 = 44.6 **(1)** = 45 m/s **(1)** to 2 sf
   (b)  displacement = zero
   (c)  average velocity = 0 m/s.
4  Twice the speed = 2 × 40 = 80 **(1)** Velocity = −80 km/h **(1)**
5  The deceleration is − 5 m/s². **(1)**

**6** Velocity is not constant **(1)**. Velocity has both size **and** direction/ (velocity is a vector) **(1)**
Since the direction is changing, the velocity is changing. **(1)**

**168. Speed, distance and time**
1 A and D are correct **(1)**
2 (a) The walker is stationary. **(1)**
  (b) Speed = (180 − 120) ÷ (200 − 140) **(1)** = 1 m/s **(1)**
  (c) Average speed = 180 ÷ 200 **(1)** = 0.9 m/s **(1)**
3 Distance = speed × time **(1)**
  Number of seconds in a year = 365 × 24 × 60 × 60
$$= 3.15 \times 10^6 \text{ s } (1)$$
  Distance = $3 \times 10^8 \times 3.15 \times 10^6 = 9.5 \times 10^{15}$ m **(1)**

**169. Equations of motion**
1 $v$ is final velocity, $u$ is initial velocity, $x$ is distance moved **(1)**
2 $u = 0$, $v = 15$ m/s, $t = 3$ s, $a = ?$ **(1)**
  $a = \frac{v-u}{t}$ **(1)**      $a = 5$ m/s² **(1)**
3 $a = -6.5$ m/s², $u = ?$, $v = 0$ m/s, $x = 70$ m **(1)**
  $v^2 - u^2 = 2 \times a \times x$ **(1)**
  $u = 30$ m/s **(1)**
  (only 2 marks if 30.2 m/s given; 1 mark if 910 m/s given)
4 (a) Velocity = (234 × 1000) ÷ (60 × 60) = 65 m/s **(1)**
  (b) Acceleration = velocity/time **(1)** = 65/42 **(1)**
    = 1.5 m/s² **(1)**
  (c) $v^2 - u^2 = 2ax$
    $x = \frac{v^2 - u^2}{2a}$ **(1)** $= \frac{65^2 - 0^2}{2 \times 1.5}$ **(1)** 1400 m to 2 sf **(1)**

**170. Velocity/time graphs**
1 (a) $a = \frac{v-u}{t}$ **(1)** $a = 17$ m/s² **(1)**
  (b)

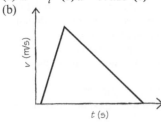

  Diagonal line showing increasing velocity **(1)**
  Diagonal line showing decreasing velocity **(1)**
  Gradient of increasing velocity greater than decreasing velocity **(1)**
  (Numbers are not needed on the sketch graph but can be included)
2 (a) $a = (15 - 0) ÷ 3$ **(1)** $= 5$ m/s² **(1)**
  (b) Distance = area under the graph **(1)**
    Distance = (1/2 × 3 × (15 − 0)) + (15 × 2) **(1)**
    Distance = 22.5 + 30 = 52.5 m **(1)**
  (c) Change in velocity = 7.6 − 15 = −7.4 m/s **(1)**
    Change in time = 1 s
    acceleration = change in velocity ÷ time
        = −7.4 ÷ 1 = −7.4 m/s² **(2)**
    (1 mark for acceleration, 1 mark for minus sign)

**171. Determining speed**
1 Swimming = 1 m/s (answer between 0.5 and 2 m/s) **(1)**
  Breeze = 5 m/s (answer between 2 and 10 m/s) **(1)**
2 Time – use a stopwatch to measure time between lamp posts **(1)**
  Distance – use a metre ruler/tape measure/trundle wheel to measure the distance between lampposts **(1)**
3 Estimate of max. speed of horse = 15 m/s (allow 13 m/s as this is correct) **(1)**
  Acceleration = (15 − 0) ÷ 5 = 3 m/s² **(1)**
  This is a third/ less than acceleration of free fall **(1)**
4 Measure the diameter of the ball using a ruler/ callipers **(1)**

Drop the ball through the light gates/The ball will break the light beam and this time will be recorded **(1)**
Speed = distance or diameter ÷ time **(1)**
Source of uncertainty – the ball may drop through so that not the whole diameter breaks the light beam **(1)**
5 As the police know the distance between the lines, they can see how far the car has travelled between photos **(1)**. They know the time between the photos **(1)**. Divide the distance by the time to calculate speed **(1)**.

**172. Newton's first law**
1 (a) Upwards arrow labelled reaction force **(1)**
    Downwards arrow labelled weight **(1)**
    Arrows the same length judged by eye **(1)**
  (b) Upwards arrow labelled drag or air resistance **(1)**
    Downwards arrow labelled weight **(1)**
    Arrows the same length judged by eye **(1)**
2 Missing answers are as follows: accelerating to the left **(1)** 0, none, stationary **(1)**
3 (a) The car is accelerating at a constant rate **(1)**. This means the thrust must be greater than the drag. **(1)**
  (b) The car is moving at a constant velocity **(1)** thrust = drag **(1)**
  (c) The car is decelerating **(1)** The drag must be greater than the thrust **(1)**

**173. Newton's second law**
1 Two boxes ticked only, bike accelerating **(1)** and plane landing **(1)**
2 $F = ma$ **(1)** $F = 2 × 5 = 10$ N **(1)**
3 $F = 10 \times 10^6$ N **(1)** $m = 2\,000\,000$ kg **(1)** $a = 5$ m/s² **(1)**
4 $F = ma$ **(1)** $m = 500$ g = 0.5 kg;
  resultant force = 10 N − 6 N = 4 N **(1)**    $a = 8$ m/s² **(1)**
5 $F = 1.7$ kN = 1700 N **(1)**
  $m = F ÷ a = 1700 ÷ 1.5$ **(1)**
  $m = 1130$ kg to 3 sf **(1)**

**174. Weight and mass**
1 (a) Mass is a measure of the amount of matter contained in a 3D space. Mass is a scalar quantity. **(1)**
  (b) Weight is the force an object experiences due to its mass and the size of gravitational field that it is in. Weight is a vector quantity. **(1)**
2 Missing values are: 130 N **(1)** 16 N **(1)** 0.36 N **(1)**
3 kg is the unit of mass and not weight. **(1)**
  The mass would be the same on the moon, but the weight would be less. **(1)**
4 (a) $W = m × g$ Divide both sides of the equation by $g$,
    $m = W ÷ g = 1200 ÷ 10$ **(1)** = 120 kg **(1)**
  (b) $g = W ÷ m = 420 ÷ 120$ **(1)** = 3.5 N/kg **(1)**

**175. Force and acceleration**
  (a) Independent variable is mass of the trolley **(1)**
  (b) Control variable is steepness of slope / falling mass / any sensible suggestion **(1)**
  (c) The slope compensates for friction **(2)** or Friction would slow the trolley down **(1)** only want one accelerating force **(1)**
  (d) $m = 200$ g = 0.2 kg **(1)**
    $W = mg = 0.2 × 10 = 2$ N **(1)**
  (e) $a = (83.3 − 20.5) ÷ 2.5$ **(1)**
    $a = 25.12$ **(1)**
    $a = 25$ cm/s² **(1)**
  (f) The mass of the trolley should be kept the same **(1)**
    The falling mass should be increased **(1)**
    The acceleration measured each time using the light gates **(1)**

## 176. Circular motion

1 C **(1)**
2 D **(1)**
3 A **(1)**
4 When the string breaks there is no resultant force keeping the apple moving in a circle. **(1)**
Arrow showing apple continuing to move in the same direction (a tangent to the circle) **(1)**. Since there is no resultant force acting / forces are balanced on the apple it will continue to move in a straight line at a constant speed. **(1)**
5 Velocity is a vector quantity **(1)** Since direction is changing the velocity must be changing **(1)** A change in velocity is an acceleration, so car is accelerating **(1)** If the car is accelerating there must be resultant force acting on it. **(1)**

## 177. Momentum and force

1 14 400 **(1)** kg m/s **(1)**
2 C **(1)**
3 The horse has a much greater mass (5 × greater) **(1)**. since momentum = mass × velocity **(1)** the horse must be moving slower (one-fifth the speed) **(1)**
4 Force = $\frac{mv - mu}{t}$ **(1)** = 270 N **(1)**
5 The momentum change remains the same **(1)**. The time taken for the momentum to change increases **(1)**. (Saying 'Rate of change of momentum decreases' gains these 2 marks.) This reduces the force of impact on the car. **(1)**

## 178. Newton's third law

1 A and D **(2)**
2 For every action there is an equal and opposite reaction **(1)**. The action and reaction forces act on different bodies. **(1)**
3 The kangaroo pushes down and the Earth pushes back with an equal and opposite force **(1)**. The kangaroo has a small mass and so the force accelerates it upwards. **(1)**
4 (a) Momentum before = 22 500 + 0 **(1)**
= 22 500 kg m/s **(1)**
(b) Conservation of momentum **(1)**
Combined mass = 1500 kg + 1000 kg = 2500 kg
22 500 = 2500 × $v$ **(1)** (allow error carried from part (a))
$v$ = 9 m/s **(1)**
5 Total momentum before the apple was thrown = 0 **(1)**. To conserve momentum as the apple moves one way the astronaut must move in the opposite direction **(1)**. The astronaut will move at a slower velocity than the apple because the astronaut has a greater mass than the apple. **(1)**

## 179. Human reaction time

1 (a) Tiredness increases human reaction time **(1)**
(b) Younger people have smaller reaction times/ caffeine **(1)**
2 (a) Hold a ruler just above the test subject's hand **(1)**. Drop the ruler and measure how far the ruler dropped before it was caught. **(1)**
(b) The test subject can't hold the ruler as they need to react to the ruler being dropped. **(1)**
(c) Teacher average = 16.5 cm **(1)**
Average = 17 cm to 2 sf **(1)**
(d) Reaction time = 0.173 s **(1)** = 0.17 s to 2 sf **(1)**
(e) Distance = speed × time **(1)**
Distance = 13 × 0.18 = 2.34 **(1)**
Distance = 2.3 m **(1)**

## 180. Stopping distances

1 B **(1)**
2 C **(1)**
3 Stopping distance = thinking distance + braking distance **(1)**
4 The thinking distance will increase as the reaction time has increased **(1)**
This will increase the stopping distance. **(1)**
5 (a) Reaction time = 0.4 s **(1)**
(b) Stopping distance = area under the graph **(1)**
Stopping distance = (12 × 0.4) + (0.5 × 1.6 × 12) **(1)**
Stopping distance = 4.8 + 9.6 = 14.4 m **(1)**
(c) Thinking distance will double/increase **(1)**
Braking distance will increase **(1)**
Increases by more than double **(1)**
Sensible suggestion 50 m (range 40 to 60) **(1)**

## 181. Extended response – Motion and forces

For full marks, the answer needs to clearly explain how to do the investigation and the correct experimental techniques required. Not all these points are needed, but for six marks there should be at least one bullet point from each heading. **(6)**
**Diagram**
• A labelled diagram such as the one on p. 175.
• Measurements
• Length of timing card using a ruler
• Mass of trolley using a balance
• Time through both light gates and time between light gates (may need a stopwatch or use of a datalogger for this)
**Variables**
• Independent – mass of trolley
• Dependent – acceleration
• Control – mass of falling mass, angle of ramp, friction between trolley and ramp
**Procedure**
• Set up as shown in the diagram
• Ramp needs to compensate for friction (slope such that trolley rolls down at a constant speed)
• Record mass of trolley
• Place trolley at the top of the slope, and release
• Record times through both light gates and time between light gates
• Repeat procedure, but increase the mass of the trolley
**Acceleration**
• Calculate the velocity/speed through each light gate using length of card ÷ time through light gate
• Calculate change in velocity
• Acceleration = change in velocity ÷ time taken between light gates

## 182. Energy stores and transfers

1 Energy cannot be created or destroyed **(1)** it can only be transferred from one store to another. **(1)**
2 (a) 19 J **(1)**
(b) The energy transferred by light would be lower **(1)** and the energy transferred by heating would be greater. **(1)**
3 Sankey diagram drawn and correctly labelled with values:
input arrow labelled: energy transferred by electricity 800 J **(1)**
one wider output arrow labelled: energy transferred to thermal store of water (720 J) **(1)**
one thinner output arrow labelled: energy transferred to kettle and surroundings (80 J) **(1)**
4 The fuel is a store of chemical energy which is transferred to kinetic energy **(1)**. As the car brakes the

kinetic energy store decreases (1). This kinetic energy is transferred to the thermal store of the surroundings. (1)

5  The store of chemical energy in the fuel decreases (1). Kinetic energy store increases as car accelerates. (1)

## 183. Efficient heat transfer

1  (a)  Insulation B, because it has the lower thermal conductivity (1). This means it transfers the thermal energy more slowly than insulation A. (1)
   (b)  Thickness of the material (1)
2  Foam contains many small air pockets so it has low thermal conductivity / is a good insulator (1) reduces heat loss through the walls. (1)
3  (a)  1200 J (1)
   (b)  Efficiency = (800 ÷ 2000) × 100% (1) = 40% (1)
4  Efficiency = 30% = 0.3
   Total energy in = useful energy transferred ÷ efficiency
   = 900 ÷ 0.3 (1) = 3000 J (1)

## 184. Energy resources

1  (a)  Renewable energy resources will not run out (1) e.g. tidal/solar/wind/wave/hydroelectricity/geothermal (1)
   (b)  Non-renewable resources are finite/will run out eventually (1) e.g. coal/oil/gas/nuclear (1)
2  When biofuels are burned they release the same amount of carbon dioxide they absorbed from the atmosphere as the plant grew (1); energy is required to grow/harvest/transport the crops so biofuels are not really carbon neutral (1)
3  (a)  Area = 40 × 30 = 1200 cm$^2$ (1)
   (b)  Energy = 1200 × 0.14 (1) = 168 J (1)
   (c)  Efficiency = useful energy transferred ÷ total energy supplied
        0.15 = useful energy transferred ÷ 168 (1)
        useful energy transferred = 25.2 J (1)
   (d)  The site may not have enough sunlight to charge the battery / there will be times when the Sun is not shining / to provide power during the winter months. (1)

## 185. Patterns of energy use

1  Increased population growth (1)
   Increased use of transport (1)
   Increased demand for electrical energy (1)
2  Burning fossil fuels releases carbon dioxide which is causing climate change/cause pollution (1).
   Renewable resources do not release carbon dioxide and will not run out. (1)
3  (a)  The colonists would need electrical energy (1) to power their equipment and for transport. (1)
   (b)  Consider.
        Renewable resources as deliveries from Earth would take too long, (1) but any source would need back up as it will not be possible to survive without electrical energy. (1)
4  Any two from: better insulation in homes; new technologies more efficient, e.g., lighting and heating; less industry in UK than in 1970s (2)
5  For full marks, must have comment from both how it changes and sources.
   How and why it changes: The demand will continue to increase (1). This is due to population increase/ developing countries increasing their energy consumption. (1)
   Sources: The percentage coming from fossil fuels will decline as it becomes increasingly expensive (1).
   The percentage from renewable resources will increase. (1)

## 186. Potential and kinetic energy

1  GPE = 300 J (1)
2  KE = 14 400 J (1)
   KE = 1.4 × 10$^4$ J (1)

3  $h = 24 ÷ (10 × 0.8)$ (1) = 3 m (1)
4  KE = ½ × $m$ × $v^2$ (1) $v$ = 13 m/s (1)
   (answer of 169 gains 1 mark only)
5  (a)  GPE = $mgh$ = 60 × 10 × 62 (1) = 37 200 J (1)
   (b)  KE = GPE (1)
        ½$mv^2$ = 37 200
        $v^2$ = 2 × 37 200 ÷ 60 = 1240 (1)
        $v$ = 35 m/s (1)

## 187. Extended response – Conservation of energy

For full marks you need to outline advantages and disadvantages of each energy source, and include a conclusion. (6)

**Advantages (of each)**
- Biogas is made from animal waste or plants. If the farm has animals, this gas can be generated from the animal waste and so the farmer would not run out of fuel.
- Biofuel is carbon neutral.
- Wind turbines require very little upkeep once they are installed.
- Wind turbines do not emit carbon dioxide.

**Disadvantages (of each)**
- If the farm does not have animals then growing crops to make the fuel would waste land.
- Wind turbines need space and can cause noise pollution.
- Wind turbines will not generate electricity continuously.

**Conclusion**
Any choice backed up by weighing up the advantages and disadvantages, e.g., I think the best choice is the biogas as this makes use of a resource which can cause pollution if not properly disposed of. The farmer will also have a continuous source of energy and not have to rely on the wind blowing at the right speed.

## 188. Waves

1  Waves transfer energy (1) without transferring matter. (1)
2  (a)  C (1)
   (b)  B (1)
   (c)  Any electromagnetic wave/s wave (1)
   (d)  Sound or p wave (1)
        The particles move back and forth/parallel to the direction wave is travelling (1)
3  If you drop a ball onto a pond the ball bobs up and down (1), but the wave travels across the whole pond. (1)
4  (a)  1 wave = 4 squares (1)
        time period = 4 × 0.2 = 0.8 s (1)
   (b)  Frequency = 1/0.8 = 1.25 (1) Hz (1)

## 189. Wave equations

1  $v = x ÷ t$ = 1000 ÷ 4.2 = 238 (1) m/s (1)
2  $v = f λ$ (1) $v$ = 4000 m/s (1)
3  $v = x ÷ t$, $x = v × t$ = 330 × 1.2 (1) = 396 m (1)
4  (a)  $v ÷ λ = f$ (1) Violet light: $f$ = 7.5 × 10$^{14}$ Hz (1)
   (b)  Red light: $f$ = 4.3 × 10$^{14}$ Hz (2)
5  Period = 10 ÷ 5 = 2 s (1)
   $f$ = 1 ÷ 2 = 0.5 Hz (1)
   $λ = v ÷ f$ = 2 ÷ 0.5 = 4 m (1)

## 190. Measuring wave velocity

1  Speed = 1.7 m/s (1) to 2 sf (1)
2  (a)  Time between claps = time ÷ number of claps
        = 4 ÷ 8 = 0.5 s
   (b)  The time between claps is very short. Increasing the number of claps reduces the effect of reaction times. (1)
   (c)  Speed = (2 × 80) ÷ 0.5 (1) = 320 m/s (1) (Answer of 160 m/s gains 1 mark only)
3  Speed = frequency × wavelength (1) Speed = 330 m/s (1)

**4** (a) Speed $= 0.5 \div (0.29 \times 10^{-3}) = 1700$ m/s **(2)**
(1 mark if answer not written to 2 sf)
(b) Time to travel 0.5 m $= 8.6 \times 10^{-5}$ s **(1)**
This is a very short period of time and would be hard to measure accurately. **(1)**

### 191. Waves and boundaries

**1** (a) Echo **(1)**
(b) The smooth classroom walls are good reflectors of sound waves, but the softer materials will absorb the sound **(1)**; this reduces the reflections. **(1)**
**2** Visible light is absorbed by the plastic **(1)**, but infrared is transmitted by the plastic allowing you to 'see' the infrared emitted by the hands. **(1)**
**3**

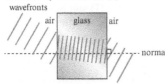

Marks awarded on diagram for change in direction **(1)**
shorter wavelengths **(1)**
Explanation: Light slows down as it enters glass **(1)**
The light changes direction **(1)**
This is called refraction **(1)**
**4** Light from the fish will be refracted/change direction as it leaves the water. **(1)**
The fish will appear to be in a different position in the water. **(1)**
**5** Any two from:
The sound travels at a similar speed in the jelly **(1)**
There will be sound transmitted into the body/there will be very little reflection **(1)** No air gap between the machine and the patient **(1)**

### 192. Waves in fluids

**1** (a) A motor is attached to a straight edged dipper **(1)**. The motor vibrates making the dipper vibrate **(1)**. The current through the motor is changed until the wavelength is easy to measure. **(1)**
(b) C **(1)**
(c) Record the time taken for a number of waves to pass a fixed point. **(1)**
Frequency = number of waves ÷ time taken **(1)**
(d) Speed $= 11 \times 4$ **(1)** $= 44$ cm/s or $= 0.44$ m/s **(1)**
(allow error carried from part (b))
**2** (a) Longitudinal waves have oscillations/particles vibrate in the same direction/parallel to the wave direction **(1)**
(b) Speed = frequency × wavelength
Frequency = 7500 Hz **(1)**
Wavelength $= 2 \times 0.4 = 0.8$ m **(1)**
Speed $= 7500 \times 0.8 = 6000$ m/s **(1)**

### 193. Extended response – Waves

For maximum marks there should be descriptions of both types of waves and some examples of wave behaviour that can be demonstrated. **(6)**
• Waves transfer energy without transferring matter.
• Longitudinal waves: the oscillations are parallel to the direction of motion.
• Transverse waves: the oscillations are perpendicular to the direction of motion.
• Water waves are transverse waves.
• Sound is a longitudinal wave.
• All waves have amplitude/wavelength/frequency/can be reflected/refracted.
• It is easy to identify the wavelength and amplitude of a water wave.
• The amplitude of a wave is the maximum distance of the wave from its rest position.
• The wavelength is the distance from one point on a wave to the same position on the next wave.

• Conclusion: The ripple tank demonstrates wave behaviour such as reflection/refraction and allows you to understand terms such as amplitude/frequency/wavelength of a wave.

### 194. Electromagnetic spectrum

**1** (a) All travel at same speed **(1)**
(b) (gaps in list are) Microwave, infrared, ultraviolet, gamma (in that order) **(4)**
(c) Frequency increases / energy of the wave increases **(1)**
**2** $v = f\lambda = 0.001 \times 300 \times 10^9$ Hz **(1)** $= 3 \times 10^8$ m/s **(1)**
(marks can only be given if working shown)
**3** $f = 3 \times 10^8 \div 0.12$ **(1)**
$f = 2.5 \times 10^9$ Hz **(2)** (max. 2 marks if answer not in standard form)
**4** $f = 99.7 \times 10^6$ Hz or $9.97 \times 10^7$ Hz **(1)**
$\lambda = 3 \times 10^8 \div 99.7 \times 10^6$ **(1)**
$\lambda = 3$ m **(1)**

### 195. Investigating refraction

(a) Normal, angle of incidence and angle of refraction all correctly identified **(3)** (Max. two marks if identified as light leaves glass instead of entering)
(b) Use a single slit to obtain a single ray of light and place the slit near the end of the ray box **(1)**
(c) Draw crosses on the light ray and then mark where the glass block is; remove ray box and block of glass and join crosses with a ruler **(1)**
(d) Points plotted correctly **(2)** Curved line of best fit **(2)** (if straight line of best fit **(1)**)
(e) Incident angle $= 50°$ or refracted angle $= 59°$
(f) As the angle of incidence increases the angle of refraction increases **(1)** As the angle of incidence increases the angle of refraction increases at a slower rate/the gradient/slope decreases **(1)**

### 196. Wave behaviour

**1** Microwave **(1)**
**2** C **(1)**
**3** For full marks there must be a statement in agreement or disagreement. For example, They are all reflected/transmitted/absorbed **(1)** different amounts depending on the material and the wavelength of the wave **(1)** Any example, e.g., radio is transmitted through walls, but light is not **(1)** all em waves have similar properties, but they are not the same **(1)**
**4** Microwaves pass through ionosphere **(1)** Receivers have to be in line with transmitters **(1)** Earth is curved **(1)** (Most) Radio waves refracted and reflected by ionosphere **(1)** (points could be made using a labelled diagram)

### 197. Dangers and uses

**1** (a) Radio waves **(1)**
(b) Any two from: X-rays **(1)** Gamma **(1)** UV **(1)**
(c) As the frequency increases the waves become more dangerous **(1)**
**2** Any two from: sterilise equipment **(1)** detect cancer **(1)** treat cancer **(1)**
**3** (a) X-rays are transmitted through soft tissue but are absorbed by bones **(1)**. The film blackens where the X-rays pass through leaving shadow pictures of the bones. **(1)**
(b) The technician does many X-rays every day **(1)** and so is exposed to much more radiation than the patient who only has one or two X-rays. **(1)**
**4** Three from: Frequency of mobile phone is lower **(1)** Power of mobile phone is much lower **(1)** Frequency is related to harm to living cells so lower frequency safer **(1)** Mobile phone less powerful so less energy transferred **(1)**

**198. Changes and radiation**

1 Electrons can only have certain discrete energy levels
(1). Protons and neutrons/nucleus also only have
certain discrete energy levels. (1)

2 (a) D (1)  (b) C (1)  (c) C (1)  (d) A (1)

3 Four from: electrons in the ink absorb radiation (1) the
electrons jump up to a high level (1) electrons jump down
in steps (1) electrons release less energy as they jump down
(1) the electrons emit visible light as they jump down (1)

**199. Extended response – Light and the electromagnetic
spectrum**

For full marks you need at least two points from each
heading and a conclusion. (6)

**Gamma radiation is used to**
• sterilise medical equipment
• in scanners to detect cancers
• treat cancers

**Risks**
• exposure to gamma radiation causes mutations
• can cause cancer or kill cells
• the larger the exposure the higher the risk

**How are risks minimised**
• sterilising done in a factory so no risk to people
• detection uses a low dose and patients are not
  exposed to it for long
• workers take precautions/wear protective clothing/
  stay out of the room
• when treating cancer, the cancer cells get the largest
  dose

**Conclusion**: the benefits of finding and treating cancers
outweigh the risks of using gamma radiation.

**200. Structure of the atom**

1 Clockwise from left: nucleus, proton, neutron, electron (4)

2 Neutron: 1 (1) 0 (1) Electron: 0 (1) –1 (1)

3 (a) $1 \times 10^5$ times bigger (1)
  (b) the nucleus is $1 \times 10^5 \times$ bigger, Atom = $1 \times 10^5 \times$
    nucleus, Atom = $1 \times 10^5 \times 5 = 5 \times 10^5$ cm (1) =
    5000 m (1)
  (c) Because the atom is 10 000 times bigger than the
    nucleus/students can refer back to their answer to
    part (b) (1)

4 Atom diameter $1 \times 10^{-10}$ (1) Number of atoms = 32 (1)

**201. Atoms and isotopes**

1 (a) The mass number is the total number of protons
    and neutrons in the nucleus. (1)
  (b) The number of protons in the nucleus (1)
  (c) Take the atomic number from the mass number. (1)

2 (a) 12 protons (1)
  (b) There are 26 – 12 neutrons (1) There are 14
    neutrons (1)
  (c) An isotope of an element has a different number of
    neutrons, but the same number of protons. (1)

3 Mass number = 235 (1) Atomic number = 92 (1)
  Symbol drawn correctly with mass and atomic numbers
  correct way round (1)

4 The mass number is an average, and for most atoms
  is approximately a whole number (1). For chlorine,
  however, the mass number cannot be rounded
  accurately to a whole number. (1)

**202. Atoms, electrons and ions**

1 (a) Protons positive/+1 (1) Neutrons neutral/0 (1)
    electrons negative/ –1 (1) (need particle and correct
    charge for each mark)
  (b) Electrons and protons have equal and opposite
    charges (1). There are the same number of protons
    and electrons in an atom. (1)

2 Diagram showing electron moving up an energy level (1)
  To move up an energy level the electron must **absorb**
  energy (1)

3 2 + (2) (allow 1 mark for positive)

4 (a) Absorb enough energy to leave the nucleus (1)
    Or be hit by a particle such as alpha or beta (1)
  (b) Gamma radiation has enough energy to help
    electrons to escape the pull of the nucleus (1) Atoms
    become ions (1) The molecule will be damaged/fall
    apart if the atoms become ions (1)

**203. Ionising radiation**

1 Beta-minus radiation is a fast-moving electron (1) and
  has a negative charge of –1.
  Beta-plus is a positron (1) and has a charge of +1 (1)

2 A nucleus can be described as radioactive. It means
  it is unstable and will undergo radioactive decay (1)
  Radiation is what is **emitted** (1)

3 Gamma and neutron have no charge (1)

4 Place an absorber between the source and a detector (1)
  Place a piece of paper, then a thick sheet of aluminium
  between them (1) If the radiation is stopped by paper
  it is alpha/if stopped by aluminium it is beta/if it is not
  stopped by aluminium it is gamma (1)

5 Alpha is a helium nucleus and has a charge of +2 (1)
  Alpha is more likely to collide with an atom (1) Alpha
  more likely to ionise an atom (1) Alpha will quickly
  lose its energy (1)

**204. Background radiation**

1 (a) Any one from: grounds and buildings/cosmic rays/
    food and drink/radon gas
  (b) 14 + 0.3 (1) = 14.3% (1) (1 mark for correctly
    identifying man-made sources)
  (c) Draughts stopped (1) radon gas builds up in the
    house (1)
  (d) There are many different sources of background
    radiation (1)
    The value would be higher if you lived in parts of
    Cornwall or Scotland (1) (or other relevant example)
  (e) Using 11.5 (1) 11.5/100 × 2.7 = 0.31 mSv (1)

2 Three from: Passengers are at less risk than the crew as
  they will be in the air for a lot less time (1) However, you
  would have to fly 675 hours in a year to double average
  dose (1) For crew there is an increased risk but not one
  to be concerned about / could monitor annual flying
  hours (1) Other factors effect your average dose e.g.
  X-rays, where you live (1)

**205. Measuring radioactivity**

1 Photographic film (1) Geiger-Muller tube (GM tube) (1)

2 Two from: Gamma is penetrating (1) Reduces risk of
  exposure for nurses/doctors administering it (1) They
  are exposed every day as part of their job (1)

3 (a) Alpha can only travel a few cm in air (1) so would
    not reach the detector (1)
  (b) Radiation is random and so repeating results (1)
    improves the accuracy/makes the results more
    accurate (1)
  (c) Mean count for background = 10 (1)
    mean count for source = 84 (1)
  (d) Corrected count = 84 – 10 = 74 (1)

4 The film badge has to detect all types of radiation.
  Gamma and beta can both penetrate the plastic
  window, (1) but alpha cannot pass through plastic/
  alpha absorbed by plastic (1)

**206. Models of the atom**

1 Atoms are neutral. An electron has a negative charge
  and is much smaller than an atom (1). The new model

had to include a positive charge **(1)** so that the atom was neutral. **(1)**

2 (a) Alpha can only travel a few cm in air/alpha would not reach the gold foil or the detection plates **(1)**

(b) Paths reflective of initial trajectory **(1)** i.e. only deflected if close enough to the nucleus **(1)** and only bounced back if aimed directly at the nucleus **(1)**

(c) Three from: as only a few are deflected **(1)** the mass/charge is concentrated in the centre **(1)** most of the atom is empty space **(1)** strong deflection **(1)** positive charge concentrated in small space **(1)**

3 Electrons exist in energy levels/orbits **(1)**

4 (a) Electrons can jump up to higher energy levels **(1)** when electrons jump down they emit radiation **(1)**

(b) The electrons can only exist on certain levels **(1)** they can only jump between these levels **(1)** the radiation will only have certain wavelengths **(1)**

## 207. Beta decay

1 In beta-minus, a neutron decays into a proton and an electron **(1)**. The mass number remains the same, but the atomic number increases by 1 **(1)**. In beta-plus, a proton decays into a neutron and a positron **(1)**. The mass number stays the same, but the atomic number decreases by 1. **(1)**

2 (a) $^{230}_{90}\text{Th}$     (b) $^{18}_{8}\text{O}$ **(2)**

3 (a) $^{137}_{56}\text{Ba}$     (b) $^{228}_{89}\text{Ac}$ **(2)**

4 In beta-plus decay a proton decays into a neutron **(1)** and in beta-minus a neutron decays into a proton. **(1)** This suggests that protons and neutrons are not fundamental **(1)** since they can be changed into other particles. **(1)**

5 The mass numbers are much bigger than the atomic numbers **(1)**. This might make them unstable. **(1)**

## 208. Radioactive decay

1 Mass **(1)** charge **(1)**

2 (a) In alpha and beta decay a new element is formed **(1)**. In neutron decay a new isotope is formed **(1)** In gamma decay the element/nucleus is unchanged **(1)**

(b) Different elements have different atomic numbers. An alpha particle consists of 2 protons and 2 neutrons **(1)** When an alpha particle leaves the nucleus 2 protons are removed and the atomic number is reduced by 2 **(1) or** In beta decay a neutron is changed to a proton/or a proton is changed to a neutron **(1)** A nucleus gains/or loses a proton; either way, the atomic number changes **(1)**

3 Gamma is an electromagnetic wave **(1)** gamma decay has no effect on the nucleus **(1)**

4 (a) $^{4}_{2}\alpha + ^{234}_{90}\text{Th}$ **(3)**     (b) $^{4}_{2}\alpha + ^{217}_{87}\text{Fr}$ **(4)**

5 Alpha decay: mass number –4, atomic number –2, Beta-plus decay: atomic number –1 **(1)** So mass number decreases by 4 **(1)** atomic number decreases by 3 **(1)**

## 209. Half-life

1 (a) Half-life is the time taken for half the radioactive atoms to decay/for the activity to halve **(1)**

(b) Activity is the number of decays per second **(1)**

2 (a) In one half-life the activity will halve. After 2 hours activity will be $1400 \div 2 = 700$ cps **(1)**

(b) 3 half-lives **(1)** 6 hours **(1)**

3 $160 \rightarrow 80 \rightarrow 40 \rightarrow 20/3$ half-lives **(1)** Half-life = $9 \div 3$ = 3 hours **(1)**

4 (a) Lines drawn to show where activity halved, e.g. where activity falls from 800 Bq to 400 Bq **(1)** Half-life = 4 hours **(1)**

(b) Line should start at 800 and always be above first line from then on **(1)** with the same exponential decay shape **(1)**

## 210. Dangers of radiation

1 Ionising radiation can remove electrons from atoms to form ions **(1)**. These ions can cause mutations/kill cells. **(1)**

2 (a) This reduces the exposure time for the class and the teacher. **(1)**

(b) The tongs increase the distance between the teacher and the source. **(1)**

(c) Protective layers absorb much of the radiation. **(1)**

3 Gamma rays are fine beams **(1)** The beams all overlap at the site of the tumour **(1)** The tumour gets the largest dose of radiation **(1)** Killing the tumour **(1)**

## 211. Contamination and irradiation

1 C **(1)**

2 Exposure to the radioactive materials would irradiate the workers **(1)**. If the radioactive materials got on their skin/into their body they would be contaminated **(1)**.

3 Since the radioactive material is inside the body and in direct contact with it this is an example of contamination **(1)**; as the seed emits radiation it is also irradiating the body. **(1)**

4 (a) Radiation kills any bacteria/fungus/microorganisms on the food **(1)**. It is the bacteria/fungus/microorganisms that causes it to rot/decay/spoil. **(1)**

(b) The food has not been contaminated **(1)**. The food itself is not radioactive. **(1)**

5 Light is a form of radiation, but it is not ionising radiation **(1)**. Irradiation is the exposure to ionising radiation. **(1)**

## 212. Extended response – Radioactivity

For full marks answer should have relevant points on all three of alpha, beta and gamma and a conclusion. The sample answer for alpha is found on page 212. **(6)**

Beta
- Beta is a fast moving electron
- Beta has a negative charge (–1)
- Beta can pass through skin and tissue

Gamma
- Gamma is an electromagnetic wave
- Gamma has no charge
- Gamma is only weakly ionising
- Gamma can pass right through body

Conclusion
- Alpha most dangerous inside the body
- Beta and gamma most dangerous outside

## 213. Work, energy and power

1 $E = 20 \times 3 = 60$ J **(1)**

2 $t = 300$ s **(1)** $P = 750\,000/300 = 2500$ W **(1)**

3 (a) $m = 0.415$ kg **(1)** $W = 0.415 \times 10 = 4.15$ N **(1)**

(b) $F = 16 \times 4.15 = 66.4$ N **(1)**
$d = 0.6$ m **(1)**
$E = F \times d = 66.4 \times 0.6 = 39.8(4)$ J **(1)**
(allow error carried)

(c) Work done is the same if the job is done faster **(1)** / supervisor is wrong
Work done depends only on the weight and the distance moved **(1)** Power would be greater **(1)**

4 $E = Fd = 30\,000 \times 3 = 90\,000$ J **(1)**
$P = E \div t$
$t = E \div P$ **(1)**
$t = 90\,000 \div 2800 = 32$ s **(1) (1)** for correct significant figures

## 214. Extended response – Energy and forces

The first part of the sample answer is on page 214. For full marks you will also need to calculate the work done going up the stairs, find the power and decide which activity is the best. **(6)**

- To calculate work done going up the stairs you would need to know the weight of the teacher and the vertical height of the stairs.
- Work done equals weight × height in metres.
- To calculate the power, you would need to record the time it took to climb the stairs and divide the work done by the time taken.
- The activity with the highest power will be the best one to do.

### 215. Interacting forces

1 C (1)
2 Vector quantities have both magnitude/size (1) and direction (1)
3 (a) The diver pushes down on the board (1) and the board pushes up on the diver (1)
   (b) The gravitational force of the Earth on the diver pulls the diver down (1) and the gravitational force of the diver on the Earth pulls the Earth up (1) **or** The air has a pushing force against the diver (1) and the body of the diver pushes against the air. (1)
   (c) The water pushes up against the diver (1) and the diver pushes down on the water. (1)
4 (a) Two magnets drawn with arrows pointing to each other (1)
   (b) Two magnets drawn with arrows pointing away from each other (1)
5 Any three from: Gravitational force acts on all objects with mass (1) Electrostatic forces act only on charged objects (1) Gravitational forces only attract (1) Electrostatic can either attract or repel (1) Both are non-contact forces (1)

### 216. Free-body force diagrams

1 (a) (as shown on page 216)
   (b) Four arrows shown and all labelled correctly (1) Thrust and drag arrows equal length (1) Upthrust longer than weight (1)
2 Line correctly drawn (1) Horizontal component = 39 N (1) Vertical component = 23 N (1) *(accept 2N more or less for each component)*
3 (a) Arrow down labelled weight (1) Arrow pointing to the left labelled drag/air resistance/friction (1)
   (b) Any three from: the resultant force does not equal zero/there is a resultant force (1) velocity is a vector (1) the ball is changing direction, so velocity is changing (1) the ball is accelerating downwards (1)

### 217. Resultant forces

1 (a) Both arrows pointing to the left (1)
   (b) Arrows pointing in opposite directions (1)
2 (a) Arrow pointing down labelled 2 N (1) Arrow pointing forwards labelled 3 N (1) 3N arrow longer (1)
   (b) Scale drawing: 2 cm arrow pointing down (1) 3 cm arrow pointing forwards (1) resultant arrow drawn (1) Force = 3.6 ± 0.2 N (1)
3 (a) (as shown on page 217)
   (b) 45 000 N − 40 000 N = 5000 N (1) to the right (1)
   (c) Upwards pointing arrow drawn 1 cm long (1) Horizontal arrow drawn 5 cm long pointing to the right (1) Resultant arrow drawn on (1) Answer: 5100 N (±100 N) (1)

### 218. Extended response – Forces and their effects

A full mark answer would include accurate calculations and explanations. (6) (Max. four marks if only calculations)
- Diagram showing horizontal component of the tension for each lead

- Student chooses suitable scale (e.g., 1 cm = 1 N)
- Lead at 30° – horizontal component = 61 N ± 2 N
- Lead at 75° – horizontal component = 18 N ± 2 N
- Owner pulls backwards with larger component when the lead is at 30°
- So shorter lead is better as pulling back with less force

### 219. Circuit symbols

1 positive terminal

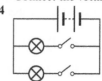

negative terminal

Correct symbol for cell (1)
Positive and negative terminals correctly labelled (1)
2 Figure A shows a fixed resistor (1) and Figure B is a variable resistor (1) The resistance of a variable resistor can be changed (1)
3 LED only allows current to flow in one direction. Reverse the LED or swap the batteries round (1) Connect the ammeter in series with the LED (1) Connect the voltmeter in parallel with the LED (1)
4

All circuit symbols drawn correctly: two lamps drawn in parallel (1) each switch placed in series with each lamp (1)

### 220. Series and parallel circuits

1 (a) The current is the same throughout a series circuit (1)
   (b) Potential difference is shared in a series circuit (1)
   (c) Current divides at a junction in a parallel circuit (1)
   (d) Components in parallel with each other have the same potential difference (1)
2 $A_1 = 1.5 A$ (1) $A_2 = 1.5 A$ (1) $V_1 = 8 V$ (1)
3 $A_1 = 1.5 A$ (1) $A_2 = 2.0 A$ (1) $V_2 = 8 V$ (1) $V_2 = 8 - 3 = 5 V$ (1)
4 Voltmeters have a very large resistance (1) All the pd is across the voltmeter/the current is too small for components to work (1)

### 221. Current and charge

1 (a) Arrow pointing anticlockwise and labelled conventional current direction (1)
   (b) Arrow pointing clockwise and labelled electron direction (1)
   (c) Electrons are negatively charged (1) so they are attracted to the positive terminal/repelled by the negative terminal (1)
2 (a) $Q = It = 3 \times 30 = 90 C$ (1)
   (b) $t = 10 \times 60 s = 600 s$, $Q = 600 \times 3 = 1800 C$ (1)
3 $I = Q \div t$ (1) $I = 120 \div 0.8 = 150 A$ (1)
4 $t = Q \div I$ (1) $t = 6.5 \times 10^3 \div 0.36 = 18\,056$ seconds (1) $t = 5$ hours (1)

### 222. Energy and charge

1 pd is the energy transferred per coulomb/per unit charge (1)
2 $E = 414\,000 J$ (2) $Q = 2350 C$ (2) $V = 24.0 V$ (2) (must be quoted to 3 sf otherwise they gain 1 mark only)
3 $E = I \times V \times t$ (1) $= 2.0 \times 12 \times 120$ (1) $= 2880 J$ (1)
4 (a) $E = Q \times V = 1.6 \times 10 \times 19 \times 1500$ (1) $= 2.4 \times 10^{-16} J$ (1)
   (b) $2.4 \times 10^{-16} = \frac{1}{2}mv^2$ (1) $(2 \times 2.4 \times 10^{-16}) \div 9.1 \times 10^{-31} v^2$ (1) $v = 2.3 \times 10^7$ m/s (1) (plus 1 for 2 sf)

### 223. Ohm's law
1  (a) pd = current × resistance **(1)**
   (b) straight line **(1)** through the origin **(1)**
2  $V = IR = 5 \times 10$ **(1)** $= 50\,V$ **(1)**
3  $R = V \div I = 14 \div 2$ **(1)** $= 7\,\Omega$ **(1)**
4  (a) $V = IR = 0.5 \times 4$ **(1)** $= 2\,V$ **(1)**
   (b) $V$ across lamp B $= 12 - 2 = 10\,V$ **(1)** $R = V \div I$ **(1)**
       $R = 10 \div 0.5 = 20\,\Omega$ **(1)**

### 224. Resistors
1  (a) (As shown on page 224)
   (b) Resistance can be calculated by dividing the potential difference **(1)** by the current. **(1)**
   (c) Increasing the resistance of the variable resistor decreases the current in the circuit. **(1)**
2  (a) $R = 8 \div 0.2$ **(1)** $R = 40\,\Omega$ **(1)**
   (b) $R = 2 \div 0.5$ **(1)** $= 4\,\Omega$ **(1)**
   (c) Resistor A $= 40 - 4 = 36\,\Omega$ **(1)**
3  (a) $I = V \div R = 10 \div 40$ **(1)** $= 0.25\,A$ **(1)**
   (b) $I = V \div R = 10 \div 20$ **(1)** $= 0.5\,A$ **(1)**
   (c) Total current $= 0.25 + 0.5 = 0.75\,A$ **(1)**
   (d) $R = V \div I = 10 \div 0.75$ **(1)** $R = 13\,\Omega$ **(1)**

### 225. I–V graphs
1
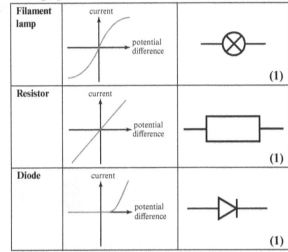

| Filament lamp | | **(1)** |
| Resistor | | **(1)** |
| Diode | | **(1)** |

2  (a) As potential difference increases, the filament gets hotter **(1)** This increases the resistance of the lamp **(1)**
   (b) In the reverse direction the diode has a very high resistance **(1)** In the forward direction there is a threshold pd **(1)** Once the threshold is passed resistance is low **(1)**
   (c) The resistance remains constant as you increase the pd **(1)** As long as the temperature remains constant **(1)**
3
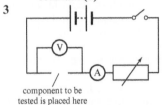

component to be tested is placed here

Ammeter in series, voltmeter in parallel **(1)** variable resistor included **(1)**
Student should plot an I–V graph **(1)** and use the shape of the graph to decide on the component **(1)**

### 226. Electrical circuits
(a)
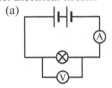

All circuit symbols correct **(1)** ammeter in series and voltmeter in parallel **(1)**

(b) $R = V \div I = 6 \div 0.3$ **(1)** $R = 20\,\Omega$ **(1)**
(c) $A_2$ (circuit B) $= 0.30\,A$ **(1)** $A_3$ (circuit A) $= 0.15\,A$ **(1)**
    $V_1$ (circuit B) $= 6.0\,V$ **(1)** $V_2$ (circuit A) $= 3.0\,V$ **(1)**
(d) In a series circuit the current decreases if you add more lamps (= increased resistance) **(1)**. In a parallel circuit the current through each lamp stays the same. **(1)**
(e) In the extended series circuit, the pd divides in three, so the pd across each bulb will be 2.0 V **(1)**. The current through each bulb will be 0.1 A [$V = 2.0$ V, $R = 20\,\Omega$, use $V = IR$] **(1)**.
    In the extended parallel circuit, the pd across each bulb will be 6.0 V **(1)**, so the current through each bulb will be 0.3 A. **(1)**
    The total current in the extended series circuit is reduced [from 0.15A to 0.1A] but the total current in the extended parallel circuit is increased [from 0.6 A to 0.9 A]. **(1)**

### 227. The LDR and the thermistor
1  (a)
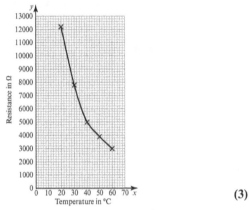
**(3)**

(–1 mark for each incorrect point plotted) (must include smooth, curved line of best fit)
(b) Idea that it's hard to measure temperature directly **(1)** Water can be heated slowly and so by measuring water temperature you know thermistor temperature **(1)**
(c) Ice can be used **(1)** to investigate resistance at cooler temperatures, where resistance changes most. **(1)**
(d) As the temperature increases, resistance decreases **(1)**
(e) Use the resistance/temperature graph to find out the temperature based on the resistance **(1)**. The thermistor's resistance changes the most between **(1)** temperatures of between 20°C and 40°C (allow 0 to 50). **(1)**
2  Method to change light intensity, e.g., move LDR away from lamp or connect lamp to variable resistor to change intensity **(1)** Place ammeter in series and voltmeter parallel to LDR **or** use a multimeter (Ohmmeter) to measure the resistance directly **(1)** Plot a graph of light intensity/distance from lamp vs. resistance **(1)**

### 228. Current heating effect
1  (a) In a kettle **(1)** the heating effect of the current is useful for heating the water. **(1)**
   (b) In a light bulb **(1)** energy is wasted as some energy is transferred to the surroundings as heat. **(1)**
2  (a) As the electrons flow through the vibrating ions they collide with the ions **(1)**. The more collisions the harder it is for the electrons to get through **(1)** and the higher the resistance **(1)**
   (b) Kinetic energy of the electrons is transferred to the ions as they collide **(1)** this makes the ions vibrate more/ions have more energy **(1)** and this increases the thermal kinetic energy of the resistor **(1)**

(c) Using a low resistance wire **(1)** Using a shorter length of wire **(1)** Using a wire with a larger cross-sectional area/thicker wire **(1)** Credit cooling the wire **(1)**

3 Three from: Appliances are added in parallel **(1)** This increases the current drawn from the socket **(1)** This can cause overheating in the cable supplying the overloaded sockets **(1)** A heating appliance will have a larger current and cause greater heating effect **(1)**

### 229. Energy and power

1 C **(1)**
2 (a) $P = IV = 230 \times 5$ **(1)** $P = 1150\,W$ **(1)**
   (b) $P = I^2R$ **(1)** $R = P \div I^2$ **(1)** $R = 1150 \div 25 = 46\,\Omega$ **(1)**
   (Could also achieve the same answer using $R = V \div I$)
3 $P = 1800\,W$, $t = 4 \times 60 = 240\,s$ **(1)** $E = Pt = 1800 \times 240$ **(1)** $E = 432\,000\,J$ **(1)**
4 (a) $E = ItV = 0.1 \times 5 \times 6$ **(1)** $E = 3\,J$ **(1)**
   (b) GPE $= mgh = 0.2 \times 10 \times 0.8$ **(1)** GPE $= 1.6\,J$ **(1)**
   (c) Efficiency = useful energy transferred ÷ total energy input, efficiency $= 1.6 \div 3 = 0.53$ **(1)** efficiency $= 53\%$ **(1)**

### 230. a.c. and d.c. circuits

1 B **(1)**
2 (a)
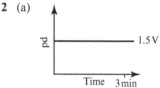

   Axes labelled **(1)** Horizontal line **(1)** Values added **(1)**
   (b) The electrons move in one direction only **(1)** This is a direct current **(1)**
   (c)
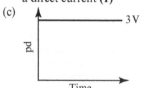

   Higher line **(1)** Line twice as high **(1)**
3 Four from:
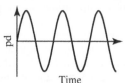

   sketch showing alternating pd with time **(1)** a.c. stands for alternating current. This means current is constantly changing direction **(1)** The frequency of this change is 50 Hz which means the current changes direction 100 times per second **(1)** The average voltage of the supply is 230 V **(1)**
4 (a) Mains electricity is 230 V a.c. This means the charger must reduce the voltage/pd to 19.5 V **(1)** change the voltage from a.c. to d.c. **(1)**
   (b) A diode **(1)** as it only allows current to flow in one direction **(1)**

### 231. Mains electricity and the plug

1 (a) The live is at 230 V and the neutral is at 0 V **(1)**. This means the potential difference between them is 230 V. **(1)**
   (b) Both wires at 0 V **(1)** potential difference equals 0 V **(1)**
2 Neutral and live have been swapped **(1)** There is no fuse **(1)** The outer cable insulation should be fixed under the cable grip **(1)**
3 (a) If a live wire comes loose and touches the metal casing the whole appliance is live **(1)**. The earth wire is connected to the metal casing **(1)** (if the live wire

touches the casing) a large current flows through the earth wire, **(1)** the fuse melts and breaks the circuit. **(1)**
   (b) Plastic is an insulator **(1)** so if live wire touches the casing it does not become live/conduct **(1)**
   (c) If the current is too high **(1)** a magnetic field opens a switch. **(1)**
4 Two from: The live wire has a potential difference of 230 V with respect to earth **(1)** If the switch/fuse is only on the neutral, the live wire would still be at this potential/live **(1)** If you touched the live wire you would be electrocuted/faulty device would still be live **(1)**

### 232. Extended response – Electricity and circuits

Answers could include the following points. **(6)**
• Fuses prevent fires, electrocutions and protect equipment.
• If a live wire touches the metal casing a large current flows to earth and the fuse melts and breaks the circuit.
• To calculate the max. current in an appliance:
  • $P = V \times I$ so the max. current $I = P \div V$, Mains voltage is 230 V
  • $I = 700 \div 230 = 3.0\,A$
• If the appliance is less than 700 W the maximum working current will be less so a 3 A fuse will work.
• If you used a 3 A fuse in an appliance rated 750 W the fuse would melt as soon as you plugged it in (as the current would be greater than 3 A).
• If you used a 13 A fuse for all appliances it would not protect sensitive equipment from a surge in current so expensive equipment like a computer might be damaged.

### 233. Magnets and magnetic fields

1 C **(1)**
2 A **(1)**
3 (a)
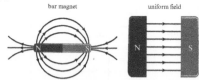
bar magnet      uniform field

   Correctly shaped fields for each diagram **(2)** Field lines have arrows pointing from north to south **(1)**
   (b) Uniform field label should be on figure 2 **(1)** Weak uniform field should be anywhere field lines more spaced apart **(1)** Stronger magnetic field should be on either of the poles **(1)**
   (c) Place a dot at the side of the compass where the arrow points (away from the magnet) **(1)** Move the compass so that the end of the arrow that was next to the compass is now next to the point you drew **(1)** Place a dot where the opposite end is pointing and repeat **(1)**
4 The paper clips are made of steel which is a magnetic material **(1)** Induced magnetism in the paper clips **(1)** Induced magnetism is caused by being in the magnetic field **(1)**
   The magnetic field becomes weaker further from the magnet **(1)**
5 Three from: A compass needle is a very small magnet **(1)** The needle points to the magnetic north **(1)** This is because it lines up with the Earth's magnetic field **(1)** The Earth's magnetic field is shaped like the field around a bar magnet **(1)**

### 234. Current and magnetism

1 B **(1)**
2 (a) Concentric circles drawn (more than one) **(1)** Arrows pointing clockwise **(1)**
   (b) The magnetic field would be stronger so the magnetic field lines would be closer together **(1)** Would also act over a larger distance **(1)**

**3** Diagram showing circular pattern around each wire **(1)** Diagram showing field patterns overlapping **(1)** Explanation that fields are added together **(1)**

**4** D **(1)**

## 235. Current, magnetism and force

**1** Three from: magnetic fields interact **(1)** increasing the current increases the force **(1)** increasing magnetic field strength increases the force **(1)** for max. force wire must be perpendicular to the field **(1)** (increasing length increases the force **(1)**)

**2** $F = 2.5 \times 10^{-3} \times 0.5 \times 0.1$ **(1)** $F = 1.25 \times 10^{-4}$ N **(1)**

**3** B **(1)**

**4** $I = F \div (B \times L) = 0.98 \div (0.8 \times 0.55)$ **(1)** $I = 2.2$ A **(1)** to 2sf **(1)**

**5** $B = F \div (I \times L) = 0.16 \div (4.5 \times 0.75)$ **(1)** $B = 47$ mT **(1)** to 2sf **(1)**

## 236. Extended response – Magnetism and the motor effect

To gain full marks you will need to include points from all three sections. Answers can appear in a labelled diagram. **(6)**

**Showing the field:**
- Place a piece of card around a vertical current-carrying wire
- Sprinkle iron filings to see the shape of the field
- Use plotting compasses to show the direction of the field
- Place a point at the end of the compass needle
- Move the compass so that needle lines up with the point, make a new dot
- Join up the dots

**Showing the direction:**
- Reverse the current
- Compass needle points in opposite direction
- Can show that if right hand thumb points at the direction of current, field is in direction of fingers

**Describing how field varies with distance:**
- Field strength decreases with distance
- Circles around the wire
- Circles get further apart as you increase distance from the wire

## 237. Electromagnetic induction and transformers

**1** (a) The needle would move to the left (opposite direction) **(1)**

(b) The needle would move to the left **(1)**

(c) Ammeter would read zero/needle stays in the middle **(1)**

(d) The moving magnetic field induces a potential difference across the wire **(1)** This causes a current to flow **(1)** The current sets up a magnetic that opposes the magnetic field that caused it **(1)**

(e) Two from: increasing the speed the magnetic moves **(1)** increasing the strength of the magnetic field by using a stronger magnet **(1)** increasing the number of turns on the coil **(1)**

**2** (a) The charger must contain a transformer **(1)**. Two from: transformer consists of a primary and secondary coil **(1)** linked by an iron core **(1)** the secondary coil has fewer coils than the primary **(1)**

(b) $I_p = (V_s I_s) \div V_p$ **(1)** $I_p = (16 \times 3.65) \div 230 = 0.25$ A **(1)**

(c) The charger must contain a diode **(1)** the diode must be placed after the secondary coil **(1)** as transformers need a.c. to work/the current must be a.c. to create changing magnetic field **(1)**

## 238. Transmitting electricity

**1** The National Grid is the wires that transmit electricity and the transformers that step up and step down the voltage **(1)**

(No marks if answer includes power stations)

**2** (a) X is a step-up transformer **(1)** Stepping up the voltage decreases the current **(1)** This is an advantage because a lower current reduces heat losses in the wire **(1)**

(b) Step-down transformer **(1)** Decreasing voltage for consumers makes it safer to use **(1)**

(c) Three from: d.c. one direction only/a.c. continuously changing direction **(1)**
Magnetic field constant for d.c./magnetic field constantly changing for a.c. **(1)**
Transformers need a.c. **(1)** The changing magnetic field in the primary induces pd in the secondary **(1)**

(d) $P = V \times I$, $P = 60\,000\,000$ W and $V = 400\,000$ V **(1)** $I = P \div V = 60\,000\,000/400\,000$ **(1)** $I = 150$ A **(1)**

(e) The answer will be less **(1)** The transformer will not be 100 % efficient **(1)**

## 239. Extended response – Electromagnetic induction

(6)
- The charger and toothbrush together make a transformer.
- In any transformer the primary and secondary coils are not electrically connected. They just need to be linked by an iron core. Since the magnetic fields can pass through the plastic the transformer still works.
- The mains electricity is a.c./the primary coil is connected to a.c.
- As the current direction changes the magnetic field changes direction.
- This induces a potential difference across the secondary coil.
- This causes a current to flow and the current charges the battery in the toothbrush.
- This is a step-down transformer.

## 240. Changes of state

**1** Mass is conserved in both physical and chemical changes **(1)**, in a physical change when the change is reversed the material recovers its original properties. **(1)**

**2** (a) Aluminium is a solid, chlorine is a gas and mercury is a liquid. **(1)**

(b) Aluminium **(1)**

(c) Aluminium is a solid, chlorine is a liquid and mercury is a solid. **(1)**

**3** (a) The particles are fixed in position in regular patterns **(1)** and are able to vibrate. **(1)**

(b) Particles have no pattern/particles moving in random directions **(1)** particles are moving fast/have lots of kinetic energy **(1)**

(c) The force of attraction between particles in a solid is high **(1)**, in a gas, the force of attraction between particles is weak/negligible. **(1)**

**4** Particles gain kinetic energy with increasing temperature **(1)**. At a change of state, energy is required to change state **(1)** to overcome the forces of attraction between the particles **(1)**, therefore energy has to be transferred to the ice cream. **(1)**

## 241. Density

**1** 2400 **(1)** 1000 **(1)**

**2** (a) $V = 1.5 \times 2 \times 5 = 15\,m^3$ **(1)**

(b) $m = \rho \times V$ **(1)** $m = 2400 \times 15 = 36\,000\,kg$ **(1)**

**3** (a) The particles in a liquid are further apart than in a solid **(1)**; this means there are fewer particles per unit volume **(1)**

(b) $V = m \div \rho$ **(1)** $V = 12\,500 \div 19.3 = 648\,cm^3$ **(1)** $= 650\,m^3$ **(1)**

(c) Since the density of liquid gold is lower, it has a larger volume (new volume = 720 $cm^3$) **(1)** this means the mould needs to be bigger **(1)**

### 242. Investigating density

(a) Use a ruler to measure the length, width and height **(1)**. The volume can be calculated by multiplying length × width × height **(1)**

(b) Three from: Fill a displacement can until water just starts to come out of the spout **(1)** Place a measuring cylinder under the spout **(1)** Place the stone in the eureka can **(1)** Read the volume from the measuring cylinder **(1)**

(c) Pour the oil into a measuring cylinder **(1)** Read the volume by looking at eye level at the bottom of the meniscus **(1)**

(d) Place a measuring cylinder on scales and zero the scales **(1)** pour in the vegetable oil **(1)**

(e) $\rho = m \div V = 128.6 \div 20$ **(1)** $\rho = 6.43\,g/cm^3$ **(1)**

(f) mass $= 128.6 - 110 = 18.6\,g$ **(1)** $\rho = m \div V = 18.6 \div 20$, $\rho = 0.93\,g/cm^3$ **(1)**

(g) $\rho = 560\,kg/m^3 = 0.56\,g/cm^3$ **(1)** This density is higher **(1)** This could be a different type of wood/could be uncertainty/error in measurements **(1)**

### 243. Energy and changes of state

1 (a) The energy required to change the temperature of 1 kg of a material by 1 °C **(1)**

(b) The energy required to change 1 kg of a material from one state to another **(1)**

(c) Specific latent heat involves changes of state, while specific heat capacity only covers one state, **(1)** and the temperature never changes, but the temperature does change with specific heat capacity. **(1)**

2 (a) Energy is transferred to the surroundings **(1)**. This is because the particles in a liquid have less energy than the particles in a gas. **(1)**

(b) $Q = 5 \times 10^{-3} \times 2257 \times 10^3$ **(1)** $Q = 11\,285\,J$ **(1)** $= 11\,300\,J$ **(1)**

(c) $Q = 5 \times 10^{-3} \times 4200 \times 80$ **(1)** $Q = 1680\,J$ **(1)**

3 (a) $Q = 50 \times 3 \times 60 = 9000\,J$ **(1)** $Q = mL$, $L = Q \div m = 9000 \div 0.030$ **(1)** $L = 300\,000\,J/kg$ **(1)**

(b) Energy from the room is also being transferred to the ice, so not so much needs to be provided by the heater. As $Q$ is lower, then $L$ will be lower. **(1)**

### 244. Thermal properties of water

(a) Diagram showing thermometer in ice with heater and insulation around the beaker. **(1)** Four from: Place the thermometer and heater directly into the ice and record the temperature of the ice **(1)** Record temperature every 30 seconds (10 seconds to 1 minute) **(1)** Read the thermometer at eye level **(1)** Use the insulation to wrap beaker/create a lid/any sensible suggestion **(1)** Stop heating after all the ice has melted/some specified time after ice melted. **(1)**

(b)

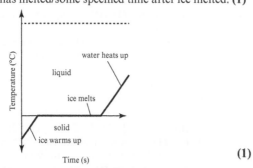

**(1)**

Change of state labelled on the flat portion of the graph **(1)**

(c) $E = Pt = 50 \times 45 = 2250\,J$ **(1)** $c = Q \div (m\Delta\theta)$ **(1)** $c = 2250 \div (0.1 \times 5)$, $c = 4500\,J/kg\,°C$ **(1)**

(d) During the experiment the ice changed state. Some of the energy transferred by the heater will have been used to change state **(1)**

If you assume all energy gone to changing temperature you will get a much larger value for specific heat capacity **(1)**

### 245. Pressure and temperature

1 (a) 27 °C **(1)**      (b) –63 °C **(1)**
(c) 293 K **(1)**      (d) 223 K **(1)**

2 Temperature is –273 °C **(1)** Particles have no movement **(1)**

3 Three from: particles moving randomly **(1)** collisions with sides **(1)** each collision exerts a force on the walls of the container **(1)** this average force over an area gives the pressure **(1)**

4 (a) Three from: Graph shows a directly proportional relationship **(1)** Increasing the temperature of the gas increases the average speed of the particles in the gas **(1)** Particles collide more frequently **(1)** Particles collide with more force **(1)**

(b) Pressure has halved **(1)**

### 246. Extended response – Particle model

For full marks an answer must include both calculations and three points of explanation. **(6)**
Explanation:
- When the steam condenses it transfers energy to the surroundings/skin
- The steam then cools down and transfers thermal energy to the skin
- Boiling water only cools down
- The energy released during a change in state is much greater than the energy released by cooling

Calculations:
- Steam changing state:
  - $Q = mL$
  - $Q = 0.05 \times 2\,257\,000 = 113\,000\,J$ (to 3sf)
- Energy transferred when water cools:
  - $Q = mc\Delta\theta = 0.05 \times 4200 \times 60$
  - $Q = 12\,600\,J$
- Total energy transferred by steam $= 113\,000 + 12\,600 = 126\,000\,J$
- This is much greater than the energy transferred just by cooling.

### 247. Elastic and inelastic distortion

1 Bending **(1)** Stretching **(1)** Compressing **(1)** All require more than one force **(1)**

2 (a) Any two examples: e.g., springs, wire (small forces), rubber **(1)**
(b) Any two examples: e.g., wool, clay, chewing gum **(1)**

3 Small forces: seat belts behave elastically **(1)** under larger forces, they behave inelastically **(1)**

4 Lycra® is an elastic material: this means it returns to its original shape when forces are removed **(1)** So stretches then fits the body tightly **(1)**. Makes the person more aerodynamic/streamlined **(1)**

5

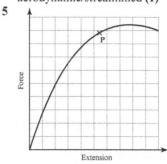

**(1)** Elastic limit (P) noted somewhere between linear and the peak of the graph **(1)**

## 248. Springs

**1** If the elastic distortion is linear the extension is directly proportional to the force **(1)**

**2** (a) Extension = 13 − 5 = 8 cm **(1)**

(b) $k = F \div x$ **(1)** $k = 4 \div 0.08 = 50$ N/m **(1)**

(c) $x = F \div k$ **(1)** $x = 8 \div 50 = 0.16$ m **(1)** (Or for both marks, double the force = double the extension = 16 cm)

Assumption: the spring is still undergoing linear elastic distortion/spring has not reached elastic limit **(1)**

(d) $x = 0.06$ m; E = $0.5 \times 50 \times 0.06 \times 0.06 = 0.09$ J **(1)**

**3** (a) Two straight diagonal lines **(1)** The steeper line labelled spring A **(1)**

(b) $E = \frac{1}{2}kx^2$ and $x$ is the same for both **(1)** Therefore the spring with highest $k$ stores the most energy **(1)**

## 249. Forces and springs

(a)

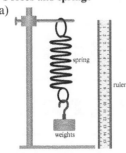

**(1)**

Measure the length of the unstretched spring using a ruler/pair of callipers **(1)** Attach 100 g and record the new length **(1)** Extension = new length − original length **(1)**

**or** Extension can be measured directly by securing the ruler at the bottom of the unstretched spring **(2)**

(b)

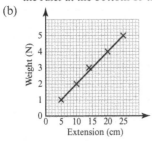

Points plotted correctly **(1)** Line of best fit drawn **(1)**

(c) Yes, since graph is a straight line **(1)** through the origin **(1)**

(d) $k = F \div x = 5 \div 0.25$ **(1)** $k = 20$ N/m **(1)**

(e) $E = \frac{1}{2} \times 20 \times 0.2^2$ **(1)** $E = 0.4$ J **(1)**

## 250. Extended response – Forces and matter

There must be a clear explanation of the method and how to compare the data and at least one point about safety and at least one about working accurately to achieve full marks. Include apparatus diagram as in topic 249 qu. 1a. **(6)**

**Method:**

• Measure the length of the unstretched spring/elastic band using a ruler/pair of callipers

• Attach 100 g and record the new length

• Extension = new length − original length

• Or extension can be measured directly by securing the ruler at the bottom of the unstretched spring/ elastic band

**Compare data**

• Plot a graph of the results

• If linear there will be a straight-line graph

• If non-linear the graph will be a curve

**Safety:**

• Use G clamps to secure the stand to the desk

• Wear safety specs

• Place a bag under the masses in case they fall

**Accurately:**

• Read the ruler at eye level

• Use callipers to measure unstretched length

# The Periodic Table of the Elements

**Key**

| relative atomic mass |
| --- |
| **atomic symbol** |
| name |
| atomic (proton) number |

Example:

| 1 |
| --- |
| **H** |
| hydrogen |
| 1 |

| 1 | 2 | | | | | | | | | | | | 3 | 4 | 5 | 6 | 7 | 0 |
|---|---|---|---|---|---|---|---|---|---|---|---|---|---|---|---|---|---|---|
| 7 **Li** lithium 3 | 9 **Be** beryllium 4 | | | | | | | | | | | | 11 **B** boron 5 | 12 **C** carbon 6 | 14 **N** nitrogen 7 | 16 **O** oxygen 8 | 19 **F** fluorine 9 | 4 **He** helium 2 |
| 23 **Na** sodium 11 | 24 **Mg** magnesium 12 | | | | | | | | | | | | 27 **Al** aluminium 13 | 28 **Si** silicon 14 | 31 **P** phosphorus 15 | 32 **S** sulfur 16 | 35.5 **Cl** chlorine 17 | 20 **Ne** neon 10 |
| 39 **K** potassium 19 | 40 **Ca** calcium 20 | 45 **Sc** scandium 21 | 48 **Ti** titanium 22 | 51 **V** vanadium 23 | 52 **Cr** chromium 24 | 55 **Mn** manganese 25 | 56 **Fe** iron 26 | 59 **Co** cobalt 27 | 59 **Ni** nickel 28 | 63.5 **Cu** copper 29 | 65 **Zn** zinc 30 | | 70 **Ga** gallium 31 | 73 **Ge** germanium 32 | 75 **As** arsenic 33 | 79 **Se** selenium 34 | 80 **Br** bromine 35 | 40 **Ar** argon 18 |
| 85 **Rb** rubidium 37 | 88 **Sr** strontium 38 | 89 **Y** yttrium 39 | 91 **Zr** zirconium 40 | 93 **Nb** niobium 41 | 96 **Mo** molybdenum 42 | [98] **Tc** technetium 43 | 101 **Ru** ruthenium 44 | 103 **Rh** rhodium 45 | 106 **Pd** palladium 46 | 108 **Ag** silver 47 | 112 **Cd** cadmium 48 | | 115 **In** indium 49 | 119 **Sn** tin 50 | 122 **Sb** antimony 51 | 128 **Te** tellurium 52 | 127 **I** iodine 53 | 84 **Kr** krypton 36 |
| 133 **Cs** caesium 55 | 137 **Ba** barium 56 | 139 **La\*** lanthanum 57 | 178 **Hf** hafnium 72 | 181 **Ta** tantalum 73 | 184 **W** tungsten 74 | 186 **Re** rhenium 75 | 190 **Os** osmium 76 | 192 **Ir** iridium 77 | 195 **Pt** platinum 78 | 197 **Au** gold 79 | 201 **Hg** mercury 80 | | 204 **Tl** thallium 81 | 207 **Pb** lead 82 | 209 **Bi** bismuth 83 | [209] **Po** polonium 84 | [210] **At** astatine 85 | [222] **Rn** radon 86 |
| [223] **Fr** francium 87 | [226] **Ra** radium 88 | [227] **Ac\*** actinium 89 | [261] **Rf** rutherfordium 104 | [262] **Db** dubnium 105 | [266] **Sg** seaborgium 106 | [264] **Bh** bohrium 107 | [277] **Hs** hassium 108 | [268] **Mt** meitnerium 109 | [271] **Ds** darmstadtium 110 | [272] **Rg** roentgenium 111 | | | | | | | | |

Elements with atomic numbers 112–116 have been reported but not fully authenticated

\*The lanthanoids (atomic numbers 58–71) and the actinoids (atomic numbers 90–103) have been omitted.

# Physics Equations List

(final velocity)$^2$ − (initial velocity)$^2$ = 2 × acceleration × distance

$v^2 - u^2 = 2 \times a \times x$

force = change in momentum ÷ time

$F = \frac{(mv - mu)}{t}$

energy transferred = current × potential difference × time

$E = I \times V \times t$

force on a conductor at right angles to a magnetic field carrying a current = magnetic flux density × current × length

$F = B \times I \times l$

potential difference across primary coil × current in primary coil = potential difference across secondary coil × currnet in secondary coil

$V_p \times I_p = V_s \times I_s$

change in termal energy = mass × specific that capacity × change in temperature

$\Delta Q = m \times c \times \Delta\theta$

thermal energy for a change of state = mass × specific latent heat

$Q = m \times L$

energy transferred in stretching = 0.5 × spring constant × (extension)$^2$

$E = \frac{1}{2} \times k \times x^2$

Published by Pearson Education Limited, 80 Strand, London, WC2R 0RL.

www.pearsonschoolsandfecolleges.co.uk

Copies of official specifications for all Pearson qualifications may be found on the website: qualifications.pearson.com

Text and illustrations © Pearson Education Ltd 2018
Typeset and illustrated by York Publishing Solutions Pvt Ltd, India.
Commissioning, editorial and project management services by Haremi Ltd.
Cover illustration by Miriam Sturdee

The rights of Ann Fullick, Catherine Jones and Faye Thorndycroft to be identified as authors of this work have been asserted by them in accordance with the Copyright, Designs and Patents Act 1988.

First published 2018

**British Library Cataloguing in Publication Data**
A catalogue record for this book is available from the British Library

ISBN 978 1 292 21375 0

**Acknowledgements**
The authors and publisher would like to thank the following individuals and organisations for permission to reproduce copyright material.

**Photographs**
(Key: b-bottom; c-centre; l-left; r-right; t-top)

**Anthony Short:** 14, 22, 29, 35, 75, 76, **NASA**: NASA/JPL-Caltech/R. Hurt (SSC) 191, **Science Photo Library:** CNRI 3t, Herve Conge, ISM 6b, **Shutterstock:** Dlumen 3b, 6t.

All other images © Pearson Education

**Notes from the publisher**

1. While the publishers have made every attempt to ensure that advice on the qualification and its assessment is accurate, the official specification and associated assessment guidance materials are the only authoritative source of information and should always be referred to for definitive guidance.
Pearson examiners have not contributed to any sections in this resource relevant to examination papers for which they have responsibility.
2. Pearson has robust editorial processes, including answer and fact checks, to ensure the accuracy of the content in this publication, and every effort is made to ensure this publication is free of errors. We are, however, only human, and occasionally errors do occur. Pearson is not liable for any misunderstandings that arise as a result of errors in this publication, but it is our priority to ensure that the content is accurate. If you spot an error, please do contact us at resourcescorrections@pearson.com so we can make sure it is correcte(d)